Green Economics and Health, Healthcare, Health Systems and Well Being

Photo Katherine Kennet: Nepal

Edited by
Miriam Kennet, Dr. Katherine Kennet, and Michelle S. Gale de Oliveira

The Green Economics Institute
2013
www.greeneconomics.org.uk
greeneconomicsinstitute@yahoo.com

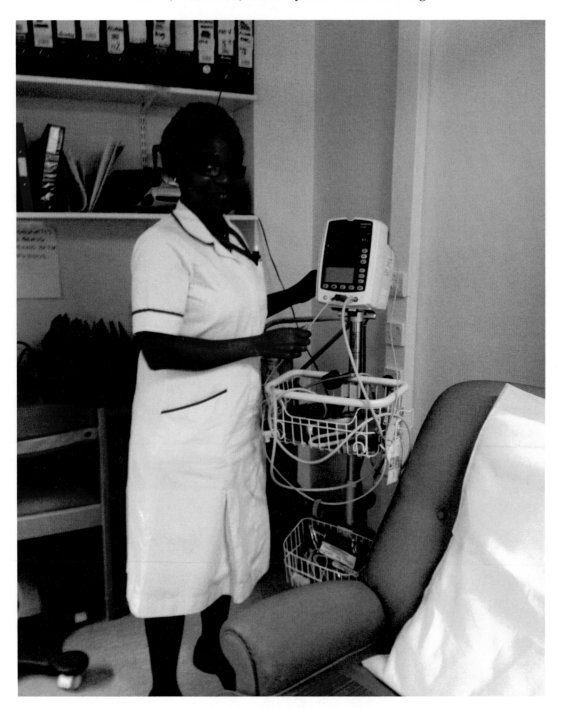

Photo Katherine Kennet. Modern Hospital Healthcare

*"A country clearly is **less well off** with a renewable resource, such as a forest being depleted. It is **not** better off, no matter what the balance sheet or graphs are telling us."*
Miriam Kennet 2013

"Maternal health is an issue that strikes at the heart of every family; every minute of every day a woman dies of a child-birth related cause[1] and the majority of these deaths are preventable. In a country with a birth rate as high as India's it is no surprise that this is a key issue, in fact, a quarter of the world's reported maternal deaths are in India[3] . What I find particularly interesting is how in India, a country currently booming economically, the maternal health remains so poor, in fact, the maternal mortality ratio for India was worse in 2005 (450) than in 2004 (440)[4]."

"As the state of Kerala shows, pregnancy in less developed areas, doesn't have to equate to life threatening danger. I believe that women's health is so intricately linked with their education, wealth and their position in society that to make strides in decreasing maternal mortality all these issues must be addressed. This may sound like a tall order but ultimately, there can be no justification for preventable and unnecessary deaths."

Dr Katherine Kennet Medical Practitioner and Global Health Specialist trained at Imperial College, London.

"The current view is that pollution is an inevitable effect of growth and growth is the imperative for profit. By externalising social and environmental costs, industry can maximize profit. Everyone including future generations is paying by allowing enterprises to have this freedom."

Dr Enrico Tezza (Italy , International Labour Organisation.)

"Modernizing the international financial institutions and global development architecture is essential to our efforts to promote global financial stability, foster sustainable development, and lift the lives of the poorest."

The G 20 2013

The Green Economics Institute (GEI)

Photo David Taylor. Meeting Space at Earthspirit Personal Development and Healing Centre

Contents

List of Contributors

Sofia Amaral (Portugal) is at NOVA School of Business and Economics, Portugal. Her field of interests include green economics and sustainable management. She is the lead editor of the Green Economics series book *Green Economics: Reforming and Transforming the Global Economy*. She specialises in looking at alternatives from around the world and how to avoid the stress of debt and poverty in Southern European Countries.

Dr Eyad Mohammed Atya (Egypt) is a Professor in the Economics Department of Zagazig University, Egypt.

Kanupriya Bhagat (India) is at the University of St Andrews. Originally, from Agra, India, she has been involved with organizations such as CRY (Child Rights and You), New Delhi, where she was part of the Digital Fundraising Department, and has a strong interest in publishing to help in this work. She enjoys collaborating with the Green Economics Institute in developing green economics into a global initiative. She is also concerned with women's safety on public transport.

Professor Dr Vinca Bigo (France and the UK) qualified at Cambridge University and is a Professor of Gender, Ethics & Leadership at the Kedge Business School in Marseille in France. She has published regularly with the Green Economics Institute and in its academic journal and her work theorises dilemmas of care and how we can change our conventional understanding of care into a model with is more inclusive and beneficial to the whole community.

Rose Blackett-Ord is a graduate of Oxford University and Le Cordon Bleu. She now works as a freelance chef and writer, and has a particular interest in rural and green issues relating to food. Her work includes local, seasonal and wild food recipes for health. Rose writes green and gourmet recipes for a number of publications, including for the Green Economics Institute, where she co-edited a number of books, including the Greening of Food, Farming and Agriculture and the Greening of Poetry and the Arts which looks at how to obtain health and well being.

Alan Cunningham trained in Public Administration and has worked as an Administrative and an Information officer. Following early retirement for family reasons, he has served on two regional working parties for public health campaigning for local action on health inequalities, the better application of public health policy by NGOs, and for recognition of the links between Public Health Practice and Sustainable Living. He has developed a local area profiling system that has been praised by MPs and by Health Observatory staff. He is an associate member of the Faculty of Public Health and of IUHPE.

Professor Dr Graciela Chichilnisky PhD (USA and Argentina) has worked extensively in the Kyoto Protocol process, creating and designing the carbon market that became international law in 2005. She also acted as a lead author of the Intergovernmental Panel on Climate Change, which received the 2007 Nobel Prize. A frequent keynote speaker, special adviser to several UN organisations and heads of state, her pioneering work uses innovative market mechanisms to reduce carbon emissions, conserve biodiversity and ecosystem services and improve the lot of the poor. She is a Professor of Economics and Mathematical Statistics at Columbia University and the Sir Louis Matheson Distinguished Professor at Monash University.

Chit Chong has been an environmental campaigner and environmental professional for over two decades. He has been a member of the Green Economics Institute since it started. He was the first Green Councillor to be elected in London and is now a member of the Alliance for Future Generations which seeks to promote the representation of future generations in the decision making processes of today. He works as an environmental consultant helping organisations and individuals to reduce their emissions from their buildings. www.LowCarbonKnowHow.co.uk

W. Thomas Duncanson, Ph.D.,(Australia) is an Associate Professor in the Department of Communication at Millikin University in Decatur, Illinois, USA. His research and writing has focused on the "speech thought" of Eugen Rosenstock-Huessy, as well as issues of communication ethics and public moral argument. In recent years Duncanson has written primarily about environmental advocacy and economic rhetoric.

David Flint is a Senior Visiting Fellow at the Cass Business School, London and specialises in Healthcare as an advisor and as a trustee of the British Pregnancy Advisory Service, and was founding chairman of Education For Choice, originally a charity providing educational resources relating to abortion and birth control and now part of Brook. He has spent thirty years studying Information Technology and its application and interpreting his findings for senior managers in business and public service. He has written two books and a great many reports, advised hundreds of organisations and lectured on four continents.

Dr Christopher Fleming (Australia) is a Director of Griffith University's Social and Economic Research Program (SERP), a Lecturer at Griffith Business School in the Department of Accounting, Finance and Economics, a founding member of Griffith University's Asia-Pacific Centre for Sustainable Enterprise, a member of the Key Centre for Ethics, Law, Justice and Governance, and a Senior Associate of MainStream Economics and Policy. An applied micro-economist with teaching, consulting and public policy experience, Christopher's research and consulting interests include, social and economic project/program evaluation, natural resource and environmental economics, the economic determinants of subjective well-being, the economics of crime, the sustainable management of natural resources and the economics of sustainable tourism. Prior to joining Griffith Business School, Christopher worked as a senior consultant for Marsden Jacob Associates and as a senior advisor within the Sustainable Development Policy Group of the New Zealand Ministry for the Environment. Christopher holds a Bachelor of Arts (Economics) from the University of Otago, a Master of Applied Economics with first class honours from Massey University and a PhD (Economics) from the University of Queensland.

Eli Gregory explored how the Kibbutz system creates feeling of community and how this leads to well being. He was a Kibbutz Lotan volunteer and CfCE

Professor Dr Sandra Gusta (Latvia) is an Associate Professor, Doctor of Social Sciences in Economy at the Latvian University of Agriculture, Department Architecture and Building (Latvia), member of the Board of LEA (Latvian Association of Economics), and a Member of the Latvian Association of Civil Engineers, Education and Science section and examines health projects in Latvia.

Volker Heinemann (UK and Germany) is an economist who studied at the Universities of Goettingen, Kiel and Nottingham. He is a specialist in international and developing economics, monetary economics and macroeconomic theory and policy. He is author of the book "Die Oekonomie der Zukunft," "The Economy of the Future," a book outlining a green structure for a contemporary economy that accepts the pressing changes that are needed to outdated current economic thinking. He is co-founder and Director and CFO of the Green Economics Institute, a member of the Institute of Chartered Accountants in England and Wales, trained at PWC and other major Institutions and is a Deputy Editor of the International Journal of Green Economics. He is a popular radio and TV speaker in Europe and a former Die Gruenen Councillor. He was on the team which organised the very first Green Economics and Well Being Retreat.

Dr Katherine Kennet is a medical doctor who trained at Imperial College, London University, UK and also is a Global Health specialist. She is now based in the UK and has practised medicine in Nepal as well. Her research focus is on women's health status and the link to wealth and poverty. She has written extensively on materal healthcare in India and outcomes for maternal health and well being in Nepal, and is also interested in mental health and pyschiatry.

Miriam Kennet is a specialist in Green Economics. She conceived and ran the world's first Green Economics and Health and Well Being Retreat. She is the Co-Founder and is CEO of the Green Economics Institute She also founded and edits the first Green Economics academic journal in the world, the International Journal of Green Economics, and she has been credited with creating the academic discipline of Green Economics. Green Economics has been recently described by the Bank of England as one of the most vibrant and healthy areas of economics at the moment.

Having worked in the UK, France,Portugal, Spain and Germany in Healthcare, she conceived and ran the first ever Green Economics and Health and Well Being Retreat and has run several since.

She is a member of Mansfield College and the Environmental Change Institute, both at University of Oxford. The BBC has made a special programme about her life and work. She runs regular conferences at Oxford University about Green Economics. Publishing regularly and having over 100 articles, papers and books. She has been featured in the Harvard Economics Review and Wall Street Journal as a leader. Recently she was named one of 100 most powerful unseen global women by the Charity One World. She is also a regular and frequently speaks at public events of all kinds, most recently to the North West Region of the National Health Service on the latest ideas in Health and Well Being. She is a popular after dinner speaker, and has advised in the Uk Parliament and the Bank of England and in Brussels on the Eurozone crisis, the high speed rail and the general economics situation.

She has taught, lectured and spoken at Universities and events all over Europe, from Alicante to Oxford and Bolzano, and to government officials from Montenegro and Kosovo to The UK Cabinet Office, Transport Department, National Government School and Treasury and spoken in Parliaments from Scotland to Austria and The French Senat and Estonia. She is also very active in spreading Green Economics in Asia, China, and all round Africa where people find it may be one of the beacons of hope at the moment in an age of Austerity and Cuts as it provides a completely new way of looking at the world. She is on the Assembly of the Green European Foundation. She has a delegation to the UNFCC COP Kyoto Climate Change Conferences and headed up a delegation to RIO + 20 Earth Summit: Greening the Economy in RIO Brazil where she is very active. She regularly speaks on TV around Europe.

Ryota Koike (Japan and the UK) is a researcher from Japan, analysing post-Fukushima Japanese energy policies. He has a broad range of academic interests from peace and development to environmental and nuclear issues. He is a regular speaker and a trainer in workshops and a popular lecturer on green economics and energy policy including at a conference held at Oxford University.

Philip Lymbery is Chief Executive of Compassion in World Farming.

Bianca Madison-Vuleta has a long experience in the areas of holistic, ecological and sustainable living. She is a PhD candidate in Green Economics. Bianca has been actively involved in the work of numerous national and international human rights and environmental NGOs as a committed and inspired campaigner, fundraiser and reknowned public speaker. A passionate humanitarian and environmentalist and Co-founder of The Sustainable Planet Foundation, Bianca works tirelessly to *be the change* in the world.

Ryte Mamacuviute (Lithuania) is a green economist from Vilnius University in Lithuania, who has worked in China on issues of transport and also has lectured in hospitals in the UK about environmental healthcare issues.

Virginie Martin, (France) is Associate Professor in Gender, Politics and Communication at the Kedge Business School in Marseille, France.

Michelle S. Gale de Oliveira (USA and Brazil) is a director of the Green Economics Institute, UK.She ran the worlds first Green Economics and Well Being and Health Retreat with Miriam Kennet. It was very well attended and a great success, inspiring her to create this book. She is very aware that human basic rights influence health outcomes and makes the connections in this book. She is a member of the Law School of the University of London School of Oriental and African Studies (SOAS), holding an MA in Human Rights Law with a focus on Islamic Law, Peace-Building, and Developing Countries. Founder of the Gender Progress Consortium, she holds degrees in Political Science and International Relations from Richmond, the American International University in London (RAIUL). She is a deputy editor of the International Journal of Green Economics. Her writing has been featured in Europe's World, one of the foremost European policy magazines. She lectures and speaks on Human Rights, Environmental and Social Justice, Gender Equity, International Development and Green Economics internationally. She also ran a conference on women's unequal pay and poverty in Reading, UK, lectured at the Oxford University Club on the human rights of land reform, is a regular speaker at international conferences and has appeared in the media in Africa, Europe, and Latin America. In 2010/2011, she was a delegate to the UNFCCC's COP15/16 in Copenhagen and Cancun, and in 2012 led a delegation to the United Nations' RIO+20, Sustainable Development Conference where she ran our three side events on green economics.

Kristof and Stacia Nordin are the co-founders of Never Ending Food, a community-based endeavor to improve the health of the planet and all of its living organisms through the use of natural, restorative, and sustainable design principles. They have been living and working in Malawi, Africa since 1997 in the areas of HIV, food security, nutrition, and community education. Stacia is a Registered Dietitian and Kristof is a Writer with a background in Social Work and Community Organizing. They both hold Diplomas in Permaculture Design. Their 9 year old daughter, Khalidwe, was born in Malawi and is already an aspiring Permaculturalist.

Don O'Neal has a BSc(Hons) in Mathematics and an MA in Environmentalism and Society. He has been the Oxfordshire Greens Treasurer since September 2000 and is a political columnist for The News and The Vincentian, national newspapers in St. Vincent and the Grenadines. He is a co-founder of St. Vincent and the Grenadines Greens. Don is a tireless campaigner and an inspiration for green causes and is involved in overcoming mainstream barriers to health and inclusion. As a beacon he has been up the highest mountain in St Vincent with a team.

Vyacheslav Potapenko (Ukraine) is based at the National Institute for Strategic Studies of Ukraine, chief consultant (from 2010); Taras Shevchenko National University of Kyiv, docent (2000-2004); The National University of "Kyiv-Mohyla Academy", docent (1999-2000). Professional interests: green economics, natural capital, governmental management, green party, environmental security, Chernobyl rehabilitation, geospace analysis. Co-author of our existing book on Green Energy Policies and specialises in looking at health issues of nuclear power plants.

Tutik Rachmawati (Indonesia and UK) is researching at the Institute of Local Government Studies, University of Birmingham with a fellowship from Japan-Indonesian Presidential Scholarship/World Bank. She is also a researcher in Center of Excellence in Small Medium Enterprises (SME) Development and a Lecturer in Public Administration Department of Parahyangan Catholic University

Professor Doaa Mohamed Salman (Egypt) of the Faculty of Management Sciences, Modern Sciences and Arts University (MSA), Egypt is a regular contributor to our Green Economics Institute work, our academic journal and led our Youth in Action, EU Programme at Oxford and Glastonbury. She is an Associate Professor, Modern Sciences and Arts University, MSA, Egypt. She holds a PhD in International Economics. She earned her BSc (1994), MSc (1999) and PhD (2004) from Ain Shams University, Egypt. Her current research interests relate primarily, though not exclusively, to the following areas: development institutional setting, and the role of entrepreneurs to robust economic systems. Dr. Doaa as a certified trainer she participated in Education Development Program for Egyptian universities (EDU Egypt) for three consecutive years, which is a milestone in bridging the employability gap. She is a member of Egypt Political and Economic Association and Middle East Economic Association, and a member in the Middle East Economic Association (MEEA). She is a reviewer of numerous academic journals including China-USA Business journal. She has taught, trained and lectured recently post and underground program in many Egyptian universities. Her current research interests relate primarily, though not exclusively, to two areas: development and growth, and effective role of institution. Her research appears in journals such as : European *Journal of Economics, Finance, Journal of International Business & Finance, International Journal of Green Economics and International Journal of Development and Conflict*. She can be reached at Modern sciences and art university, MSA, Egypt.

Lawrence Sappor (Ghana and UK) is a health worker from Ghana and the UK. In 2006, he began research related to HIV/AIDS which was nominated as the best study in the department that year. His work aims at analyzing the spread of HIV/AIDS, and seeks to track its spread, since it was first reported in Ghana. He has been engaged in improving access to equal education, health and economic resources in Ghana for a little over two years, which has been an enjoyable experience. In addition, Lawrence has undertaken short courses in health and care for the disable including the aged for the past four years, themes about which he is very enthusiastic. His work has for many years has entailed supporting the care and life of persons suffering with health related illnesses including COPDs, autism, asthma, dementia, and stroke. He has also undertaken training in medication and other themes involving supporting disabled people. Lawrence has collaborated with the Green Economics Institute, particularly on the subject of people suffering from COPDs in Windsor at the King Edward II Hospital with a focus on the effect of pollution on health and healthcare. As a green economist, his postgraduate degree in 2010 aimed to correlate deforestation and flooding to desertification, trying to find a link with natural circumstances that rehabilitate these regions. The thesis explored what happens when humans exploit natural resources and the consequences using Erdas Emagine software. During his studies, he used MapInfo to explore dotted mapping of health issues.

David Taylor is the Co-Founder of Earthspirit with Bettina Von Coels (Germany, Portugal and UK). The centre provides one of the most important spaces in the Uk for Green Education and Green Health Courses to take place. He runs the centre with Francoise his partner (France and the UK). The Green Economics Institute runs many of its courses and retreats at the centre and takes students there for field trips as it has very good and practical green systems in place. David is a life long green activist. He was influential in the Glastonbury music festival litter pick, and in founding the Green Gatherings, Green CND and also the Library of Avalon. He is a well known, very accomplished and popular national speaker on green issues, specialising in a more natural human centred and more feeling approach to professional activities. He has appeared on many TV and radio broadcasts and taught Miriam Kennet about Green issues and how to speak in public. He has also had a high profile in green politics. He is increasingly worried about runaway climate change and the effects it will have on his two children and he is currently seeking to unite disparate elements of the green movement to work more closely together in the face of humanities' most catastrophic threat in historic times and to address the threat from the current mass extinction of species.

Dr Enrico Tezza (Italy) is a senior training specialist and has a background in social research and evaluation studies. After a career in the Italian Ministry of Labour and local public institutions, he joined the International Labour Organisation in Turin in 1992. He is labour market advisor for the Green Economics Institute. Subjects covered vary from training policy to employment and active labour market measures. His current focus interest is on social dialogue for green jobs. His main publication was Evaluating Social Programmes: the relevance of relationships and his latest publications include Dialogue for Responsible Restructuring and Green Labour Market for Transitions.

Sir Crispin Tickell, GCMG, KCVO, FZS, is a British diplomat, environmentalist, and academic. He went to Christ Church, Oxford, graduating in 1952 with first class honours in Modern History. He joined the British diplomatic service in 1954, serving at the Foreign & Commonwealth Office in London until 1955. He was responsible for looking after the British Antarctic Territory; the experience gained may have laid the foundations for long term interests in the environment. He then had posting at the British Embassy in The Hague (1955–58)); Mexico City (1958–61); London (1961–64); Paris (1964–70); and Private Secretary various Chancellors of the Duchy of Lancaster (1970–72) during negotiations for the UK entry into the European Community. He was later Chef de Cabinet to the President of the European Commission (1977–1980), British Ambassador to Mexico (1981–1983), Permanent Secretary of the Overseas Development Administration (now Department for International Development) (1984–1987), and British Ambassador to the United Nations and Permanent Representative on the UN Security Council (1987–1990). He was appointed MVO in 1958 and later knighted as a KCVO in 1983 on the Royal Yacht Britannia, to mark the conclusion of Queen Elizabeth's Official Visit to Mexico. He was appointed GCMG for his work at the UN in 1988. Sir Crispin was President of the Royal Geographical Society from 1990 to 1993 and Warden of Green College, Oxford between 1990 and 1997, where he appointed George Monbiotand Norman Myers as Visiting Fellows. He was President of the Marine Biological Association from 1990 to 2001. From 1996 until August 2006 he was chancellor of the University of Kent when Sir Robert Worcester took over the position. He is currently director of the Policy Foresight Programme of the James Martin 21st Century School[5] at the University of Oxford (formerly the Green College Centre for Environmental Policy and Understanding) and Chairman Emeritus of the Climate Institute, in Washington DC. He has many interests, including climate change, population issues, conservation of biodiversity and the early history of the Earth.

Margaret Thatcher credits Tickell for persuading her to make a speech on global climate change to the Royal Society in September 1988 (though the speech was written by Thatcher and George Guise). He chaired John Major's Government Panel on Sustainable Development (1994–2000), and was a member of two government task forces under the Labour Party: one on Urban Regeneration, chaired by Sir Richard Rogers, now Lord Rogers (1998–99), and one on Potentially Hazardous Near-Earth Objects (2000). A man of strong environmental convictions, he has been described as influential in Britain, although his environmental message has not always travelled as easily abroad, particularly to the United States. His 1977 book 'Climatic Change and World Affairs' argued that mandatory international pollution control would eventually be necessary. Despite his non-scientific background, he is internationally respected as having a strong grasp of science policy issues. He has been the recipient, between 1990 and 2006, of 23 honorary doctorates. He is currently the president of the UK charity Tree Aid,[7] which enables communities in Africa's drylands to fight poverty and become self-reliant, while improving the environment. He is also a patron of Population Matters.

His main recreations include climatology, paleohistory, pre-Columbian art and mountains. Formerly he was :Non-executive Director, IBM UK (1990–1995),Trustee, Natural History Museum (1992–2001),Trustee, Baring Foundation (1992–2002),Publications: *Climate Change and World Affairs*, with a preface by Solly Zuckerman (1977, second edition 1986, Harvard International Affairs Committee).and *Mary Anning of Lyme Regis*, with a preface by John Fowles (1996, 1998 and 2003). He became Sir Crispin Tickel KCVO and GCMG in 1988.

Jigme Tashi Tsering (Bhuttan) is currently working as a Senior Analyst in the Department of Investment, Druk Holding and Investment, the commercial arm of the Royal Government of Bhutan. Jigme has a Bachelors in Civil Engineer from the Indian Institute of Technology (ITT) Delhi, and a Masters in Environmental Engineering from the University of Melbourne. He has over eleven years of working experience and has worked in various capacities in the Government (engineer, technical auditor, and environmentalist). He enjoys travelling, which goes hand in hand with his passion – photography.

Dr Jeffrey Turk (Slovenia and Belgium) holds a doctorate in particle physics from Yale University and after working as a physicist at the European Laboratory for Particle Physics (CERN) he earned an MA in transition economics at the Central European University in Budapest and then a Dphil in contemporary European Studies from the University of Sussex and a research fellow at the Scientific Research Centre of the Slovenian Adademy of Sciences and Arts, where he researches realist biography and European Policy. He ran a research conference at the University of Leuwen on critical realist narrative biographical methods. He has produced many articles on Green Economics and methodological innovation. He specialises in biographical methodology and looking at the whole person in an analysis of what consitutes data and research and is head of research at the Green Economics Institute.

Dr Michelle Wishardt lectures at Leeds Metropolitan and has worked as a researcher on a variety of projects funded by a range of international organisations. Some of these have entailed periods of work in East and West Europe. She has recently contributed to four ESPON projects (1.1.1 Polycentricity, 1.1.2 Urban-Rural Relations, 3.2 Spatial Scenarios and 3.3 Competitiveness and Sustainability) and is currently working on the Interreg IV SURF (Sustainable Urban Fringes) project. Michelle has also undertaken research outside the university sector including work as a Parliamentary researcher. Michelle's research activity has been primarily European in focus and most recently been concerned with issues of regional governance, migration and European spatial planning. She has developed expertise on EU territorial instruments and their evaluation and has regional expertise in Central and Eastern Europe. Particular areas of knowledge and interest relate to European planning and Cohesion policy, social inclusion, transport developments and various aspects of sustainability. Geographically areas of study have included North Yorkshire, Ireland and Central and Eastern Europe, particularly Poland.

Tracy, Marchioness of Worcester is a campaigner for the greening of food, farming, agriculture and cruelty free farming that opposes agribusiness. She is a patron of International Society and Culture, a trustee of the GAIA Foundation, The Schumacher Society and the UK Soil Association.

Photo by Miriam Kennet. Medicines

Part 1: Health, Healthcare and Health Systems

Global health

Looking ahead to 2015

"Ahead of the Sept 25 2015, The United Nations General Assembly, which will evaluate the efforts made towards achieving the **Millennium Development Goals**, and look ahead to the post-2015 Development Agenda, a special issue of *The Lancet* focuses on the Countdown to 2015.

A new analysis of interventions to reduce maternal and child deaths in developing countries reveals that if current trends continue, just nine Countdown countries will meet internationally agreed targets to reduce the number of deaths of children under 5 to fewer than 20 deaths per 1000 births by 2035. " *The Lancet.*

Photo Miriam Kennet, of an original Photo in an exhibition taken by Hein du Plessis as part of an exhibition on South African Gold Miners and silicosis. South African Gold Mine Workers create much of the wealth of South Africa but they don't see it themselves or enjoy it. Nearly all of them develop Tuberculosis and many of them get Silicosis- and then they receive almost no pension and no state sickness benefit. Often they have to look after several generations of families as well, even if they are very sick indeed or terminally ill. Their labour and suffering is to create conventional economic wealth but they have no part in the bonanza they create and their health is extremely compromised- to allow for the greed and pride of others. We don't think there is any place for such inequalities in a Green Economy. This photo is from a series exhibited in the House of Commons in the UK to highlight their plight. Dr Cowie 1987, "The well-recognised association between silicosis and pulmonary tuberculosis has a special significance in this working population," caused by inadequate occupational health or dust protection. Not long after this photo was taken many miners in South Africa were shot dead by the security forces for striking.

1.1 Introduction: Green Issues in Health today in the 21st century

By Dr. Katherine Kennet, MBBS BSC. And Miriam Kennet

Health, Healthcare, Health systems and the Well-being of the planet, nature, humans and other species are all essential aspects of a Green Economy. Economic, social and environmental justice all intersect at this critical point, as our species seeks to define the way forward, in terms of improving our standards of living, the human healthcare experience, and the best way to interact with the rest of our planet's species and nature itself.

The Green Economics Institute first started to address this interconnected issue with its first *Green Economics and Well Being Retreat* which it held at the Earthspirit Centre near Glastonbury about 7 years ago. Over 100 people came to this event which had a guiding principle of Multiple Intelligences (Wenger) and the care and health of the whole person, forming the bedrock of any concept of health and well-being. Every aspect of a person is valued from a Green Economics Perspective. Additionally we recognise that the start people have in life can present serious challenges to health and well-being, much as the Marmot Review (2010), (a sort of Stern Review (2008)) for Health, has just outlined.

In November 2008, Professor Sir Michael Marmot was asked by the then, Secretary of State for Health to chair an Independent Review to propose the most effective evidence-based strategies for reducing health inequalities in England from 2010. "The Report Fair Society, Health Lives, was published in February 2010, and concluded that reducing health inequalities would require action on six policy objectives:

- **1. Give every child the best start in life**

- **2. Enable all children, young people and adults to maximise their capabilities and have control over their lives**

- **3. Create fair employment and good work for all**

- **4. Ensure healthy standard of living for all**

- **5. Create and develop healthy and sustainable places and communities**

- **6. Strengthen the role and impact of ill-health prevention.**

- One of the authors of our current book gave a lecture in December 2012 to the North Western Area of the entire National Health Service of England to put forard suggestions as to how this could be implemented.

Photos from the official NHS photographer for the event, which was held at Manchester United famous Old Trafford football stadium and was very well attended.

We, as Green Economists, also make the links and interconnections and even causality between Democracy, Economic Power, Wealth and Health and Well Being as well. The row over Obama Care in the United States helps us to understand this interconnectedness of Health, the Economy and the Environment with very strong vested interest and business lobbies spending $10 million to pushing against a health programmme intended to be of benefit to the general population designed by the elected President. Those vested interests are the same people who funded the climate change deniers to the tune of $60 million and are also themselves in the top 10 of the biggest oil and gas polluters in the USA and also the attacks on the Green Jobs Programme. On repeated occasions organizations specifically funded, have led the same assault on climate science and scientists, "green jobs," renewable energy and climate policy progress. Now they are funding opposition to Obama's Health Care Reforms. (Greenpeace report).

Poverty, as several chapters in this book explains, impacts on health outcomes negatively and therefore it is crucial to try to eliminate inequality and to increase equal and fair access to health for everyone. The Green Economics Institute is committed to trying its utmost to challenge inequality and to end the lack of access to health and resources, so that everyone on the planet can realise their full potential unhampered by health issues and supported by free healthcare at the point of need. For example an case coming to international attention is the very low life expectancy in countries like Sierra Leone where it is only 41 years and the Health Service has all but disintegrated due to wars. Maternal and child mortality is the worst in the world and one in eight women die in childbirth often for lack of the most basic of amenities such as clean water or any experienced birth attendant or any hospital facilities and simply bleed to death. (*BBC* and *Amnesty International* Websites, acessed 26th September 2013). The cost of this injury to public health is very high and affects the whole economy. Hence as Green Economists we see this lack of investment in a significant part of the population as happening at the intersection of human rights, democracy, peace and investment. No woman in 2013 should be dying in routine childbirth.

Our book also discusses how economic "growth" impacts on our own health and the health of our planet. How does our physical Well-Being result from the Well-Being and respectful interaction with our planet and with its other species, both plant and animal? Can we justify and where do we stand, on controversial issues such as factory farming, the obliteration of fish populations in the oceans, and the increased consumption of certain crops leading to deforestation? Are we conscious of, or even concerned with, how these daily choices impact the global environmental crisis our planet is experiencing?

How do social policies impact the way our human communities develop, and how can we ameliorate the prospects of the poorest and most marginalised among us? With 2015 looming on the horizon, to what extent have the Millennium Development Goals been successful, and what has our success-rate been towards the eradication of poverty and its resulting and related maladies? These questions and more are among the issues driving the discussion of Health, Healthcare, and Well-being from a Green Economics Perspective and we regard them all as linked together, indivisible inter related determinants of health outcomes, which we began to explore in our books -*Green Economics and the Citizen's Income,* Lord, Felton and Kennet (2012) and in *Womens Unequal Pay and Poverty,* (Kennet, Gale de Oliveira, Felton and Winchester. 2012) both of which books are influencing policy outcomes in some cases in governments and Ministers are using them to formulate government strategy. We hope this current book will do the same.

There are two main aspects that we might propose to be the most important health issues in the modern world. The first is the investment in seeking out new and technical solutions to illness we either don't understand, or just can't cure yet. The second, and in our opinion, far more interesting and green aspect of health care is the real quest for knowledge to inform us about how to deliver the skills, technology and medicines we already have, and in some cases have had for decades, to the people who need it. Distribution to people and access to health care is one of the biggest challenges of the 21st century. One c o – author of this paper, Dr Katherine Kennet, says that in her practise, around the world , she has seen whole hospitals without a single bar of soap. If you consider how in the developed world we know that the use of cleaning and disinfecting and even soap will be really effective barriers to infection spreading. Denying patients the rights to this basic level of technology is what really impacts global health outcomes.

We have known for over a century that a lack of basic sanitation is more than enough to kill vulnerable people and creating hygenic conditions is one of the most effective health care remedies. The newer, and greener, discipline of *Global Health (The Lancet)* looks at not just modern solutions to illness, but also considers the socio-economic barriers to rolling out at any level the solutions we already have. A medical doctor's work is not always about modern science, pharmaceuticals and impressive and expensive machines. Rather it is increasingly about our responsibility to care for our patients. As Hippocrates said and all new doctors recite, *"first do no harm."*

It is very moving to hear 300 new Medics reciting the *Hippocratic Oath* together as we recently did at Imperial College, London University and I think it is worth reminding readers what it says. Although some parts are clearly outdated, considering that it is 2300 years old, it is remarkable in its relevance for us here.

The Hippocratic Oath as amended by the British Medical Association in 1997

"The practice of medicine is a privilege which carries important responsibilities. All doctors should observe the core values of the profession which centre on the duty to help sick people and to avoid harm. I promise that my medical knowledge will be used to benefit people's health. They are my first concern. I will listen to them and provide the best care I can. I will be honest, respectful and compassionate towards patients. In emergencies, I will do my best to help anyone in medical need.

I will make every effort to ensure that the rights of all patients are respected, including vulnerable groups who lack means of making their needs known, be it through immaturity, mental incapacity, imprisonment or detention or other circumstance.

My professional judgement will be exercised as independently as possible and not be influenced by political pressures nor by factors such as the social standing of the patient. I will not put personal profit or advancement above my duty to patients.

I recognise the special value of human life but I also know that the prolongation of human life is not the only aim of healthcare. Where abortion is permitted, I agree that it should take place only within an ethical and legal framework. I will not provide treatments which are pointless or harmful or which an informed and competent patient refuses.

I will ensure patients receive the information and support they want to make decisions about disease prevention and improvement of their health. I will answer as truthfully as I can and respect patients' decisions unless that puts others at risk of harm. If I cannot agree with their requests, I will explain why.

If my patients have limited mental awareness, I will still encourage them to participate in decisions as much as they feel able and willing to do so.

I will do my best to maintain confidentiality about all patients. If there are overriding reasons which prevent my keeping a patient's confidentiality I will explain them.

I will recognise the limits of my knowledge and seek advice from colleagues when necessary. I will acknowledge my mistakes. I will do my best to keep myself and colleagues informed of new developments and ensure that poor standards or bad practices are exposed to those who can improve them.

I will show respect for all those with whom I work and be ready to share my knowledge by teaching others what I know.

I will use my training and professional standing to improve the community in which I work. I will treat patients equitably and support a fair and humane distribution of health resources. I will try to influence positively authorities whose policies harm public health. I will oppose policies which breach internationally accepted standards of human rights. I will strive to change laws which are contrary to patients' interests or to my professional ethics."

Environmental Health

John Snow is usually regarded as the father of *"Epidemiology "* and he made the connection and discovered the relationship between the environment and health. He made his great discovery linking a fatal outbreak of cholera with a pump on Broad Street in Soho, London and there was an exhibition to commemorate his work, this year at the London School of Hygene and Tropical Medicine. The water, he realised, was contaminated by sewerage, making the local residents incredibly ill. This revelation, as recent as 1854, showed the scientific community that there was no escaping the link between environment, social infrastructure and health and how to spatially map the geography of diseases.

The discipline of *"Public Health "* evolved over the years to become *"International Health"* and eventually arrived at its current incarnation of *"Global Health"* which now widens its scope to encompass a *Health Systems* approach, i.e. a view to healthcare which takes not just an ill patient into account, but it also considers the social and economic landscape which created the illness and also strives to find solutions to their current illnesses , and the prevention of future outbreaks of disease.

Millenium Development Goals (MDGs of the United Nations Developmnt Programme)

This issue of the lack of access to healthcare is today regarded as one the key obtsacles to development, in every sense. So much so, that the United Nations has made it a priority, with its famous 8 "M illenium Development Goals":[1]

1. To eradicate extreme poverty and hunger;
2. To achieve universal primary education;
3. To promote gender equality and empower women;
4. To reduce child mortality;
5. To improve maternal health;
6. To combat HIV/AIDS, malaria and other diseases;
7. To ensure environmental sustainability
8. To develop a global partnership for development.

Helen Clark the Head of the *United Nations Development Programme* and who was a lecturer at a UK Government training course for women leaders which one of the current books co -authors taught on gave an interesting speech outlining how much progress has been made as a result of the focus provided by the MDGs. She spoke about,

"There has undoubtedly been progress on many of the indicators targeted by the MDGs. The proportion of people living in extreme poverty, on under $1.25 per day, is now half of what it was in 1990. Good progress has been registered on access to improved water sources. The world is within reach of seeing every child enrolled in primary school, and has achieved parity in primary education between girls and boys. Some of the lowest income countries have made the greatest strides. Considerable progress has

also been made on MDG Six on HIV/AIDS, malaria, and TB.
Alas, there are also the goals and targets where too little progress has been made – for example on maternal mortality reduction, universal access to reproductive health, and improved sanitation."

She outlined the aim to be:
Accelerating MDG progress in the last 1000 days
"Despite the progress made on the MDGs, those major challenges remain: reducing hunger and undernourishment, poor sanitation, and high maternal death rates have proved to be among the most difficult targets to attain.

As well, aggregate figures on MDG progress mask large disparities within and across countries – a matter which groups like those representing people with disabilities are emphasizing in the post-2015 consultations."

Helen advised in her speech that we will still in 2015 need to acknowledge that

"By 2015 almost 1 billion people will still live in extreme poverty. Many still will not have clean water or improved sanitation. Many will still be suffering from hunger, malnutrition, the burden of preventable ill-health, gender discrimination, and more. Whether or not global MDG targets are met, such suffering is inconsistent with the vision for dignity, equity, freedom, peace, and prosperity of the Millennium Declaration."

And it's not just the 191 UN member states who feel these subjects are key to address. *The Lancet* , one of the world's leading health journals, has become a specialised *Global Health* journal because Professionals feel its so important. The Royal Society of Medicine in London started an annual *Global Health Conference* in 2012. Its inaugural meeting was on *child and maternal health* and its second was on the *global burden of psychiatric disease.* Both these topics are not found in mainstream economics or medicine and we think it's worth exploring why. They are both 'unfashionable' and don't fit with the traditional Marxist view of development and nor do they fit with traditional economists' view s, which are often quoted as being those of the views of " *rational economic man",* " homo economicus. " These issues were swept under the carpet, or treated in novels as an object of terror in the attic like Bertha Mason the wife of Mr Rochester in the famous novel *Jane Eyre* by Charlotte Brontë (1847) or or people were stuffed into asylums when young and never come out again, a fate which even befell two of the queen's own cousins -Nerrissa and Katherine Bowes – Lyon.

Population Control and women's health and education

However as the medical and global health communities are slowly realising, these issues and perspectives really do form a most integral part of healthcare. Interestingly, it has been shown that the most effective form of population control (a major issue facing modern society) can only be achieved through the empowerment of women. Where women have access to family planning, and the education to be able to use it and the choice of a career, women choose to have children later, fewer of them, and both the mother and child are healthier. Gone are the traditional roles of children as an insurance policy for old age. In its place is to be found a women's economic contribution to the household and society, making both stronger. This argument has never been played out more violently than in our "modern" world where Malala Yousafzai, a 14-year-old Pakistani young girl was shot to prevent her using her right to education and her iconic struggle back to health continues to inspire global leaders who graphically now realise the importance of this issue to the human species over all. Women and children's health is no longer a sub-speciality, when it comes to global economics, health and development it is the main performance. Without it everything else collapses.

It is true that our ancient ancestors ten thousand years ago could successfully perform T*repannation* , as early as 7000 BC in Ensisheim, in the French region of Alsace (a Neolithic early form of craniotomy to relieve raised inter -cranial pressure). It is not only new surgeries, pharmacology and the technologies which are true the modern innovations, but actually the new discovery is much more how they are able to be used, how they are shared and who gets access to them which is the economic, and 'global health' new issue. The latter is the set of issues which is exciting the medical community.

The Marmot Review in the UK has excited social scientists and the National Health Service Management and its main message is that social deprivation leads to deprivation in health outcomes. What you put in in terms of socio economic status determines, very largely, the outcome for a person, in terms of their Health status and this is a constant theme throughout our book. Improving a person's socio economic status, means that their health will improve. The two are completely inter- linked.

Additionally, Green Philosophy suggests that the prevention of ill health and the maintenance of Well Being is an important part of health. Hence greens tend to consider the whole body. However this is not in our opinion the same thing as happiness which has become a fashionable altenative buzz word in recent years in the economics literature. In particular , we find this challenging as the " Greatest happiness of th e greatest number is a Benthamite concept from the mainstream.

The *greatest happiness principle*, or *the principle of utility*, forms the cornerstone of all Bentham's thought. By "happiness", he understood a predominance of "pleasure" over "pain". He wrote in *The Principles of Morals and Legislation*:

Nature has placed mankind under the governance of two sovereign masters, pain and pleasure. It is for them alone to point out what we ought to do, as well as to determine what we shall do. On the one hand the standard of right and wrong, on the other the chain of causes and effects, are fastened to their throne. They govern us in all we do, in all we say, in all we think ..

In practical terms and also philosophically it would mean that in a world of say 7 billion inhabitants – it would be acceptable if 1.5 billion were starving as all the others were fine. However in Green Economics, we would argue that if one person out of the 7 billion is still starving then the economic theory is wrong and other approaches need to be sought. There has also been great excitement over the Gross National Happiness Index in Bhuttan. However, it must be remembered that inspite of people from the west visiting to check this out, the fact remains - the choice our own Bhuttan team has taken for their part of this current book is for the advent of basic sanitation, so far from being a beacon of best practise, once again, its the basics that people really need to maintain good health, rather than fancy fashionable solutions. Even after phenomenal growth rates of up to 17% in 2007, the people of Bhuttan still lack basic amenities for good health and their nominal per capita income is $2,000 per year.

Mental Health

As an Institute we take a particular interest in health challenges and our team is diverse and as with any community we will find it contains people with a variety of health issues. Economists and accountants because of the type of work have generated a whole literature called post autistic economics. It is a very interesting term for many reasons. One is that it could be deemed offensive to people on the autistic spectrum as it's is being used in a negative way. It is also fascinating as the view of the profession was that they too must exhibit these more challenging personality profiles in order to get on at work. We run regular workshops about these issues and they are mostly led by people who have a condition themselves. We try to help everyone achieve their absolutely fullest potential with our institute as this gives them a thorough grounding for their successful life and on going career.
We pride ourselves in how we provide really solid foundations for people with perhaps personalty challenges or syndromes to join our team and in several cases to lead it- and we all work together in teams across the world to achieve our common goals and we have been remarkably successful with our programmes in this respect. In particular at our annual conference at Oxford University we ran workshops on autism and how to help ourselves, and others if we find we recognise it also how to take a wide balanced view of theory and of economics to include many facets that are missing in main stream disccourses and literature. The workshop was run by Caroline Hearst from "Autism matters."

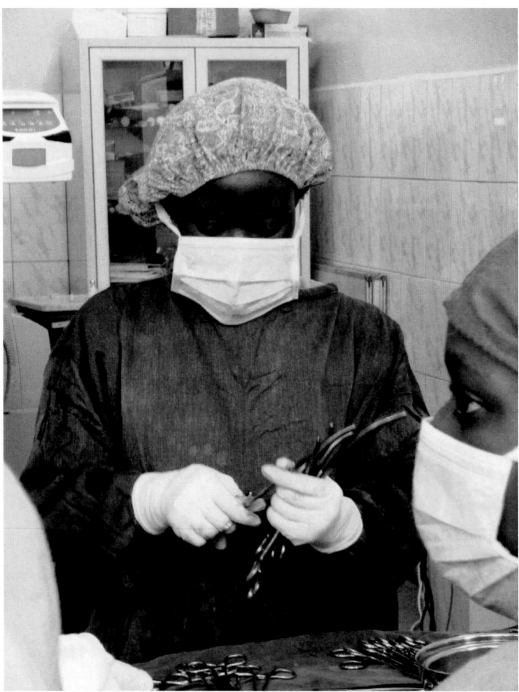

Photo Tone Hedvig Berg and Aase Seeberg (Norway). Healthcare today in Zambia

The United Nations , http://www.un.org/disabilities/default.asp?id=1545, shows that mental health is now ranked with depression as No. three in the global burden of disease,

"Millions of people worldwide have mental health conditions and an estimated one in four people globally will experience a mental health condition in their lifetime. Almost one million people die due to suicide every year, and it is the third leading cause of death among young people. Depression is the leading cause of years lost due to disability worldwide. Mental health problems, including alcohol abuse, are among the ten leading causes of disability in both developed and developing countries. In particular, depression is ranked third in the global burden of disease, and is projected to rank first in 2030. Persons with mental and psychosocial disabilities often face stigma and discrimination, as well as experience high levels of physical and sexual abuse, which can occur in a range of settings, including prisons, hospitals and homes.

The economic cost of mental health problems is vast, while reasonable investment in mental health can contribute to better mental health for people. Poor mental health is both a cause and a consequence of poverty, compromised education, gender inequality, ill-health, violence and other global challenges. It impedes the individual's capacity to work productively, realize their potential and make a contribution to their community."

In fact the latest global The United Nations has started to try to manage th extreme burden of mental health deficits and illness around the world seeing it as a key blocking factor to development largely due to the stress of modern life and perhaps rapid modernisation and globalisation within one generation in many countries and the breakdown of communities and their traditional support networks. Mental health once the poor relation has become one of the key targets for improvement and is now included as an important part of overall health delivery.

The change in the United Nations and generally in research communities supports our own views in the Green Economics Institute expressed in the following United Nations quotation, that," *Mental health well-being is closely associated to several Millennium Development Goals and economic development sectors including education, labour force participation, and productivity. Limited access to mental health care increases patient and family suffering. Unmet mental health needs have a negative effect on poverty reduction initiatives and economic development. Untreated mental conditions contribute to economic loss because they increase school and work absenteeism and dropout rates, healthcare expenditure, and unemployment." Ngul et al (2011).*

The Commodification of Care and the Elderly and Frail

A key contemporary causal factor in this is the commodification and globalisation of care. Whilst some healthcare is now paid for rather than offered by the community in the traditional model, today the person being cared for is taken out of the community, isolated and cared for in a home for money. This contributes to the calculation of the GDP figure for the nation state but it means that a whole swathe of society is removed from public life.

For example, in elderly care, in traditional societies , the elder was a term with almost chief like status. Everyone deferred to them and when I was young people would get up for older people on the bus as a mark of their status. Indeed it is believed that humans uniquely survive their menopause years and the input of wise elders is what has given us such an amazing power as a species. Today, we put older people away in homes and pay institutions to care for them for money. A really regretable consequence of this process means that their knowledge is lost to the rest of the community and already the literature says children today are not as academically able as previous generations, so they need the " grandparent " input desperately to return . Also for those communities that can't afford to pay for caring services , then this is done in the home, and not in the community, as older people become invisible and something to be ashamed of and so the invisible care is done by the mother of the house hold and the women in the community alone, putting them under even more strain. Indeed women in their fifties often have to stop work to care for their children, their mothers and any other elderly relatives. This work is not paid as " women's" work is assumed but not included in the GDP figures and not reported and is simply regarded as domestic work and so as Waring (1990) exposed – womens' work is not counted and it needs to be for a healthy society. Many women provide all the meals for elderly parents whilst maintaining a j ob and a family of their own. Additionally , even paid caring work is regarded as the lowest of the low and in hospitals " care assistants" are about the lowest paid as caring is not valued at all. We have a major chapter near the end of this book which presents many of leading writers, theories and ideas connected with the care dilemmas an d the value we place on" elders " and how much we are loosing out in terms of practicality and wisdom. However, it is also true that infants and patients who are not " cared for" do not thrive or get well. In fact caring can make all the difference between surviving or not surviving and getting well or succumbing to illnesses.

Hence all sorts of aspects of Well Being are addressed by Greens. Green philosophical stances encourage the use of retreats, quiet times, and at Poundbury "eco" village built by Prince Charles , there is a Quiet Space Building. When I asked John Elkington author of the book, *Cannibals without forks* and of the *Green Consumer Guide* and the inventor of the Triple Bottom Line, what will happen in the 21st century , in 1999 he told us -and we will never forget, it will be the century of spirituality. I thought he was mad or mistaken or both, but no one could have foreseen that not only was he right but that wars would once again be fought and people completely redefining themselves by their spirituality ,in some cases as a backlash against the modernity in what has been termed a *crisis of modernity*, and globalisation and unfettered consumerism. Thus a range of alternative healthcare ideas have grown up. Many of these are based on traditional practises with a modern tinge. People use sweat lodges which the ancient indigenous Americans used to use, like a precursor to a modern sauna, festivals where people camp out for days are increasingly popular. Healing fields at such gatherings are very very popular with all kinds of alternative therapies on offer. There is huge interest in *Stone Henge* as an original gigantic health spa from 5000 years ago.

Alternative healthcare includes massage, reflexology and many other aspects. Etienne Wenger's Multiple Intelligences informed our first Retreat, the idea of the whole person being valued and that our intelligence and our uniqueness includes, art, music, dance, physical activity and not just academic work. It also includes being close to nature, as it has been proven that humans are happier when they can see trees and natural surroundings, and patients get better more quickly.

Similarly, when a patient has been cured of a disease we don' t just cast them out to fend for themselves, the elderly and frail then need occupational therapy to avoid the same problem again and learn how to cope perhaps with a changed mobility status. Modern healthcare deals with the whole person ,past, present and future.

As greens we want healthcare status for everyone on the planet to be high and not just for those who are wealthy. All of society does better economically when everyone has a high health status and the more equal a society is, the better its outcomes for everyone.

HIV and AIDS

The HIV and AIDS epidemics cure has been described as 'one of the greatest success stories of modern science, not society, but science'. This seems perverse at first hearing but when examined it proves to be a very true statement. Never before has a new disease had a causative agent recognised and understood, as well as its mechanism of transfer, not just identified but fully preventable Although we still don't have a full cure, the life expectancy of those who contract HIV and are identified early is no shorter than those without it. However, all of this was known to the scientific community and the world before the bulk of the global burden of this disease occurred. This brings us on to examine why the HIV and AIDS pandemic happened at all. The answer of course , lies in the politics, economics and social issues surrounding the subject. For us this is the perfect example of the importance of access to medicines and lack of stigma in finding a cure.

Photo Dr Katherine Kennet , Seeing the Doctor in Nepal, a total lack of privacy and space and time as 3 patients are seen at the same time at the same desk.

The modern doctor training in the UK today, will learn that gone are the days of paternalistic medicine, where the doctor knows best. No longer is a doctor necessarily a man. Our own grandmother was dissuaded from becoming a doctor, as it was considered not a " suitable job for a nice girl" and all the doctors at that time were men. Today in the west, your doctor is just as likely to be a woman and slightly more women are training at the UK's s top Medical schools than men. The present day medical trainee will   be taught that at the heart of their medical practice is so called "*patent centred medicine*" which is the the idea that the patient's informed choice is to be taken as gospel. We are taught that it is not the doctor's role to choose the treatment, or the lack of treatment in some cases, but to provide the necessary education for a patient to make these decisions themselves, and facilitate whatever choice they make, thus giving each patient autonomy over their body and their own healthcare.

This is certainly not the case everywhere. There are many hospitals throughout the developing world where paternalistic medicine is very much alive and well. In rural hospitals in Nepal, for example, time and financial pressures mean that a visit to the doctor involves the patient describing their health issues to a very busy Doctor in front of a whole room full of people, a brief examination, and a prescription written in English (which the patient usually cannot read), with no explanation of what the medication is for, and often little insight into the clinicians' diagnosis. One really cannot get further from patient centred medicine. Yet despite these global differences in the practicalities of modern medicine, most new doctors still recite the Hippocratic oath, a 2000 year old promise to "first do no harm" and essentially (although the details have changed a bit since its first incarnation) to do right by our patients.

What we that hope the reader takes from this book is this; that health is a key (one could argue *the* key) human right and not just because health of itself is important, but also because without it. all other developments cannot even begin to take place!

References:

http://www.instituteofhealthequity.org/projects/fair-society-healthy-lives-the-marmot-review Accessed September 26th 2013
Stern Review of Climate Change, (2008) HM Treasury.
http://www.amnesty.org/en/news-and-updates/report/maternal-death-rate-sierra-leone-quothuman-rights-emergencyquot-20090921 Accessed September 26th 2013
BBC website http://www.bbc.co.uk/learningzone/clips/14005.html acessed 26th (September 2013)
http://www.greenpeace.org/usa/en/campaigns/global-warming-and-energy/polluterwatch/koch-industries/
Lord, Felton, Kennet (2012) Green Economics and the Citizens Income.
Kennet, Felton, Winchester, Gale de Oliveira, Mekonen (2012) Womens Unequal Pay and Poverty. The Green Economics Institute
http://web.bma.org.uk/pressrel.nsf/wall/776B5BE6D9D1D2D0802568F50054301D?OpenDocument The Hippocractic Oath of the BMA 1997
http://www.undp.org/content/undp/en/home/presscenter/speeches/2013/02/27/2013-global-mdg-conference-opening-remarks-helen-clark-undp-administrator-/ Helen Clark and the MDG accessed 26th September 2013

WHO website, "the Milenium Development Goals " accessed 27/09/13. http://www.who.int/topics/millennium_development_goals/about/en/index.html

If Women Counted (1988) by Marilyn Waring, former New Zealand Member of Parliament

http://www.ncbi.nlm.nih.gov/pmc/articles/PMC2935265/ Accessed 27th September 2013. Mental Health.

Ngul (2011) (Murali & Oyebode, 2004, p. 217). according to Ngul et al (2011). 010)

http://www.who.int/mental_health/policy/mhtargeting/mh_policyanalysis_who_undesa.pdf [WHO]

Elkington J. (1996) Cannibals without forks. Capstone Press

Wenger, Etienne (1998). *Communities of Practice: Learning, Meaning, and Identity*. Cambridge: Cambridge University Press.

Bentham J. (1789) The Principles of Morals and Legislation:

Photo by Dr Katherine Kennet. A Doctor washing her hands. Sanitation and washing hands with soap and water is one of the most modern and effective weapons in the fight to maintain human health.

Photo Miriam Kennet. A bird in Germany. Understanding our role in nature and learning to share with and help other creatures, and more importantly, seeing ourselves as one of them is a really important part of our Health and Well Being as well as that of society as a whole.

Photo Dr Katherine Kennet. A Doctor in her Scrubs Uniform prepares for patient care

1.2 How saving the planet will improve our health

By David Flint

Concern for the natural world is central to all Green thinking and, therefore, to Green economics. The political philosopher Professor Andrew Dobson has argued (Dobson 1960) that the two most distinctive principles of green political philosophy are the inherent value it ascribes to the natural world and its respect for the limits that world sets to both possible and proper human activity.

Our understanding of these limits has changed considerably in the last forty years. There's now a general acceptance that human emissions of greenhouse gases will create catastrophic climate change unless they are sharply reduced. We have also come to understand that the Earth's capacity to absorb greenhouse gases is far from the only limit that we are approaching. The most authoritative recent examination of limits is the Planetary Boundaries work, discussed by Mark Lynas (2011), which identifies nine distinct boundaries.

But what has this to do with health? Are there such things as green health policies? Indeed there are and most of them are the same as the policies needed to ensure we live within the planetary boundaries.

Although respect for the boundaries requires many policies a full analysis would be very lengthy. I will therefore concentrate on one, greenhouse gas emissions (GHGE). I will show that the policies we need to reduce GHGE are generally beneficial to human health and wellbeing and should therefore be favoured by people of all political persuasions, even those few sceptical of climate change, provided only that they value human health.

My argument has three parts:

1. Reducing fuel consumption, deforestation and meat consumption will improve our health
2. The Green alternatives will improve our health
3. The Green social justice agenda will improve our health.

Reducing fuel consumption, deforestation and meat consumption will improve our health

Electricity generation

Though all fuel burning creates some pollution there's no doubt that coal is much worse than the other main fuels. It's also extremely popular and this is doubly unfortunate because it produces more greenhouse gases and more pollution per kilowatt-hour (kWh) than the other main fuels. A sharp reduction in coal consumption is probably the single most important policy for climate change mitigation.

New Scientist reported (McKenna, 2013) research by the International Energy Agency (IAE) (Husebye et al, 2002) which showed that coal is the most dangerous fuel used in electricity generation. Coal-related deaths are predominately due to the pollution and this arises from extraction and transport as well as combustion. It is interesting to note that when disasters are included the most dangerous generation technology is hydropower; though most of the increase is due to events in China in 1975.

Fuel	Deaths per 10B kWh – normal operation	Largest disaster	Deaths from largest disaster	Deaths per 10B kWh – all
Coal	2.8-32.7			32.7
Hydroelectric	1.0-1.6	Dam failures in China, 1975	230,000	54.7
Natural gas	0.3-1.6			1.6
Nuclear	0.2-1.2	Chernobyl, 1986	9,000	1.2

Markandya et al (2009) have modelled the effect of reducing GHGE from electricity generation and distribution on fine particulate matter (PM2.5) concentrations in the air and thus on health. It found that a 50% GHGE reduction by 2030 would save 4,000 premature deaths in the EU. In China and India smaller GHGE savings would produce much larger benefits - 57,000 and 93,000 premature deaths in the respectively. The benefit is greatest in India because its air quality is currently the worst.

All generation systems have other health impacts as well:

· Coal: "the fly ash emitted by a power plant—a by-product from burning coal for electricity—carries into the surrounding environment 100 times more radiation than a nuclear power plant producing the same amount of energy" (Hvistendahl, 2007)

· Oil: Oil extraction has pernicious effects on local people in some places. Oil spills in the Niger delta have often damaged the health and livelihoods of local people.

Reducing our use of fossil fuels, especially coal, would have major benefits for climate and health.

Travel

The private car is a major source of GHGE. A reduction in car use is therefore a key climate change mitigation policy (together with improvements in fuel economy the introduction of electric and hybrid vehicles). It also provides some health benefits through reduced air pollution (Haines, 2012).

Greens generally favour lower speed limits and many campaigners have pushed to reduce urban speed limits from 30 to 20 mph. According to Grundy et al, 2006, the 20 mph speed limits imposed on London roads reduced deaths by 42%.

Deforestation

Deforestation is a key environmental concern and a major source of GHGE. It's also the reason that Indonesia is the third largest emitter of greenhouse gases in the world! There's a simple pattern. Agrobusinesses operating in Indonesia clear forests in order to plant palm trees (needed to meet international demand for palm oil). Fires started accidentally or deliberately consume the felled wood emitting vast amounts of carbon dioxide. In June 2013 the Guardian reported (Vidal, 2013) that over 800 fires were burning. They also set light to the peat, starting underground fires that are immensely difficult to extinguish and may burn for months.

These fires create vast smoke clouds that carry pollution across Indonesia itself and into adjacent countries – even as far as Hong Kong. The harm is hard to estimate but is clearly significant. For instance, during the winter of 1997/8 the smoke cloud covered an area larger than Europe! At least 20 million people were treated for smoke-related illnesses and many more were too poor to afford treatment. There were several collisions at sea and a plane crash in Sumatra killed 234 passengers. Deforestation also harms the health of local people by polluting watercourses and dispossessing indigenous peoples.

Stopping deforestation would obviously reduce GHGE and improve public health.

Meat consumption

Farming was responsible for about 10% of the UK's GHGE in 2011. Meat production requires more resources – land, water, fuel, pesticides – than producing vegetable food with the same nutritional value. Greens therefore favour eating less meat and many are vegetarians or even vegans.

Friel and co-workers (2009) modelled the health implications of a 30% reduction in meat consumption. Meat is a major source of dietary saturated fat and cholesterol and the study predicted a 15% reduction in ischaemic heart disease. There may also be reductions in cerebrovascular disease and colon cancer.

Overall

A study by the Netherlands Environmental Assessment Agency estimated the financial benefits of the lives that would be saved by climate change mitigation policies (Bollen et al 2009). They found that "Measures to reduce emissions of greenhouse gases to 50% of 2005 levels, by 2050, can reduce the number of premature deaths from the chronic exposure to air pollution by 20 to 40%." The scale and timing of benefits vary considerably between countries. In China, for example, policies that reduced GHGE by 80% relative to business as usual would deliver health benefits worth 4.5% of the Chinese GDP by 2050. The costs, however, would be 6.5% of GDP so health benefits alone would not justify the proposed policies. As a side-effect, however, 4.5% of GDP is very impressive!

The Green alternatives will improve our health

Travel

Travel in the UK, as in other developed countries, is dominated by the motor car. In consequence car use was responsible for 16% of the UK's carbon dioxide emissions (other than international shipping and aviation) in 2011. To reduce these emissions requires a significant reduction in car use and this implies increases in walking, cycling and the use of public transport.

Walking and cycling are, of course, much healthier than driving or being driven whether in cars or buses and the current epidemics of obesity and diabetes, to name but two, are due in part to our failure to take enough exercise. Though visits to the gym help most people who join gyms soon give up. Walking and cycling are good alternatives to the expensive artificiality of the gym.

Switches to walking and cycling are associated with lower levels of ischemic heart disease, cerebrovascular disease, hypertensive heart disease, dementia, diabetes, breast and colon cancer and depression. Research by Woodcock et al (2009) considered changes in physical activity, air pollution and the risk of road traffic injury resulting from reductions in car use. They found savings of 7,500 disability-adjusted life-years per one million population. Their calculations did include increases in traffic accidents affecting pedestrians and cyclists.

The Ramblers have summarised the health benefits of walking (Ramblers, 2013). A study of 30,000 people in Copenhagen (Anderson, 2000) found that cycling to work for 3 hours per week reduced mortality by 40%.

Photo Miriam Kennet. The joys of mountain life! Mountains are some of the most threatened environments on earth but they provide huge benefits for health, fitness and relaxation as well as sources of many of the world's most important water sources. Threatened water sources are becoming more evident and affecting the economy of whole areas and the Green Economics Institute was asked to help the government in South Tyrol in the Alps where HEP was already being affected by climate change and this was affecting local businesses. Reducing car use is a climate change priority and increasing levels of exercise is a health priority. The priorities of Public health authorities and climate change campaigners converge in this respect.

Housing

Buildings are a critical part of the emissions picture since 40% of global emissions are buildings-related. Because buildings – even bad ones – last for many decades it's obviously important that we start building the low-energy buildings that we will need by 2030 and 2050 now. This is not happening at even 1% of the scale needed.

A key reason is that that many supposedly low-energy buildings are nothing of the sort (Tofield, 2012). Some use as much energy as buildings in which no special energy-reduction measures have been taken. However, a method of producing very-low energy buildings does exist. It's called passivhaus (http://www.passivhaus.org.uk/) and has been extensively used in Germany and Sweden. Passivhaus buildings (which may be schools or offices as well as houses) often use only 10% as much energy as conventional ones.

So Passivhaus is great for the climate. But what about the users?

It's good for them too, which should be no surprise since user comfort was the original inspiration for passivhaus. In his review Bruce Tofield produces evidence that passivhaus buildings are more comfortable and that the occupants of passivhaus offices both think they are and are more productive. And a report by the Westminster Sustainable Business Forum (Janowska, 2011) estimated that good low-energy office buildings would reduce sick leave by three days per year. They would also increase the productivity of office workers. Some similar data is given in Greening the Bottom Line (Romm and Browning, 1994).

The evidence here is indicative rather than compelling but it does point to health benefits that will presumably apply to homes as well as to offices.

A study by Wilkinson *et al.*, 2009 looked at the results of a possible programme to reduce GHGE due to the UK's housing stock by 26% by improved insulation, ventilation control, switching to electric heating, etc. The study found that consequential reductions in exposure to fine particles (PM2.5) would reduce premature deaths by 5,400 per year. This must be an underestimate since it ignored both cold-related deaths – currently a serious problem in the UK – and heat-related deaths – which are likely to become commoner as the climate warms.

The social justice agenda

Green economists have always sought social justice and very few environmentalists have favoured inequality. This commitment was originally founded on conventional Enlightenment moral principles: Since all are equally human they deserve equal respect from fellow citizens and institutions and equal opportunities to learn, work and play.

But Green economics, unlike most other sorts, seeks to base itself on science and it was therefore very satisfying to find, in 2010, that science supports the Green commitment to social justice. In their now famous book *The Spirit Level* sociologists Richard Wilkinson and Kate Pickett reviewed a vast body of research on the consequences of inequality. They found that unequal societies have higher levels of obesity, drug use, teenage pregnancy, infant mortality, murder and mental illness. And, the wellbeing of their children is lower.

They also established, at least to my satisfaction, that inequality CAUSES this array of social problems. It is not the only cause but it is one that we understand and can therefore address.

Finally, in a nicely circular fashion, more equal societies recycle more of their rubbish thus reducing (if only by a little) their GHGE.

Conclusion

This brief survey strongly suggests that most of the policies required to avoid climate change will have significant health benefits. In some cases the financial value of the benefits, in medical costs avoided and extra economic production, will be comparable with the costs. Both the financial benefits and the obvious human benefits – lives saved, suffering avoided – should be considered in assessing proposals for climate change mitigation.

There is, of course, a sense in which this discussion misses the point. Uncontrolled climate change will produce a global catastrophe in which millions will die from famine, flooding, disease and war. To avoid this is worth almost any cost.

But perhaps these deaths are just too many and remote, in both time and space, to engage today's policy-makers. Perhaps the likely deaths of thousands will weigh more heavily than the possible deaths of millions. We can only hope so.

References

Anderson, Lars Bo, 2000: *"All-Cause Mortality Associated With Physical Activity During Leisure Time, Work, Sports and Cycling to Work"* Archives of Internal Medicine Vol 160 No. 11 June 12, 2000. http://archinte.ama-assn.org/issues/v160n11/full/ioi90593.html

Barrett, M. and M. Holland, 2008 *The Costs and Health Benefits of Reducing Emissions from PowerStations in Europe*, Air Pollution and Climate Secretariat http://www.airclim.org/reports/documents/APC20.pdf

J.C. Bollen, C.J. Brink, H.C. Eerens, A.J.G. Manders, 2009: *Co-benefits of climate policy*. Netherlands Environmental Assessment Agency.

Dobson, Andrew, 1960: *Green Political Thought*. Unwin Hyman.

Friel, S., Dangour, A.D., Garnett, T., Lock, K., Chalabi, Z., Roberts, I., Butler, A., Butler, C.D., Waage, J., McMichael, A.J. and Haines, A. (2009): *Public health benefits of strategies to reduce greenhouse-gas emissions: food and agriculture*. Lancet 374, 2016-25.

Grundy, Chris, Steinbach, Rebecca, Edwards, Phil, Green, Judith, Armstrong, Ben, and Wilkinson, Paul, 2007: *Effect of 20 mph traffic speed zones on road injuries in London, 1986-2006: controlled interrupted time series analysis*- BMJ 2009; 339:b4469.

Haines, Andy, 2012: *The health co-benefits of policies to reduce greenhouse gas Emissions.* In Vardoulakis and Heaviside 2012. Online at http://www.hpa.org.uk/webc/HPAwebFile/HPAweb_C/1317136682288.

Husebye, Sverre, et al, 2002: *ENVIRONMENTAL AND HEALTH IMPACTS OF ELECTRICITY GENERATION.* International Energy Agency (IEA).

Hvistendahl, Mara, 2007: *Coal Ash Is More Radioactive than Nuclear Waste* . Scientific American. http://www.scientificamerican.com/article.cfm?id=coal-ash-is-more-radioactive-than-nuclear-waste

Janowska, Peter, 2011: *Leaner and Greener: Delivering Effective Estate Management*, Westminster Sustainable Business Forum, London, February 2011, http://www.policyconnect.org.uk/sites/default/files/Final%20version%20-%20blacktype%20-%20Leaner%20and%20Greener.pdf.

Lynas, Mark, 2011. *The God Species*.

Markandya, A., Armstrong, B.G., Hales, S., Chiabai, A., Criqui, P., Mima, S., Tonne, C. and Wilkinson, P. (2009) *Public health benefits of strategies to reduce greenhouse – gas emissions: low carbon electricity generation. Lancet* 374, 1917-29.

Meadows, et al, 1972: *The Limits to Growth* by Donella H. Meadows, Dennis L. Meadows, Jørgen Randers, and William W. Behrens III.

McKenna, Phil, 2011: *Fossil fuels are far deadlier than nuclear power*. New Scientist, 23 March 2011.

Ramblers, 2013: *The case for Walking for Health: a briefing for Scheme Coordinators.*

Romm, Joseph J and Browning, William D, 1994. *Greening the Bottom Line.* US Department of Energy and the Rocky Mountain Institute.

Tofield, Bruce, 2012: Delivering a low-energy building: Making Quality Commonplace. Adapt Low Carbon Group, University of East Anglia, October 2012. http://www.uea.ac.uk/mac/comm/media/press/2012/October/passivhaus-bruce-tofield

Vardoulakis, Sotiris and Heaviside, Clare, (eds) 2012: *Health Effects of Climate Change in the UK 2012. Health Protection Agency.* Online at *www.hpa.org.uk/webc/HPAwebFile/HPAweb_C/1317135969235*.

Vidal, John, 2013. *Indonesia's forest fire smoke blows deeper into Malaysia.* theguardian.com, Monday 24 June 2013.

Wilkinson, P., Smith, K.R., Davies, M., Adair, A., Armstrong, B.G., Barrett, M., Bruce, N., Haines, A., Hamilton, I., Oreszczyn, T., Ridley, I., Tonne, C. and Chalabi, A. (2009) *Public health benefits of strategies to reduce greenhouse-gas emissions: household energy. Lancet* 374, 1917-1929.

Wilkinson, Richard, and Pickett, Kate, 2010: *The Spirit Level: Why Equality is Better for Everyone.* See also the Equality Trusty website at http://www.equalitytrust.org.uk/.

Woodcock, J., Edwards, P., Tonne, C., Armstrong, B.G., Ashiru, O., Banister, D., Beevers, S., Chalabi, Z., Chowdhury, Z., Cohen, A., Franco, O.H., Haines, A., Hickman, R., Lindsay, A., Mittal, I., Mohan, D., Tiwari, G., Woodward, A. and Roberts, I. (2009): *Public health benefits of strategies to reduce greenhouse-gas emissions: urban land transport. Lancet* 374, 1930-1943.

1.3 Low Carbon Pathways to Healthcare

.

By Alan Cunningham

Introduction

This chapter suggests that many decisions on health have sustainability effects and that many decisions on sustainable living have health effects and that this points to the existence of a preferred combined health/sustainable living pathway. This pathway is difficult to identify in practice but it may be mapped in part by using the Health Policy Framework of the World Health Organisation and the International Policy Framework for Sustainable Living as guides to community organisation.

The Policy Context The World Health Organisation and Public Health Academics believe that community health is a function of the way society is organised (4) and that community health is affected by Determinants of Health including the Social Determinants of Health which are not distributed evenly throughout society (6,7,8,9). Thus any decision to move for change in society including change in accordance with a 'Green Economics' agenda or change to a 'Transition Town' agenda is likely to have implications for community health

The developing Policy Framework of the World Health Organisation from 'Health for All' (2) and'Health21'(Europe)(5) to 'Health 20/20'(Europe)(20) is based on a 'Rights' based approach to health and a 'Rights' based approach to sustainable living.

The International Policy Framework for sustainable living can be traced from 'Agenda21', the United Nations Agreement on the Environment (The Rio Agreement in 1992 (3) to the new set of Millennium Goals to be introduced in 2015 (16, 17)

Both the Health Policy Framework and the Sustainable Development Policy Framework, with their associated research and indicators can be used as a guide to community organisation. They can be used to derive a notional sustainable community standard - this being the choice of a rational group of people who have autonomy, who are fully informed on health, fully informed on sustainable living and who seek to organise their lives accordingly.

It is obvious that a decision to start an allotment or community garden to obtain cheap local food will also bring with it increased exercise and sunlight that are likely to be beneficial to health, similarly a decision to walk or cycle to reduce fuel use is also likely to bring health benefits. A successful Health Promotion Campaign to reduce the incidence of serious illnesses such as Cancer, Heart Disease or Stroke by tackling the determinants of ill health such as alcohol, obesity or smoking is likely also to reduce the massive carbon costs which are implicit in intensive medical care.

There is a body of evidence that nature and green spaces have the potential to enhance physical, mental, spiritual social and environmental health (Mark Dooris), Interacting with nature improves mental health, social interaction, community cohesion and perceived well being, it reduces the effects of the risk factors for health (19)

The 'Biophilia ' hypothesis was formulated by E O Wilson- Closeness to Nature increases wellbeing as well as increased likelihood of understanding and caring for nature. It suggests that we have an innate sensitivity to and need for living things as we have co-existed for thousands of generations, we seek connections with other life, and nature has an emotional effect on us. Nature deprivation can create problems. Psychological benefits flow from nature, prisoners and hospital patients have been healthier when they could see farmland or trees.(10,11,12,19)

A recent report by the Faculty for Public Health in association with Natural England (22) suggests   contact with green spaces can improve a number of aspects of mental and physical wellbeing: 1) It can reduce symptoms of poor mental health and   stress   and   can   improve   mental   wellbeing   for   all   age   groups. 2) Access to green spaces can increase levels of physical activity for all ages. 3) Having green spaces in an area can contribute to reduced health inequalities. 4) Safe green spaces can increase levels of communal activity across different social groups   as   well   as   increase   resident's   satisfaction   with   their   local   area. 5) Green spaces can help with our response to climate change through their potential to reduce the impacts of heatwaves and reduce flooding and reduce CO_2 emissions. 6) Green spaces and natural environments can improve air and noise quality and support sustainability through increasing biodiversity, encouraging active transport and community participation.

In 1977, the World Health Assembly decided that the major social goal of governments and WHO should be the attainment by all people of the world by the year 2000 of a level of health that would permit them to lead a socially and economically productive life. In 1981, the Assembly unanimously adopted the Global Strategy for Health for All by the Year 2000. Within Europe this led to the Health21 Policy Framework, which included 21 targets for health to be attained by the 21st Century. This was also rooted in the United Nations Declaration on the Environment (the Rio Agreement (1992).

Health Policy has also been influenced by the Ottawa Charter on Health Promotion (1986)(14) 'Health is created and lived by people within the settings of their everyday life, where they learn, work, play and love'.. .'People should not be seen in isolation of the larger social units in which they live'

According to the Ottawa Charter Health Promotion is the process of enabling people to increase control over, and to improve, their health. To reach a state of complete physical, mental and social well-being, an individual or group must be able to identify and to realize aspirations, to satisfy needs, and to change or cope with the environment.

Health is, therefore, seen as a resource for everyday life, not the objective of living. Health is a positive concept emphasizing social and personal resources, as well as physical capacities. Therefore, health promotion is not just the responsibility of the health sector, but goes beyond healthy life-styles to well-being.

The fundamental conditions and resources for health were: peace, shelter, education, food, income, a stable eco-system, sustainable resources, social justice, and equity. Key strategies for health under the Ottawa Charter included the need to build healthy policy, create supportive environments, strengthen community action and reorient health services.

WHO Health Policy thus formed the basis of many successful international policy initiatives such as Healthy Cities, action to challenge the Social Determinants of Health and Healthy Ageing. It is currently being updated into a new emerging European Policy Framework, Health 20/20. Whilst the present writer does not have the authority to produce such a pathway, anyone who is reasonably well informed could produce an example of what such a pathway might look like.

Advantages of Using the International Policy Framework Locally
- Increased thought given to the possibility of local decision making.
- Better quality and better informed local decision making.
- Less reliance on the kind of vested interests identified by Ivan Illich and David Simon, as this approach should help people minimise their vulnerability to such interests.(15,18)
- If the WHO and Health Academics such as Sir. Michael Marmot demonstrate a relationship between Healthy and Sustainable Living, which they do, then any process of green economics which fails to recognise that relationship is likely to create or exacerbate inefficiency and unfairness and this is likely to undermine its effectiveness.
- In decisions on food and nutrition this approach could support the better attainment of health and sustainability criteria. It would reduce the market impact of big actors such as Asda, McDonalds and TESCO.
- It would tend to reduce the effects of the massive deficit in movement which lies at the heart of many health problems whilst reducing the impact of carbon intensive forms of transport such as driving (13).
- It could be integrated into the newly emerging Millennium Goals to be introduced in 2015.

Decision making at every level is likely to be fairer and more efficient if the health and sustainability effects are taken into account.

Any strategy for change could have implications for any or all of the categories identified in both Health and Sustainable Living Policy Frameworks and such decisions could be improved by importing the available fund of knowledge and research into local decision making. In Britain a wide range of social and economic indicators are mapped down to Lower Level Super Output Areas (Office for National Statistics), small local geographic areas which typically contain 1500 residents or 400 households. There are also very detailed studies of land use available from Ordnance Survey, Office for National Statistics, local authorities and other sources.

Local projects such as Green Economics or Transition Initiatives have the potential to realise very detailed local information about areas and populations as well as sound theory based on the WHO Policy Framework, the Rio Agreement as well as more recent work to replace the Millennium Goals.

Conclusion

It is recommended that increased use be made of the International Health and Sustainable Development Framework in local organisation and decision making including the use of a notional sustainable community standard - this being the choice of a rational group of people who have autonomy, who are fully informed on health, fully informed on sustainable living and who seek to organise their lives accordingly.

References

United Nations Declaration on Human Rights (1948).

Declaration of the World Health Organisation (1977)

United Nations Agreement on the Environment (Rio) (1992)

City planning for health and sustainable development - WHO Europe (1992)

Health 21 – Health for all in the 21st century – WHO Europe (1999)

Social Determinants of Health- The Solid Facts – Sir. M. Marmot and Richard Wilkinson (2003)

Report of the WHO Commission on Social Determinants of Health – Chair Sir Michael Marmot (2008)

Fair Society, Healthy Lives – The UK Marmot Report (2010) Chair Sir Michael Marmot.

The Spirit Level Richard Wilkinson and Kate Pickett (2009)

Biophilia E. Wilson (1984) Harvard University Press

Healthy Parks, Healthy People. The Health Benefits of Contact with Nature in a Park (2002) Maller C, Townsend M, Brown P and St. Leger L

Health & Wellbeing: Trees, Woods and Natural Spaces, Paul Tabbush & Liz O'Brien, Forestry Commission(2002)

: Steps to health. A European framework to promote physical activity for health WHO (2007)

Ottawa Charter on Health Promotion –WHO (1986)

The Wire HBO DVD, David Simon

The United Nations Millennium Goals http://www.un.org/millenniumgoals/

Redefining Sustainable Development, Stockholm Resilience Centre http://www.stockholmresilience.org/21/research/research-news/3-27-2013-redefining-sustainable-development.html

Deschooling Society (1973), Disabling Professions (1987), Ivan Illich
University of Central Lancashire, Healthy Settings Development Unit Bulletins
2002,2005 Edited by Mark Dooris (*The material in italics is derived wholly from these bulletins*)
 Health 20/20 The European Policy for health and wellbeing
http://www.euro.who.int/en/what-we-do/health-topics/health-policy/health-2020-the-european-policy-for-health-and-well-being
 (21)UK Government -Office for National Statistics- 'Multiple Deprivation Indices' (2010) Area   Profiles.
(22)Great Outdoors: How Our Natural Health Service Uses Green Space To Improve Wellbeing. Faculty of Public Health/Natural England (2010)

Photo Miriam Kennet. Rural Calm in France

1.4 The intergenerational oppression of unfettered population growth

By Chit Chong

The issue of population is divisive in society, and is especially so amongst many from the left of the conventional political spectrum who see it as a threat to a women's right to control her body and reproduction. In tandem with this is a strong belief in Gandhi's maxim *"Earth provides enough to satisfy every man's need but not for every man's greed"* leading many to say that all that would be needed to feed a population of 10 billion would be equity between people and nations and efficient distribution of food.

This chapter will show that these these beliefs are not only wrong but morally indefensible and in the harsh light of climate change represent intergenerational oppression under the fig-leaf of feminism and equality. I will look at food production in the UK as a model of the world and ask whether the UK in particular could eed itself in a 4 degree world.

Setting the scene

There is little doubt that we are entering the anthropocene, a epoch of the Earth with high carbon dioxide in the atmosphere created by the activities of humans as they release the fossil fuels locked up by plants over millions of years during the Carboniferous epoch 300 million years ago

Humanity's presence on the planet for only 50,000 years is an eye-blink compared to the 5 million years of chimpanzees our nearest relative. It was only in living memory that we have come to destroy the environment to the extent that we have. About 200 million shared the planet with Christ, and it took 1800 years for the population to reach 1 billion. Now, every14 years or so, sees another billion is added to the population and we are expected to reach 10 billion give or take a billion by 2050.

In tandem with this increase in population, humanity has fritted away both non-renewable and renewable resources at a rate which would take 1.5 worlds to provide more profligate nations like the US running at a rate of 3 worlds. This consumption has been at the cost to other species, which have been going extinct at an alarming rate as we destroy their habitat to feed our greed and our growing population.

A key resource that has been frittered away, has been the ability of the planet to absorb our pollution, including for example the whirlpools of plastic waste trapped by ocean currents, which are killing successive generations of sea creatures from turtles to albatrosses. Undoubtedly, the most crucial of this is the planets' ability to re-sequestrate the fossil fuels laid down carefully by nature over millions of years, that we have released since the industrial revolution, most of which has been since the 1970s.

The result of this, is that carbon dioxide has built up from the 280 parts per million to the 400 ppm which it has now reached. As we have singularly failed to do anything to stem the increase in emissions, we are moving towards a world which will increase in temperature by 4°C by the end of the century, even if we are lucky.

The impact of this on all aspects of our life will be catastrophic. It is important to bear in mind that the errant weather that the world has seen in the past decade has been in part the result of the 0.5 °C of warming since the industrial revolution and as the time that CO_2 spends in the atmosphere is about 100 years, is only the damage caused arguably the result of Brunel and his industrial revolution. The impact of our more recent and current emissions is yet to come and will make the errant weather we have had seem mild.

Refuting arguments against population as a climate change issue.

Feeding 10 billion

The Green Revolution of the 1960s brought with it much higher yields but also a much higher reliance on fertiliser and pesticides. This, in tandem with transport and food processing has led some scientists to calculate and equate one calorie of food requires 10 calories of fossil fuel, compared to US agriculture in the 1940s which produced 2.3 calories of food for every 1 calorie of fossil fuel, or Chinese agriculture up to the 1960s which used virtually no fossil fuel in its production.

That said, Fairlee S. has calculated that Britain which currently imports 50% of food[1] could grow enough to feed our 60 million mouths using a low meat diet and low input organic agriculture. However the land required for such agriculture would have to be increased, reducing the land not used for agriculture down from 28% to 14%, inevitably destroying habitats used by other species.

This low input organic agriculture would have to be radically different from today's high input organic agriculture. It would use human waste as the main fertiliser supplemented by green manure compared to conventional organic agriculture which uses significant quantities of fertilisers like dried seaweed and its attendant processing and transport carbon costs. The result is that conventional organic food delivered to the supermarkets is only 30% less carbon intensive than conventionally farmed counterparts. (Pollan M) would have to be substantially improved.

Given the historic example of China and the possibility of feeding a densely populated island like the UK from within its own borders, it may be possible to feed 10 billion people using low input agriculture, so long as climate remains benign and food is shared equally.

However, the changeable and inhospitable weather that climate change will bring, as well as increasing water scarcity worldwide, simply spells out famine for many. The aberrant weather of the last decade has shown how agriculture can be adversely effected. The European heat wave of 2003 resulted in 70,000 deaths as well as a 10% reduction in grain production in the European Union. More recently, the 2012 heatwave in the US,which is one of the world's major bread baskets, resulted in an 8% reduction in grain production. Clearly, as climate change bites, with increased likelihood of prolonged draughts, interspersed with prolonged flood,s as well as more frequent and violent storms, the impact on agriculture would be severe. In such a scenario, an extra 3 billion mouths to feed on top of the 7 billion today may well be an extra 3 billion to starve.

Equity

It is often argued that it is possible to feed everyone in the world so long as it is fairly shared. To emphasise this, Gandhi quote *"Earth provides enough to satisfy every man's need but not for every man's greed"* is frequently cited. However it misses a crucial caveat added by Gandhi who goes on to say *"So long as we cooperate with the cycle of life, the soil renews its fertility indefinitely and provides health, recreation, sustenance and peace to those who depend on it"*[2] As climate change clearly shows, we have broken the cycle of life and the soil may not renew its fertility.

Also, unlike homeopathic cures, which only work when divided into infinitesimal portions, people require a basic intake of food to survive and cannot be divided up in a similar fashion. The National Health Service in the UK , for example, says that the healthy diet for an average man, this is 2500 calories and for an average woman 2000 calories, and all that separates health from obesity is the addition of a large burger and fries a day with an additional 1500 calories Conversely, 1,000 calories less leads to semi starvation[1]. Clearly, the resources required to fulfil these needs will be far less with a vegan diet than on a meat based diet, however basic food needs represents a finite point, below which, equity of food distribution cannot provide enough for all.

In a finite world with finite needs, all that is done by avoiding population stabilisation and reduction is that a more difficult job is left to future generations.

Cutting Consumption and/or cutting population

Environmentalists, who are concerned about climate change, sometimes believe that reducing consumption is the key to addressing climate change. In the short-term, this is clearly the case, as reduction in the birth-rate takes many years to feed into a reduction in population, especially when it is occurring at the same time as longevity is increasing.

However, reduction in consumption is easier said than done, for example, reducing heating temperature is the cheapest form of energy saving and the Energy Savings Trust in the UK advises the public that setting the thermostat 1 °C lower equates to a 10% saving, This assumes that the outside temperature is 10°C and the inside temperature is 20°C. To achieve really significant savings such as the UK government's 80% target by 2050 would require a room temperatures of 12°C which is untenable except for the most hardy. Also as mentioned above, food consumption has a basic level below which consumption cannot be reduced.

[1]   Minnesota Starvation Experiment 1944
http://en.wikipedia.org/wiki/Minnesota_Starvation_Experiment

As the impact on the environment is proportional to average consumption times population, once consumption is reduced, the only way of reducing our impact on the environment is by reducing population. Since population has such a long-term effect, lasting not just the lifetime of a generation but also that of their offspring, reducing consumption without addressing population inevitably hampers long-term reductions of our impact on the environment.

Women's rights.

The hard fought rights of women in the west and the continued oppression of women in the rest of the world makes population a difficult issue for many. This is because reducing birth rate and by inference reducing the average number of children that a women should have is seen as a threat to these rights, especially if the message comes from men. However the issue of population is a species issue and is one that all individuals, male and female have a stake in.

It is often argued that improving rights and education for women would be the most effective means of reducing birth rate. This would have the ideological benefit of strengthening women's right to control whether they have children as well as raising their level of equality. However it is not axiomatic and depends on the cultures involved. Nigeria and the Philippines both have relatively high levels of female education in tandem with high birth rates. Further, research shows that states in India show a greater correlation between access to television and reduced birthrate than female education1. Making women responsible for population through rights and education will now doubt help reduce the rate of population increase, but is this enough and is it fair that women have the sole responsibility for such an important species issue?

However perhaps more important, is the fact that the rights of children are rarely if ever talked about in the context of birth rate. Few would argue that parents have a duty to do their best to ensure that their children have sufficient resources to ensure fulfilling lives, especially so when climate change threatens to reduce the resources available to our children.

This argument may purport to uphold the rights of women but undeniably ignores the rights of children.

Other species

Like children, other species hardly merit a footnote to discussions about population, yet they are crucial to the ecology of the planet.

Animal rights and wildlife organisations are strangely quiet on this issue even though human pressures are a leading cause of habitat destruction and with it the extinction of species. Clearly, this is an animal rights issue, but equally important is the impact of chipping away at the biodiversity that species extinction represents. The reduced biodiversity inevitably reduces the ability of the planet to resist climate change and act to mitigate it by sequestering carbon.

The issue of other species is rarely heard in the context of human population and like future generations of humans, the voice and rights of other species should be integral to discussions on both human populations and human induced climate change.

Many non human species activities' help to regulate the climate, even humans and primates help seed the forests which in turn help with climate control.

Conclusion

Population is a climate change issue and should be tackled in tandem with emissions reductions. Efforts to reduce emissions and adapt to climate change will be difficult and increasing numbers of people merely magnify the difficulty.

Morally, not addressing population issues now only postpones the need to do so more drastically for future generations, who will then have the problem magnified by the increased numbers, which we in our generations have failed to address. It represents another failure of people living today to fulfil their side of the contract between generations, which is to look after the future of future generations so that they will look after us in our dotage.

Lets work together to create more innovative solutions to this problem and start to think about how we can really make a difference that our descendents will respect and value. Lets start that process now Dear Reader.

Editors Note: This paper represents a personal view which is controversial but which the editors feel is balanced and useful opening of the debate to do something about the problem of having too many humans on the planet and probably not enough of the other species!

1] Working together on imported food, Food Standards Agency 2010

2] *Gandhi on Providence and Greed Y. P. Anand and Mark Lindley*

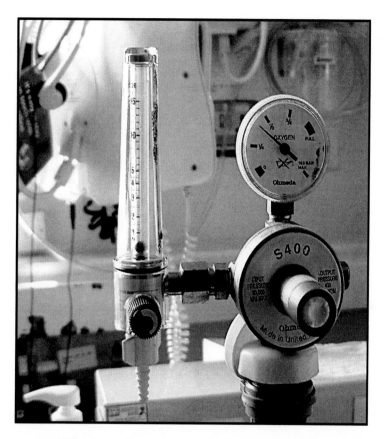

Photo: Medical Equipment by Judith and Antony Felton

1.5 The Descent of Authority in Public Discourse on Environmental Health

by W. Thomas Duncanson

Experientially, 'environmental health' is one of the key dimensions of the size of our world. Those of us who grew up in the United States east of the Mississippi River, for instance, have always had a bounty of water near at hand; given the water shortages over much of the planet, we enjoy an almost embarrassing plenty of lakes, rivers, streams, ponds, and wells. But we are taught to not drink a drop that did not come treated from the tap, even when we are out in the beautiful countryside, for our water runs 'poison' with industrial pollution, mining and agricultural 'run-off', and the taint of human sewage. Rather than our world being a vast and enticing place, it is the size of our canteen or water bottle, the amount of water we can bring from home and possibly replenish from a public spigot. We may be standing on the shore of a lake, but at the bottom of our canteen is anxiety and thirst. Poor environmental health may not strike us ill on the spot, but it imposes limit after limit on what Ralf Dahrendorf (1979) called 'life chances'. How many life chances does one have, if the environment dictates one stay home, or if workplace conditions force one to go home and recuperate, or if one's community is so stripped of essential resources one is required to spend every day from dawn to dusk in a single-minded search for water, fuel, grain, and protein? Environmental health is life and death, disease and disability, freedom and consciousness. Considering environmental health begins us thinking about the remarkable limits we have passively internalized about toxicity, resourcelessness, and the small space that remains for our life. These concerns are not jejune. That we live conditioned by our environment is not a bad thing; that we are prisoners of our own filth is monstrous. And that this is a project of political-economic reform there can be no question.

If our physical body is ill, we visit the physician. Who then is the physician of the environment? Is it the environmental scientist? Hans-Magnus Enzenberger wrote presciently in 1974 that no person could begin to possess all the science of the environment, and that we would be routinely frustrated that scientists would not provide us with straightforward solutions to our environmental problems. Donna Haraway (1997) acknowledges that people trust scientists and technologists, until they do not trust them, and then the publics' passive acceptance of science explodes in incoherence; passive acceptance of the work of huge institutions of science is not enough of a give and take relationship to carry the uncertainties. We cannot always even decide who or what is an environmental scientist—an ecologist certainly, but a geologist, a civil engineer? I think one of the best ways to think of Kennet and Heinemann's 'green economics' project (2006) is being about creating new 'authorities' in environmental matters. By 'authority' I do not mean who has sovereignty, or what sort of bureaucratic structure to follow, but 'authority' in the rhetorical sense of who we listen to and why. Of course, this is the great grinding political-cultural issue in the West for two centuries now, and today the global dynamic: only a scientific and mathematically sophisticated elite is able to judge in matters of technological adaptation, economic development, and environmental risk. This is such a central focus of cultural concern, it is almost embarrassing to bring it up. The book shelves groan under the weighty tomes on the subject (as but one example, Saul 1992). Some wag will dismissively observe this was the unabomber's fixation (Chase 2003). The problem is played out every weekend in the cinemas, with contemporary 'Frankenstein' stories told about new technologies. In this gloomy view the 'lay person' is a helpless victim with nothing to add to the conversation, and our democratic political structures produce mountains of pointless palaver. As many have written, on the big environmental issues, the 'DAD' model is followed (Depoe & Delicath 20040: officials meet with their business and scientific advisors and DECIDE, they ANNOUNCE their decision to the public, and then DEFEND it against public criticism. Kennet and Heinemann think these closed and simulated processes need to be opened up to new voices who will be taken seriously; as just one for instance, they hold that women have a great deal to say on matters of sustainable, equitable, development. Non-orthodox economists also have much to contribute. These new authorities need to be heard in many venues, including those where public policy is set.

Democratic Problem, Elite Problem

Often those of us who write about environmental communication do so as advocates for citizen participation. Mostly what we have learned gives us, at best, minimal optimism for increasing the power of new voices in environmental advocacy. We know the average citizen rightly fears to become involved in speaking out on environmental issues from overcoming her or his fear of public speaking to being condescended to, insulted, lied to, lied about in public, betrayed by allies, and disappointed in the final outcome (Frantzich, 2008). People rightly mistrust their governments which may well exhaust them and divide them to conquer them, may beat them if they protest (Roy, 2002), and will likely re-classify their 'voices' as 'noise'

(Dikeç, 2004; Williams, 2012). The key thing for advocate success, more than, say, knowledge of ecology, may be people's conceptions of themselves as effective human beings and as citizens (Cantrill, 1993; Kurtz, 2005; Bravo, 2009). In this regard, encouragement, education, example, and practice all matter.

Many nations have formal hearings and written public comments on major land development projects. It is doubtful that citizens are adequately invited to these meetings. We know that citizen participants in these hearings are disregarded as 'emotional' (Peterson,1997), that in what is regarded as a technical decision ordinary citizens are dismissed as apt to speak in anecdotes about ways of life and to employ religious and spiritual language (Patterson and Lee, 2000), that when they do make science-based contributions to the proceedings their contributions are often mis-summarized and answered with existing documents the citizen was attempting to refute (Endres, 2009), and that the participation is not intended to discern the *decisive* argument but to methodically fulfill a process requirement and somehow establish environmental safety and health by thorough rhetorical collection expressed in a written document (Opie and Elliott, 1996). Who is surprised when this results in 'dueling experts' who justify the *status quo* with their public stalemate (Roy, 2002). Political officeholders use the public participation features of the law to create a 'balance' of competing interests, wherein 'balance' is understood as both a means and an end, increasingly divorced from actual environmental outcomes (Patterson and Lee, 2000).

What every citizen is able to bring to an environmental deliberation is local knowledge. We know that appeals to 'localism', as in the Stansted Airport expansion controversy are frequently successful, if at times tainted with popular paranoia (Griggs and Howarth 2008). Worries about blockheaded, *bourgeois* 'NIMBY-ism' have not stood up to critical evaluation; citizens with local environmental concerns have proved able to take up universalistic and impressive scientific arguments about their local issues (Kraft and Clary 1991; Smith and Marquez 2000). Environmental controversies are often occasions for extensive learning and deep thinking in communities.

This chapter is different from the usual study of environmental communication, because it is not about broad citizen participation. Instead, here we take up the possibility of introducing a new elite actor into local, regional, and national environmental issues. In evolving, in 'descending' in Darwin's term, new authorities able to address us on environmental issues, we here think on paper about the *physician* as a new authority for environmental health, able to open up environmental policy controversies with special clarity.

Ethos

Human being are geniuses, performing, perhaps, a quadrillion mental operations per second; but human beings are also famously intellectually lazy, taking drastic shortcuts in their inferences, and ignoring the careful qualifications that attend the rationales for their actions, even when the subject is a matter of life and death. No matter our brain power, the truly engaging problems we face are most often ones where there are no certainties, where the situation requires superb *judgment*. Often the cognitive shortcut we take in these judgments is a reliance on authority. We displace the problem of *what* to think over on to the question of *who* to believe and follow. Who we believe cannot be separated from the larger cultural apparatus, and in a startling number of situations people seem willing to believe the dominant male, the person with the longest *curriculum vitae*, the person with the most medals and ribbons, the person with the most money, or, as Ernest Becker wrote in *Escape From Evil*, the one who comes pre-qualified with a narrative of death dealing and death defying. Most of these shortcuts in judgment are part of the deep structure of our sexism that makes it difficult to hear and value the life sustaining experience of women. No sooner do we establish, if only implicitly, a regime of authority, the material value of the authority is so great, people will try to simulate the signs of authority, and confuse the types of authority. This is exactly our predicament in environmental controversies.

Critically reading, listening, and viewing public environmental discourse would quickly illustrate that most, even the best of it, is full of conclusions, for which no evidence is provided. The more popularly these discourses are written or spoken, the more 'conclusionary' they are. Clearly, we are relying on the training, methods, resources, institutional checks, and determination of environmental scientists to serve as the authority for these claims.

Taking other people's word for things is the mark of a stupid, an irrational person, right? Our intelligence lies in our ability to verify the claims of others. But how can we ever verify these technical matters? I kindly suggest that upon closer examination, the test of rationality that we verify every claim is sophomoric. As the profound British philosopher Gillian Rose wrote in her valedictory book *Love's Work* (2011; 1995), we rational creatures must be on the look out for new forms of authority to trust and believe in, that we must be aware of the reasons we trust as much as the reasons we should doubt one-another. But an even greater objection against believing in environmental claims from authorities comes from the anti-humanists among us. They hold we will be soon be swamped under for all our ingenuity and efforts. We are the new dodo birds, and will not leave any witnesses to testify to our stupidity. The environmental damage we have done is too great, too irreversible; and we are too ignorant, too slow, too vain, and too short-sighted to understand, much less correct the problems. If there is any hope at all, we would have to stop listening to people, to privilege the voice of nature, and it still will be too late. We are a disease on this planet, a brutal trial for our fellow creatures, and will soon enough be gone. Again, it is a clever sophomoric position, but we, in fact, have a billion hungry people, on a warming planet. The green economics project is obstinately humanist and optimistic, and is extraordinarily interested in getting more, right voices to the table, no matter the glib pessimism some would employ to derail environmental action.

The most commonly taught rhetoric in the world is Aristotle's and his famous student notes known to us today as the *Ars Rhetorica* tells us the speaker has three great resources: the speech, the speaker herself, and the audience, known to university students and even prep schoolers everywhere as the *logos, ethos,* and *pathos.* We teachers mostly teach and study a rhetoric of messages, of *logos*, because that is the part of persuasion we can "hold still" for our analytical microscopes, coach, and easily assign a 'mark'. Students inevitably stop on *ethos*, the who you are of the speaker. Aristotle himself implied that he thought *ethos* was the most often decisive part of the great rhetorical trinity, and there is a good historically irrefutable reason why: so many of our greatest leaders are horrible speakers and writers, yet somehow their inept presentations have spoken to, spoken *for*, millions of people. There was or is some attribute of their person, including that sense of speaking for—the throngs, God, history —that has made them a force with which to reckon. For the record, many of us who have looked at the problem of persuasion persistently tend to see it in its biggest part the problem of *pathos*, what audiences possess to bring to occasions—preferences, sureties, emotions, even ambivalent emotions. And today, we would add that there must be a fourth leg in any complete rhetoric, the consideration of the media or channel by which a message is sent or received, channels which, straightforwardly have their own *ethos* or relative trustworthiness and prestige. We call it credibility, which I like to make very literal and ask, would you give me credit? What history, what resources, what references, what guarantors, what plain good sense understood as proportionality—must you or I offer to get that credit?

Aristotle made of *ethos* a moral problem, a characterological issue. People who have high *ethos* are those who are morally good people, well qualified by education and experience to speak on a topic, and who have the audience members' best interest at heart on the present matter. But this is the "Pollyanna" version. For while *ethos* is all those things, it is certainly also age, and the length of one's *curriculum vitae* whether relevant or not, and attachment to prestigious institutions whether relevant or not, and how tall you are, and how fat you are, and how deep your voice is, and whether or not you are wearing a uniform, and how many men stand behind you carrying machine guns, and how many people have you killed, how many millions you have in the bank, how many platinum albums you have recorded, and on and on. Ernest Becker, in *Escape From Evil*, without a thought for rhetoric, argues that we will always privilege the death dealers and death defy-ers who face down the lion and reach into another's chest and fix their beating heart, and we will always be in awe of, and therefore listen to, those who can make the biggest display of prosperity.

Our students are quick to tell us we are talking about celebrity. And indeed, the power of celebrity in environmental matters is awesome. We see this with James Cameron and his actors from *Avatar* stopping the Belo Monte Dams project in Brazil when no one and nothing else could do so (Jampolsky 2012). But how many celebrities are going to stop by when you are trying to stop a coal mine from opening in your county or trying to prevent the location of a pcb-laden industrial dump site over your regional aquifer? We need authorities for environmental health in our communities.

Photo Miriam Kennet. The roads in Brighton are still clogged up with motorists making it difficult and more dangerous for cyclists. We need safe and separated cycle lanes now that people understand the health benefits of cycling and other greener modes of transport.

The Physician and Environmental Health

In some ways physicians are not likely candidates to lead environmental health efforts. They are committed to a curative model of disease. This is not some obtuseness on their part: they open their practice every morning to a waiting room full of people demanding cures. Further, physicians are increasingly organized into complex organizations cemented into leviathan social institutions that do not suggest much possibility of social change. Many physicians are badly indebted coming out of their educations and overworked in their positions; they have little time for asking big questions and getting involved with 'politics'. Many physicians are, for many reasons, politically conservative and would be loathe to associate themselves with the full agenda of related progressive advocacy. In this regard, their relative insularity with their peers in clinics may be a powerful force in policing progressive tendencies in their thought. But for all of that, the physician is probably the central character in improving environmental health in our communities.

Every survey of occupational prestige and trust, from every nation where such surveys are conducted, puts physicians at the top or near the top behind sentimental favorites such as firefighters. But let's be clear, almost no one thinks of a firefighter, military officer, or teacher the way they think of their physicians. The physician is the everyday scientist in our community, connected to science as both a body of knowledge and as a conversant with other flesh and blood medical specialists. We rely on the medical conversation to be conducted with high standards of evidence meant to persuade the many skeptical participants. This conversation is backed up by an enormous body of settled fact and a massive on-going research tradition, and it is staunched by a wide public urgency to solve the unsolved puzzles of human health. In this endeavor, the physician takes on heroic stature. They save us from pain, diminished lives, and death. We are grateful, and tempted to believe we have been in the presence of miracle workers who stand close to the powers of existence. In every nation physicians are the best paid professionals, and in small to medium sized communities they are often among the most affluent individuals.

The work of physicians appeals directly to our self-interest. They work with us one-on-one, actually listening to and responding to our complaints and worries. They possess remarkable technology and direct a team of other caregivers. People across most of the world are accustomed to relying on physician judgments and submitting to their disciplines. And they are not far away at famous universities, they are in our towns. They know us, they know our community. Taking all of this together, there is no question that physicians have remarkable *ethos* and are in an unsurpassed position to speak of or confirm assertions of environmental health.

For this chapter a brief, anonymous survey was conducted among a small group of university students. The outcomes will not be reported here in any detail, and no statistical significance is claimed from a few participants. Physicians were contrasted with ecologists, physicists, chemists, geologists, economists, attorneys, city planners, sociologists, journalists, and business leaders, in trust, believability, and desire to hear their testimony. Three separate environmental advocacy scenarios were proposed, with two questions concerning each, where the contributions of eight hypothetical professionals were contrasted. The physician's testimony was ranked third most trusted/believable in three of the six questions against other professionals who had specific contributions to make concerning environmental matters. Environment is aesthetics, jobs, devotion to other life forms, and many other things, but the human interest in human health is plainly one of our deepest pre-occupations about the environment.

Physician Advocate

Environmental health is a recognized medical specialty, and among physicians there is an organization for environmental advocacy called the International Society of Doctors for the Environment and there are national organizations with similar names and purposes. These physicians are the obvious candidates in helping their colleagues to see environmental health advocacy as a part of their job. We can easily enough say it should be so, but it is better to skip that particular exhortation.

What remains to be described is environmental advocacy with and without physician participation. In the last year in the community where I live there has been a huge controversy about siting a coal mine in a small town. A citizen can stand before a city council meeting and say that the mine will almost certainly free the heavy metals mercury, arsenic, and selenium into the small town's waste stream and into the regional watershed. A physician can say why that matters, how they and other health care providers downstream would 'see' those heavy metals in their practices. They are the authority. They are the living breathing mediators of that information to our lives. But no physician joined the conversation, and this and other assertions remained 'loose ends' in the debate. We all deserve fewer loose ends when we think about the places we live. It is, an evolutionary problem. Our ability to engage in environmental communication is slowly descending, but the progress is frustratingly slow. We need more, better talk, to get more action. Getting the physicians involved would be one of the most important steps in this evolution at the present time.

References

Aristotle (1963) *Ars Rhetorica,* W.D. Ross, trans., Oxford: Clarendon.

Becker, E. (1975) *Escape From Evil,* New York: Free Press.

Bravo, M. (2009) 'Voices from the sea ice: The reception of climate impact narratives', *J. Historical Geography*, Vol. 35, No. 2, pp. 256-278.

Cantrill, J.G. (1993) 'Communication and our environment: Categorizing research in environmental advocacy', *J. Applied Communication Research*, Vol. 21, pp. 66-95.

Chase, A. (2003) *Harvard and the Unabomber: The Education of an American Terrorist,* New York: Norton.

Dahrendorf, R. (1979) *Life Chances: Approaches to Social and Political Theory,* London, Weidenfeld & Nicolson.

Depoe, S. and Delicath, J. W. (2004) 'Introduction', *Communication and public participation in Environmental decision making,* Albany: SUNY Press, pp. 1-10.

Dikeç, M. (2004) 'Voices into noises: ideological determination of the unarticulated justice movements', *Space and Polity*, August, Vol. 8, pp. 191-208.

Endres, D. (2009) 'Science and public participation: An analysis of public scientific argument In the Yucca Mountain controversy', *Environmental Communication*, March, Vol. 3, pp. 49-75.

Enzenberger, H.-M. (1974) 'A critique of political ecology', *New Left Review*, March-April, Vol. 84, pp. 3-31.

Frantzich, S.E. (2008) 'Wouldn't you just love to live here? Lois Gibbs', *Citizen Democracy: Political Activists in a Cynical Age,* 3rd Ed., New York: Rowman & Littlefield.

Griggs, S. and Howarth, D. (2008) 'Populism, localism, and environmental politics: The logic and and rhetoric of the Stop Stansted Expansion campaign', *Planning Theory*, July, Vol 7 pp. 123-144.

Haraway, D.J .
(1997) *Modest_Witness@Second_Millenium. FemaleMan(c)_Meets_OncoMouseTM: Feminism and Technoscience,* London: Routledge.

Jampolsky, J.A. (2012) 'Activism is the new black: Demonstrating the benefits of international celebrity activism through James Cameron's campaign against the Belo Monte Dam' *Colorado J. Int. Environmental Law and Policy*, Winter, Vol. 23, pp. 227-256.

Kennet, M. and Heinemann, V. (2006) 'Green economics: setting the scene. Aims, context, and philosophical underpinning of the distinctive new solutions offered by green economics', *Int. J. Green Economics*, Vol. 1, Nos. 1/2, pp. 68-102.

Kraft, M.E. and Clary, B.B. (1991) 'Citizen participation and the NIMBY syndrome: Public response to radioactive waste disposal' *Western Political Quarterly*, Vol. 44, pp. 299-328.

Kurtz, H.E. (2005) 'Alternative visions for citizenship practice in an environmental justice dispute', *Space and Polity*, April, Vol. 9, pp. 77-91

Opie, J. and Elliott, N. (1996) 'Tracking the elusive Jeremiad: The rhetorical character of American environmental discourse' in Cantrill, J.G. and Oravec, C.L. (Eds.)

The Symbolic Earth: Discourse and Our Creation of the Environment, University of

Kentucky Press.

Patterson, R. and Lee, R. (2000) 'The environmental rhetoric of "balance": a case study of regulatory discourse and the colonization of the public', in Coppola, N.W. And Karis, B. (Eds.) *Technical Communication, Deliberative Rhetoric and EnvironmentalDiscourse: Connections and Directions*, Stamford, Connecticut: Ablex Publishing.

Peterson, T.R. (1997) *Sharing the Earth: The Rhetoric of Sustainable Development*, Charleston:University of South Carolina Press.

Rose, G. (2011; 1995) *Love's Work*, New York: New York Review of Books.

Roy, A. (2002) *The Algebra of Infinite Justice*, London: HarperCollins.

Saul, J. R. (1992) *Voltaire's Bastards: The Dictatorship of Reason in the West*, New York: Free Press.

Schwarze, S. (2003) 'Juxtaposition in environmental health rhetoric: Exposing asbestos contamination in Libby, Montana' *Rhetoric & Public Affairs*, Vol. 6, No. 2, pp. 313- 336.

Smith, E.R.A.N. and Marquez, M. (2000) 'The other side of the NIMBY syndrome' *Society & Natural Resources*, Vol. 13, pp. 273-280.

Toker, C.W. (2002) 'Debating "What ought to be": The comic frame and public moral argument' *Western J. Communication*, Vol. 66, pp. 53-83.

Williams, T.T. (2012) *When Women Were Birds: Fifty-four Variations on Voice*, New York:Farrar, Straus, and Giroux.

Photo by Miriam Kennet. Three Green modes of Transport- Walking,Cycling and using public transport, here the Train in Sweden.

1.6 Retreats

Retreat ideas
By Miriam Kennet

Photo Miriam Kennet at EarthSpirit.

The idea of a retreat is to spend some time away from the everyday and have a think about what matters to you and to recharge your batteries.

The term **retreat** has several related meanings, all of which have in common the notion of safety or temporarily removing oneself from one's usual environment.

It helps to have nice surroundings and to feel relaxed and safe and supported. So one of the most important things is to make a decision at the beginning that everyone wants to enjoy their experience too and so we decide that we will be supportive to each other and positive towards them and what they say. We wont interrupt, but we won't hog the time, we will listen fully to other people and also encourage them in their retreat to find out what really matters to them. If we are working on personal issues in a workshop we never say anything to hurt them and nothing negative that they can't do anything about. We wont be racist, sexist, ageist, etc. We wont prejudge people based on their looks or what we assume about them. All the people who have booked are fascinating and interesting people and one ideal thing to achieve is to take time to find out about them over the weekend.

The term **retreat** can also be used in the sense of to back off or run away from danger. In the sense that economics, has been used over the last two hundred years to justify all sorts of things including war.

A retreat gives you a chance to put aside the concerns and demands of your everyday routine. By getting away from the noise and clutter of the city or where ever you come from, you can begin to relax and open up.

Many people who go on retreats feel more grounded, calmer and in touch with themselves. Those who go on retreat regularly find these qualities pervading the rest of their lives, and can live more and more from their human potential.

Going on retreat gives you the opportunity to share time, and inspiration with like-minded people from all walks of life. Many people find that a sense of community develops as a retreat progresses, and lasting friendships are born from their experience.

But retreats are not 'holidays'. They are an opportunity to deepen your awareness of yourself, other people, and the world around you. They give you space to clarify what is essential in your life. And as such, a retreat can be a challenging, life changing experience.

Most retreats include periods of quiet, and other activities such as talks, workshops, study groups, and something physical. They also have short work activities and free time.

There is no smoking in the building. Some people have come here for real healing, or may be feeling quiet or off colour, some people may be feeling very excited about new projects and want to share and we'd like everyone to contribute what they can from where they are at the moment.

No session is compulsory- I have tried to provide an alternative at all times- even if it is just to go and sit quietly or to go for a walk. But we need to respect other people's rights to enjoy a session. This also means finishing all sessions on time with no slippage. If a speaker says something you don't like – please let them finish and ask why they have suggested something- its hard being a speaker – can be nervous making – so treat them as you would wish to be treated if you were the speaker for that session.

Many of us feel fear about economics, and even the economists and banks admitted that the new credit instruments were impossible to understand and they felt alienated. The trouble was no one dared to say so for fear of feeling foolish and so look what a mess we have got into as a result. People feel shutting out when others talk about economics. This weekend is designed to show you that sometimes people may have wanted to encourage that feeling that economics is only for and done by white middle class men- "what economics terms "Homo economicus." As with all things this is a way of maintaining a particular group in power and putting forward a particular perspective. Green Economics is characterised by the fact that economics is practised by everyone equally on the planet and its for everyone equally on the planet and for non human species too.

The Retreat is about reclaiming economics for ourselves and we have been busy trying to create a new philosophy of economics that will make this possible and we will try to share some of that work with you.

There is a lot of excitement around about our work, we have had interest from ministers and from people in Japan, China, Venezuela, Nigeria, Estonia and Kenya and so what we are doing and what we are talking about here this weekend is part of a growing international dynamic movement for change. As far as we know no-one ever tried a Green Economics Retreat- or even an economics retreat before– so you are participating in the development of a new concept and a new process of opening up economics- and so its important and exciting work. We are participating in the complete reform of economics and we think that will enhance everyone's well being. So we hope you enjoy it thoroughly and find it interesting.

Miriam Kennet 2007

The Earthspirit Centre for Personal Development
By David Taylor

The EarthSpirit Centre, in the Somerset English rural village of Compton Dundon is an holistic healing centre providing a venue for a wide variety of groups with a focus on holistic wellbeing, complementary health and personal development.Itis situated five miles from Glastonbury in the UK.

The centre hosts groups working with a wide variety of complementary therapies including reiki, massage, homeopathy, pilates, the Bowen Technique, the Rosen Method, Body Harmony and yoga, amongst others that work with the mind, body and spirit.

As the centre is residential, groups are able to spend several days studying their therapy in some depth. Many of the groups offer qualifications in their respective therapy.

In addition to the more mainstream therapies the centre hosts various teachers who offer personal and soul healing, working within different spiritual and shamanic traditions from around the world. One example of this is breathwork where participants use particular types of breathing to help release emotion and trauma, and to recover memory.

A great deal of attention has been given to the design of the buildings , working on the premise that people appreciate and relax more, and therefore get more healing benefit, when surrounded by natural materials such as thatch, stone and wood.

The centre also incorporates many eco-features including a grey water system, 12kw of solar arrays, rainwater harvesting, compost loos and organic gardening.

Photo David Taylor: The Garden at the EarthSpirit Centre

Photo the Main Hall at the EarthSpirit Centre Photo David Taylor

Photo. Contemplation space at Earth Spirit Centre Photo David Taylor

1.6: Alternative Therapies

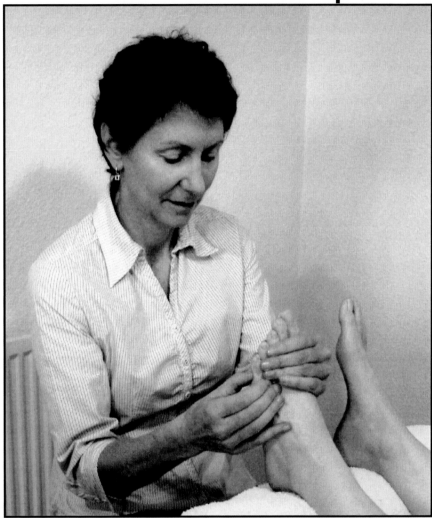

Photo: Judith Felton. She is a Green Economist and former Occupational Therapist who created our Trust and our global network and is seen here in her Reflexology Practice.

1.7 Is there a Relationship between Health and Wealth? Evidence from Egypt

By Dr Doaa Mohamed Salman and Dr Eyad Mohammed Atya

This chapter investigates the relationship between health and wealth in the Egyptian economy during the period 1960-2010. We use life expectancy at birth as a measure for the health and gross domestic product per capita (constant 2000US$) as a measure for the wealth. We employ cointegration analysis and utilize the linear and nonlinear forms. This chapter concludes that for the linear model, the results indicate that there is a positive and significant relationship between health and wealth. For non-linear model, the results show that health and wealth have inverse U-shape relationship. This conclusion will help policy makers and researchers in developing countries with high fertility rate to consider a strategic health program to achieve impacts on nation's health and human wealth. However, further work need to be done in order to specify exactly which policies will be effective in improving economic growth and development in LDCs. Policy recommendations are proposed.

1. Introduction

For decade's researchers have documented the positive links between income and a wide array of health indicators (see reviews by Deaton, 2001; Robert, 2000b; and Wagstaff and Pamuk, 1998). In lower income countries, Case et al. (2002) there is evidence that these countries experience higher rates of asthma, heart conditions, hearing problems, digestive disorders and elevated blood lead levels. While in high income level countries they witness better health level. On the other side, there is a gap in the literature between the relation between wealth and health. This is a surprising fact because we view wealth as a basic measurement that affects a person's health. The question is whether the same relationship exists between wealth and health.

The relation between wealth and health are interrelated and require decision makers to realize the core channels to achieve growth and development. Health's role is vital for economic growth and the nation's wealth. The direct effect of wealth on health occurs via different levels. First, finance channels, saving provide a direct effect on health. In poor countries with low saving rates face a challenge to protect ill people. The second channel involved is education, as people with better educated level are able to protect their health, and able to use the preventative and curative medical system.

Third, financing agencies represented in: public sector, such as, governmental hospitals and clinics, and university hospitals, while private sector such as: private insurance companies, unions, nongovernmental organization (NGO) and household sector. Finally, the quality of the service provider represented in staff.

Improvement in health based on various macro input factors represented in the quality of education system, sufficient government expenditure scheme, effective clean environment regulation, quality of the service providers, and the cost of health service. These factors reflect on the human being health and the level of productivity in positive trend. We believe that population can be a curse in case if they are unproductive or a bliss if government invest them to sustain growth and wealth. Changes in fertility behavior in addition to health and investing in human capital is expected to have to have effects on life expectancy and economic growth. This paper contributes to literature by investigating Egypt as one of the developing countries characterized by high population density and volatile economic growth in the context of demographic transition. Initially, we explore the role of health as being an intermediate channel affecting wealth. Then we overview the literature and discuss empirical specifications and result. Finally we draw our conclusion and recommendations.

The Egyptian population started the 20th century with 10 million people and by the end was almost 70 million. Most of the increase that took place since the end of World War II, was due to an initial rapid decline in mortality, and decline in death rate. Before World War II, more than 250 out of every 1,000 Egyptian infants died before reaching their first birthday (Fargues 2000). Since the late 1940s, the infant mortality rate has dropped quite steadily. For at least 20 years this decline in mortality was not matched by a drop in birth rates. Data from the World Fertility Survey suggest that the total fertility rate (TFR)[1] for all of Egypt was 7.1% in the early 1960s, the TFR declined between from 5.9% in 1970 to 4.4 % in 1990 and finally to 2.7 % in 2010. United Nations projections suggest that the population will exceed 127 million by 2050 (United Nations Population Division 2003).

The rapid population growth was the result of a substantial decline in mortality triggered by the increased use of antibiotics and vaccinations, and by the spread of disease control and sanitation programs. These improvements substantially increased life expectancy at birth. But achieving "Good health" is obviously a multidimensional aspect and the impulsive need to pull off good health relies on complex factors. Egypt Human Development Report 2010 (EHDR) recorded values for the progress of the income index indicating a noticeable improvement in its income level, the increase in average GDP per capita between the 2008 and 2010 EHDRs took place despite the rise in the percentage of the poor from 19.6% to 21.6%, and the increase in the absolute number of poor.

Egyptian government health policy increased health expenditure remarkably during the period 1995 to 2010, figure one records the increase in per capita government expenditure on health (PPP int. $) in Egypt from 50 percent in 1995 to 108 percent in 2010. However, the increase in health expenditure did not meet the needs of the population demands and the demand of human resources for health. In Egypt, the Ministry of Education and Ministry of Higher Education control the supply of human resources for health (e.g. doctors and nurses) from a side, while the Ministry of Health controls a large part of the demand of human resources for health; as the government is committed -by law- to hire graduates of the faculties of Medicine and Nursing and schools of nursing. The main concern of the Ministry of education is to tune the balance between the demand required by health foundations and the available capacity of educational institutions rather than the quality of the population health. The demand for human resources for health in Egypt is influenced by many things other than population needs.

In addition, the progress in Egypt total expenditure on health as a percentage of gross domestic product during 2000 record was 5.6%, that increased to 6.3 % in 2006, then droped to 4.7 in 2010 (WHO, 2011). Although, the Egyptian government expenditures on health as a % of total expenditure on health was not maintaining a stable increase in this level, it recorded 40.7 % as a percent of the total expenditure on health during 2000 to drop to 37.4% by 2010. These values are considered to be low percentages compared with the Egyptian population.

It is worth noting that despite improvements in life expectancy rate at birth total (years) from 70 to 73 there is still a significant number of Egyptians live in slums, with poor and overcrowded housing, limited food supply, and inadequate access to clean water, good quality health care, and education. The poorest 20 percent of the Egyptian controlled only 9 percent of wealth during year 2008, while the wealthiest 20 percent controlled 40 percent of the country's wealth with a drop 2 percent in year 2000, (WDI, 2011). This inequality in income rooted to the government policies as it focuses on the Northern cities e.g. Cairo and Alexandria in its investment plans more than the south rural areas.

Inequality also spread to a certain extent to the education sector as the household wealth level is a major determinant of higher education enrollment. However, we found that almost half of those who are or have been to university came from the richest wealth quintile (richest 20%); only 4% came from the poorest wealth ones (poorest 20%). In 2008, United Nation Population Division report reasoned this to the free higher level of education that the government adopted since 1962. Resulting in an urban/rural differential where 39% of rural youth compared to 61% of urban youth finish higher education[2]. Consequently, youth in rural area with limited capacity for learning and working endure higher limitation in human developments that is transmitted to their children. Egyptian Government efforts to raise the human level of development focusing on the education, health and income are not sufficient as it is still facing continuous inherited problems.

2. Literature Review

From the theoretical point of view, the standard neoclassical model of the limits of improvement in health and life expectancy highlights that increased life expectancy increases the population number while reducing the capital-labor ratios and decreasing the per capita income. However, endogenous growth models in the tradition of Becker and Barro (1988) propose that human capital investment and fertility responses may offset the severe predictions of the neoclassical model. Other researchers provide a strong relationship between initial levels of health and economic growth, using life expectancy at birth as their basic measure of overall health of the population. They conclude that improved health is associated with faster economic growth and supported the positive relationship between health and economic growth (Gallup, Sachs and Mellinger, 1999).

Nora Lustig (2006) conducted in Mexico during 1970-95 to study the relationship between health and growth using life expectancy and mortality rates of different age groups as health indicators. It was observed that health is responsible for approximately one-third of long term economic growth. Results showed that low health levels are linked to poverty trap. There is a clear imperative to focus on improving the health status of the population to unleash higher economic growth and lower poverty rates. Moreover, Acemoglu (2006), in a study entitled "impact of life expectancy on economic growth" investigated the recent agreement in scientific assemblies and policy making bodies that disease environment and health status at present have been created through high income differences among the countries. The study discussed that health status improvement does not only improves the quality of life but also stimulates rapid economic growth. The conclusions drawn from this study was that the increase in life expectancy led to a considerable increase in population; however considerable birth rate was not controlled to compensate increased life expectancy

A recent paper by Acemoglu and Johnson (2007) further investigated the changes in life expectancy with dates of global health interventions to combat 15 major diseases. They studied 47 countries at various levels of development, during period 1940 to 1980; they offer little evidence for the causal effect of life expectancy on income per capita differs during different phases of development. Cervellati and Sunde (2009) argue that the increase in life expectancy reduces income per capita in countries that did not go through the demographic transition. In post-transitional countries the gains in life expectancies leads to an increase in per capita income. Additionally, Bloom, Canning and Fink (2009) argue that Acemoglu and Johnson's results are based on the assumption that initial health and income do not affect the subsequent economic growth. The healthiest nations in 1940 are those that benefitted least from the health interventions and also the ones that grew the most, giving a negative relationship between health interventions and growth. Furthermore, Cervellati and Sunde (2011) studied 47 countries showing that wealth exhibits a V-shaped relation with health. Thus, they argue that only after the onset of the demographic transition, life expectancy had a causal positive effect on wealth.

On the other side, Zachary Zimmer (2008) studied the relation between wealth and disability in one of the world's poorest regions – rural Cambodia. The research presents a U shape relation but the paper speculates on possible causal directions (both from wealth to health and vice-versa). Moreover, Hansen C. (2012) used panel data from 119 countries during the period 1940 to 1980. He discovered that wealth traces a U-shaped path as a function of the level of national health and that excluding the possibility of a nonmonotonic path might lead to wrong conclusions about the wealth–health nexus. Therefore, the main message is that when studying this relationship over time, a form of nonlinearity for health should be included in the empirical model. Scholars' results using panel data to identify the relation between health and wealth either presents a U – shape or V- Shape relation. The reasons rely on the stage of development and the demographic transition for each country. In an early stage of development, the effect of health improvements on wealth is negative because, at this stage, the only effect is to increase the size of the population which possibly has an adverse effect on wealth.

3. Empirical specifications and results

We investigate the relationship between health and wealth in the Egyptian economy during the period (1960-2011). The basic empirical specification is given by the following reduced form relationship between wealth and health.

3.1 Model and data

We employed linear and nonlinear models so we estimate the following two models.

GDP represents the level of wealth measured by the log of Gross Domestic Product per capita (constant 2000 US$). Life represents level of health which is measured by log of life expectancy at birth[3]. We collect data for Gross Domestic Product (GDP) and life expectancy at birth from the World development indicator.

3.2. Empirical Results

Our methodological approach in this paper is structured as follows: first, we test for stationarity in the time series for all the variables using the augmented Dickey–Fuller (ADF) test (Dickey and Fuller, 1979). The results indicate that the variables are non stationarity as we see from table (1).

Table 1: Augmented Dickey-Fuller unit root tests

Variables	Lags	Constant	lags	Constant and trend
LGDP	1	-0.4636	1	-2.7009
DLGDP	0	-4.104277***	0	-4.0604**
LLife	3	-2.1289	3	-0.116317
D(Llife)	2	-0.252436	2	-0.436988
DD(LLife)	1	-0.943081**	1	-0.685901**
LLife2	3	-0.010527	3	-0.873052
D(LLife2)	2	-0.711936	2	-0.389649
DD(LLife2)	1	-2.924523*	1	-0.3.657034**

(*), (**) and (***) indicate 10 %, 5% and 1% level of significant, respectively.

Akaike Information Criteria (AIC) is used to select the lag length

DX represents the first difference of variable x

DDX represents the second difference of variable x

The second step is to test for cointegration using the Johansen technique (Johansen, 1995), which is carried out in a context of a vector auto regression (VAR) model. Whether or not the variables included in the VAR model they are cointegrated. It has implications for the form of that model and for the type of causality test supporting it is the appropriate technique. If the Johansen tests support the conclusion that the variables are not cointegrated, then causality tests must be based on a VAR model in first differences. If, however, the variables are cointegrated, then causality tests should be based on an error correction model (ECM). So, the third step is to test for causality by employing the appropriate types of causality tests. Table (2) shows that we have long –run relationship among the variables. So we will proceed to estimate the Error Correction Model (ECM).

Table (2): Johansen cointegration tests (1995)

Model 1			
Rank	**Eigen value**	**Trace statistic**	**5% Critical value**
0	.	22.1454	15.41
1	0.36174	1.0421*	3.76
2	0.02193		
Model 2			
0	.	88.7028	29.68
1	0.81221	8.4263*	15.41
2	0.12718	1.8973	3.76
3	0.03876		

We proceed to estimate error correction model (ECM) for the models. Table (3) presents the results of error correction model for both models. The first model (linear model) shows positive and significant correlation between health and wealth at 1 % level of significance. This means that the improvements in the health will lead to an increase in the wealth of the Egyptian economy. We use the non-linear model to estimate the shape between the health and wealth. Column (2) shows a positive B1 and negative B2 – both statistically significant at the 1 % level of significance. This means that the curve which describe the relationship between wealth and health take an inverse U-shaped relationship for the Egyptian economy and the turning point is 69 years.

To explain the inverse relation between wealth and health it passes through two stages. In the first stage, the improvements in the wealth (measured by life expectancy) will lead to improvement in wealth. i.e.: the worker will be healthier and so productivity is expected to be high. In the second stage, we have two opposite effects. The first is an increased productivity of the labour (positive effect). The second effect is increased population size (as a result of the improvement of the health). Consequently, this will make pressure on the economic growth and exhaust the benefits seen from improving the health. In the second stage the negative effect was higher than the positive effect and this will lead to a negative relationship between health and wealth.

Table 3: Error Correction Model

	GDP	GDP	Turning point
LLife	3.2789***	12.12516***	-
	(0.118732)	(2.6985)	
LLife2		-1.429004***	69
		(0.34728)	

*** indicate 1 % level significant. Standard errors (SE) in parentheses

6. Summary and Concluding Remarks

This research adds to the literature of the relation between health and wealth via empirical analysis to the Egyptian economy, during the period 1960-2010. We try to focus on one country using time series data and apply cointegration analysis. Previous work relied on panel data but in this study we tried to focus on one country using time series data and apply cointegration analysis. We estimated linear and non-linear models. For the linear model, the results indicated that there is a positive and significant relationship between health and wealth. For non-linear model, the relationship between health and wealth follows an inverse U-shape relationship, Egypt witness an inverse relationship with a turnaround value of about 69 years of life expectancy, i.e., this means that improving the health in the long run put more pressure on the economic growth and consumes it, and health problems is an obstacle ahead of enjoying the growth in economic growth.

Improving health in Egypt among all governorates is a challenge the government is facing, especially with present of high inequality among governorate. The unavailability of data among governorate over a long time posed a limitation in the present work for a deep analysis in each governorate. And, to achieve better government expenditure allocation in the health sector must be parallel with higher quality of the service provider. The issue that required a new perspective to restructure insurance health program to be a tool for investment not consumption approach.

For policy implication, we believe that the way to improve the economic growth is to improve the skills of the labour via education to prevent transmission of poverty across generation. This is in agreement with previous reports supporting the direct effect of education on poverty. Furthermore, the ministry of education and higher education need to match the market needs with the supply from the educational institutions. This is expected to be one of the effective policies that can be implemented in the health and wealth sectors which will results in improved economic growth and development. We think that if the population exceeds 127 million by 2050, as it is estimated to be, while the government adopting their insufficient policies to deal with health expenditure, then the health measurement will deteriorates pressure and will have severe negative impacts on economic growth in the near future.

References

[1]   Acemoglu, Daron and Simon Johnson, 2007. " Disease and Development: The Effect of

Life Expectancy on Economic Growth, *Journal of Political Economy*, 115(6): 925–985

[2]   Arab Human Development Report, 2009. "Challenges to Human Security in the Arab Countries", United Nations Development Programme (UNDP), Regional Bureau of Arab States (RBAS) New York

[3]   Becker, Gary S., and Robert J. Barro, 1988. "Reformulation of the Economic

Theory of

Fertility", *Quarterly Journal of Economics*, 103(1): 1–25.

[4]   Bloom, David; Canning, David and Sevilla, Jaypee, 2001. "The Effects of Health on

Economic Growth: Theory and Evidence". NBER Working Paper No: 8587

[5]   Bloom, D., Canning, D. 2004. "The Effect of Health on Economic Growth, a Production Function Approach", World Development, 32, 1-13.

[6]   Bloom, David E., David Canning and Gunther Fink, 2009. "Disease and Development Revisited". NBER Working Paper No. 15137.

[7]   Casper Worm Hansen, 2012. "The relation between wealth and health: Evidence from a world panel of countries". *Economics letters* 115: 175- 177.

[8]   Case A, Lubotsky D, Paxson C., 2002. "Economic status and health in childhood: The origins of the gradient". American Economic Review 92:1308-1334.

[9]   Cervelatti, Matteo and Uwe Sunde, 2009. "Life Expectancy and Economic Growth: The

Role of Demographic Transition", IZA Discussion Paper No. 4016

[10]   Dickey D.A. and W.A. Fuller, 1979. "Distribution of the Estimators for Autoregressive Time Series with a Unit Root", *Journal of the American Statistical Association*. 74, 427-431.

[11]   Deaton, Angus, 2001. "Health, Inequality, and Economic Development". NBER Working Paper No. 8318, Cambridge, MA.

[12]   Fargues, P., 2000. "Generations Arabes. Paris: Fayard. Gadalla, S. 1978.Is there hope? Fertility and family planning in a rural community in Egypt". Chapel Hill, NC: Carolina Population Center, University of North Carolina

[13]   Gallup, John L., Jeffrey D. Sachs, and Andrew D. Mellinger, 1999. "Geography and Economic Development", International Regional Science Review, 22(2): 179–232

[14]   Robert, Stephanie A., 2000b. "Socioeconomic Inequalities in Health: Integrating Individual-, Community-, and Societal-Level Theory and Research." In Gary L. Albrecht, Ray Fitzpatrick, and Susan C. Scrimshaw, eds., Handbook of Social Studies in Health and Medicine. London: Sage Publications Johansen S. (1995), Likelihood-based inference in cointegrated vector autoregressive models. Oxford: Oxford University Press.

[15]   Lustig, Nora, 2006. "Investing in Health for Economic Development: The case of Mexico".

UNU-WIDER Research Paper No. 2006/30

[16]   Pamuk E, Makuc D, Keck K, Reuban C, Lochner K , 1998. "Socioeconomic Status and Health Chartbook. Health", United States, Hyattsville, MD: National Center for Health Statistics.

[17]   Wagstaff, Adam, and Eddy van Doorslaer, 2000. "Income Inequality and Health: What Does the Literature Tell Us?" Annual Review of Public Health 21:543–567.

[18]   Weil, D. N., 2005. "Accounting for the Effect of Health on Economic Growth". National Bureau of Economic Research, 11455

[19]   World Health Organization, 2011

[20]   United Nations Population Division , 2003

Zachary Zimmer, 2008. "Poverty, Wealth Inequality and Health among Older Adults in Rural Cambodia. Social scienc

[1] The total fertility rate (TFR) is a useful measure for examining the overall level of fertility. It can be interpreted as the number of children a woman would have by the end of her childbearing years if she were to pass through those years bearing children at the currently observed rates. The TFR is calculated by summing the age-specific fertility rates. It is presented for women age 15-44 and women 15-49 to facilitate comparisons with other surveys in which the age range of interviewed women may differ from that in the 2005 EDHS.

[2] This high unemployment can be explained by the fact that young people in poor households have a lower reservation wage, and hence accept any possible form of employment. While, young graduates from the highest socio-economic classes rely on their parents to remain unemployed.

[3] The total life expectancy at birth is the average number of years a child

would live if prevailing patterns of mortality of the total population at the time of his/her life. This also is expected to have direct relationship with the rate of economic growth in the economy. This is because as the living condition improves, human longevity is expected to be enhanced and vice-versa. This is achieved when there is improvement in health expenditure.

Part 2: Health, Pollution, and Environmental Justice
2.1 The Unsustainable Heaviness of The Impact of Air Pollution on Workers' Health

By Dr Enrico Tezza

Commons includes air, sky, light
Res communes omnium (Giuseppe De Nittis, 1868)

The current debate about air pollution

Air quality and tolerable levels of pollution might seem debatable concepts when they replace the absolute concept of air, a good of itself, to admit the right of industries and consumers to pollute. The current view is that pollution is an inevitable effect of growth and growth is the imperative for profit. By externalising social and environmental costs, industry can maximize profit. Everyone including future generations is paying by allowing enterprises to have this freedom. Resource management, introduced to reconcile pollution with sustainability is a false concept when its operational meaning is dictated by the bottom line principle. As a result, pollution becomes the partner of the free market ideology. Since the 1950s when the great acceleration took off, human activities have reached the tipping point in terms of extraction, production and consumption. Air pollution is an effect of this growth and its impact on workers' health has raised strong concerns.

Air pollution and the susceptibility of workers

Air pollution exerts a different impact on different populations and factors contributing to these variations can be explained by susceptibility. Workers are forced to experience inferior respiratory conditions both at work, due to the indoor air pollution and during their free time thanks to the outdoor pollution. Air pollution aggravates risks accumulated by some categories of workers (vulnerability vector) seriously threatening their health. As reported by the ILO, an estimated 2 billion workers breathe in dangerous levels of air. Occupational epidemiology provides statistics on the impact of air pollution on workers' diseases and death therefore raising the concern about the relation between air pollution and public health. Exposure (concentration, dose and inhalation time) is studied to mitigate the risk of air pollution, but the interaction effect (chemical reaction among multiple pollutants) impedes evidence on the true effect on workers' health.

The problem: the transformation of air composition.

Owing to the growth and related increase in emissions in the atmosphere, the composition of air is changing and the marginal part of it (78% Nitrogen, 21% Oxygen, 1% Traces gases) plays a decisive role in worsening workers' health. Conventional primary pollutants contribute the largest volume of air quality degradation: Sulphur compounds (SO_2), Nitrogen compounds (NO_x), Carbon oxides (CO_2, co), Metals (Lead, Mercury), Halogens (CFCs), particulate material, volatile organic compounds (VOCs). Indoor air pollutants, including formaldehyde, asbestos, toxic organic chemicals, randon, tobacco smoke, are considered unconventional pollutants. In addition secondary pollutants, not directly emitted as such but formed when primary pollutants react in the atmosphere, include ozone which is formed when hydrocarbons (HC) and nitrogen oxides (NO_x) combine in the presence of sunlight. Toxicology science, Occupational Epidemiology and WHO provide evidence of the impact of these pollutants on human health. Effects vary from acute (reversible) and chronic (irreversible) illness and diseases. Each pollutant has its own effect. For instance, particulate matter affects the respiratory systems and genetic structure leading to death. Sulphur dioxide inhibits the respiratory system as well adding cardiovascular diseases and lung cancer. Carbon monoxide interferes with the blood's ability to provide an adequate supply of oxygen to body tissue, causing brain damage, angina pectoris, and foetal abnormalities. Nitrogen dioxide affects the respiratory systems, lowering resistance to infection. Lead affects the blood, nervous and renal system. Ozone impacts on lung inflammation, breast cancer. Pollutants may last even as long as 30 years in the atmosphere and they migrate around the world at heights of up to 17 kilometres. Human breathing which needs 11 m3 every 24 hours, is exposed to both air pollutants and secondary pollutants which cause mutagenic effects (mutagens). Epigenetic science has proved that air pollution changes the human genetic structure (DNA) leading to death.

The solution: the prevention strategy.

The aim of air pollution prevention is to avoid and reduce the quantity and the hazardous character of pollutants. Literature on prevention includes three areas following the cycle of pollutants: sources, transportation and receptors. At source, emission ratios and type of pollutants are studied within other physical variables such as height, temperature, pressure and the speed of exit. The transportation issue includes wind speed, moisture, temperature, physical transportation and chemical reactions, atmospheric chemistry and physics. Receptors, in their turn, include sea, earth, humans, animals, monuments, buildings and the atmospheric itself. While air pollution prevention cannot be applied in the transportation phase, prevention at source and at receptors is applied.

The European Union is the most influential actor on the international scene regarding prevention policy even if its legal framework is not binding for member states. The

Directive on Industrial Emissions replaces previous legislation and represents a sound legal framework on prevention policy, covering definitions, general principles and prevention obligations, best available technologies, emission limit values, installations requirements, environmental inspections, controls of emissions and monitoring and special provisions for installations and activities using organic solvents. Technical issues are presented in the Annexes. The decision to designate 2013 as the Year of Air reflects the concern about the impact of pollutants on human health. The European Environment Agency plays an important role in prevention policy. Air Quality in Europe Reports provide data on sources and effects of Particulate Matter, Ozone, Nitrogen Dioxide, Sulphur Dioxide, carbon Monoxide, heavy Metals and Benzene.

Air Pollution Prevention includes the adoption of green technologies, prevention programmes in enterprises and integrated approaches (prevention and recycling). Cooperation among science, industry and educational institutions is a key determinant in achieving results from prevention policy. Progress on sustainability science is also needed so as to overcome two obstacles impeding the comprehensive view for air pollution prevention: the complexity of the problems and the concomitant specialisation of science that seeks to address problems. Due to the "mobility" of air pollution sustainability science and policy makers should provide uniform solutions to different (even if global) problems. This overarching strategy should overcome the compartmentalization of disciplines and be based on a trans-disciplinary approach. Collective action is also required following the comprehensive perspective on sustainability and air pollution prevention. The collective action points out that a single action has a limited impact. Without the orchestration towards a comprehensive prevention policy all activities by numerous actors have a marginal effect. By strengthening a network of networks, sustainability knowledge is shared, learning processes become mutual, skills and resources are used in complementary way and the innovation toward air pollution prevention is breathed collectively. Educational institutions must play the key role in achieving this collective action.

Introduction

Air pollution is the introduction of harmful substances into the environment. Air Pollution has been a public health problem since the discovery of fire. The term Pollution stems from the Latin polluere alteration or defilement and was first coined by John Spengler in 1983 (Spengler, 1983). Seneca noted the "heavy air of Rome in 61 A.D while King Edward in 1272 banned the burning of sea-coal. The origin of modern air pollution problems can be traced to eighteenth century England and the birth of the Industrial Revolution. The history of air pollution includes disasters and related policies to prevent them. (United States Environmental Protection Agency, 2003). In 1940 the air pollution problem, defined as "smog" forced regulators to act in USA. The episode of London fog in 1952, when over 4.000 people died might be the symbol of air pollution's anthropocene effect - terms coined by Eugene Stoermer and used to mark the evidence and extent of the impact of human activities on the Ecosystem starting from the 1950s. The second half of the 20th century is unique in history since many human activities reached take off points and sharply accelerated towards the limits reported at the end of the century relating to population growth, CO_2 concentration, N_2O concentration, CH_4 concentration, water use, fertiliser consumption, urban population, ocean ecosystem depletion, motor vehicles, telephones, tourism, etc.

"The air we breathe contains emissions from motor vehicles, industry, heating and commercial sources, as well as tobacco smoke and household fuels" (WHO, 2005). This United Nations official sentence legitimates the concept of air quality and the intrinsic right of industries to pollute.

The current view is that pollution is the inevitable effect of profit and profit is the imperative for growth. By externalizing social and environmental costs, industry can maximize profit. Everybody and even future generations is paying for this freedom of enterprises.
Policy decision makers try to reconcile pollution as a "natural effect" of growth introducing resource management and legislation to mitigate the pollution impact on human health and the environment. Resource management in itself is a false concept when its operational meaning is dictated by the imperative of the bottom line. As a result, pollution becomes a natural partner of the free market ideology. Legal systems, based on this framework, foresee a crime when a person poisons another but not when the culprit is the intermediary pollution.

Science studies emissions from natural sources such as volcanoes or forest fires and related air composition and equates natural pollutants with pollutants coming from human action. A solution is seen in the legislation that makes the polluter pay for pollution and the payment must be high enough to act as a deterrent. But, to date, this principle has failed as a deterrent.

Epidemiology takes for granted the chain emissions-transportation-receptors and measures the tolerable levels of impact.

The tolerable level of pollution confirms the right of industries to pollute replacing the concept of air with air quality, therefore eliminating the absolute concept of air, good in itself. It is said that exposure to air pollutants is largely beyond individuals' control and that it requires action by public authorities at regional, national and international levels. Mitigation and adaptation are concepts used by all UN Agencies, therefore perpetuating the logical framework based on the growth-pollution relationship.

While the hazardous properties of many common pollutants are still under intensive research, evidence-based policies demonstrate that decisive health protection is possible and effective. For example, phasing out leaded petrol decreases blood lead levels in children and reduces their risk of impaired neurobiological development. Controlling air pollution, both indoor and outdoor, can significantly prevent diseases. But this is not enough. A different strategy is needed.

This different strategy and counter arguments are supported by international documents relating to human and environmental rights such as the 1972 Stockholm Declaration, UN Resolution 37/ 7, 1982, the World Charter of Nature and human development, the Rio Declaration of Human Rights (UNCED, 1992).

How can we guarantee any of the human rights and freedom such as life if we poison our air? Breathable air and the amount of 11 m3 required for breathing every 24 hours are essential to support all life, including that of the polluters.

In this approach air is treated as natural heritage of humankind and the misleading effect of the air quality concept is highlighted.

The tragedy of the commons is a concept developed by Hardin (Hardin, 1968) and states that when a commons or common natural resource like air is exploited disproportionally by one or more persons at the expense of all others, it is tragic. In a sense, Air pollution is exploiting air.

Air pollution is an example of the problem when a commons is privately rather than publicly owned therefore creating a fundamental inequity or anti-commons situation. When an industry is allowed to pollute until a tolerable level is the tragedy of the commons.

This chapter highlights the air issue, in the year of air, so as to understand sustainable conditions and related actions to be taken by science, policy makers and educators.

Several misleading concepts have to be overcome and new strategic prevention has to be adopted. A new scientific approach following the ecology realm and not the free market ideology is also needed.

A communication policy is furthermore needed to convince people that air is not far from daily thoughts, it is visible, heavy and material especially when its particulate matter causes neurobiological changes leading to premature death.

Linking science, policy and the public is the aim of the European Environment Agency publications where links between air pollution and death or illness are documented.
A further publication acquires stronger relevance in the year of air: the ILO report on Worker Safety and Health, issued on the international day of Safety and Health at Work (28 April).

EU and ILO reports show how important the air is for the working environment and the interdependency between air pollution and a healthy workplace. What follows takes the findings of mentioned reports with the aim to improve the preventive strategy towards air as the "Commons". The composition of air has a dramatic impact on our health and well-being in terms of respiratory diseases and genetic modification. Air pollution damages forests, waters, the acidity of the soils and corrodes buildings. Climate change is affected by pollution as well, aggravating the human condition through related effects on human security and health.

The vulnerability of workers due to the accumulation of polluted air inhaled both in the workplace and during free time is the focus of the following sections.

The aim is to highlight determinants of air composition, related effects on health and feasible solutions to prevent pollution at large.

Without detailing specific sectors, such as the chemical sector or specific tasks like those operating in hazardous indoor plants, the purpose is to recall salient pollutants involving the whole population therefore aggravating the poor health conditions of those already vulnerable.

This chapter is organised in a somewhat unconventional manner since the emphasis is on workers' health rather than air pollution in itself. This is why the opening sections are dedicated to susceptibility and exposure. The following section discuss air pollution and its effect on workers' health. The final part outlines air pollution prevention strategy recalling the European Union's policy. The last section stresses the need for education on sustainability science.

1. The concept of susceptibility

It is worth beginning by highlighting the different reactions of workers to air pollution. Since individuals respond differently to exposure to air pollution, susceptibility explains factors contributing to these variations (WHO, 2005). The concept of susceptibility explains how one is discriminated even in every breath he or she takes. Workers must face poorer breathing conditions both at work, due to the indoor air pollution and during their free time, thanks to the outdoor air pollution. Work environments are obviously not all the same and workers closer to industrial process experience poorer quality breathing compared with colleagues working in managerial centres. Hence, it is worth understanding, monitoring and preventing the negative impact of air pollution on vulnerable workers. Vulnerability refers to the inability to withstand the effects of a hostile condition. When some risks are frequently accumulated by certain categories of workers, a "vulnerability vector" is determined with the result that the health of these workers is endangered. (F. Eyraud, 2007). In particular, a clearer understanding of the individual characteristics which increase the health risks of air pollution goes hand in hand with reducing risks for the more susceptible and prevention mechanisms.

Susceptibility refers to an altered degree of individual responsiveness. In considering the likelihood of an adverse response to an inhaled pollutant, the degree of exposure is considered in conjunction with individual characteristics. The relationship between exposure and response may take different forms, depending on the mechanism by which the pollutant causes illness or disease. In general, it is accepted that increased exposure leads to a consequent increase in risk.

Multiple factors influence susceptibility. Some factors include inherent individual characteristics (e.g. sex, age) and exposure to other agents that also have adverse effects on the same target organ (e.g. cigarette smoke or asbestos). This interaction between secondary factors, such as cigarette smoke, increases the risk from air pollution.

Socio-economic factors.

The main factor influencing susceptibility is economic status.
Surveys on susceptibility have shown the close relationship between air pollution health effects and socioeconomic status. Some studies suggest that residents of economically deprived inner cities are at greater risk of mortality and morbidity. It is acknowledged that a lower socioeconomic status is associated with an increased level of exposure and with behaviour, lifestyle, malnutrition, and hygiene conditions predisposed to unhealthy status. (M.S. O'Neill, 2003). It is undeniable that people with lower incomes are more likely to live in polluted major cities and near busy roads, industrial plants or other pollutant sources.

Type 2 diabetes, recognized as a major risk modifier for PM health effects is more common among adult inner city residents (J. F. Bach, 2002).

Individual health

A second cluster of factors refers to precarious health status.
Laboratory exposure studies suggest that people with asthma or coronary and respiratory diseases experience a particularly high rate of mortality. (P. Brimblecombe, 1987). People suffering from these same diseases are more vulnerable to the adverse effects from exposure to sulphur dioxide and carbon monoxide, even at lower concentrations.

Lifestyle

A third group of factors coincides with lifestyle. Aspects of lifestyle, in fact, aggravate the risk of an adverse effect from inhaled pollutants. Alcohol, tobacco and illegal drugs impair defence mechanisms and induce chronic inflammation and permanent structural damage in the brain and other organs. The combined effect of lifestyle and air pollutants is classified by WHO as additive or synergistic. The adverse effect is multiplied by increasing the "dose" of pollutants delivered by multiple sources or amplified by catalyzing the chemical process occurring between two or more different pollutants. When pollutants from air interact with pollutants linked to drugs, such as cocaine or heroine, the metabolic system changes, leading to genetic disjunctions.

Additive and synergistic effects are concomitant when the pollutants of the working environment are added to pollutants deriving from workers' lifestyle. In some cases ultra-fine particles react with the genetic structure (nitrogenous base) causing cancer.

Genetic factors

Technological advances in molecular biology have increased the understanding of the pollutant mechanism, specific genes and the genetic susceptibility factors. Candidate genes include tumour necrosis factor $\sim$, inflammatory cytokines, the toll-like receptors and antioxidants systems. Another candidate genes most implicated in air pollution responses is glutathione S-transferase which is an important enzyme in the glutathione pathway for protection against oxidant injury as reported by recent epidemiology (D. Peden, 2005). This enzyme, present in 40% of the United States population, has a null allele with no protein expression that reduces antioxidant protection. These are some examples of increasing susceptibility due to genetic interaction between air pollution and genetic structure. What is worth noting refers to the polymorphism in drug metabolizing enzymes and cell mutation due to the reaction with the chemical component of air pollutants (K. Vahakangas, 2003).

Demographic age structure

Demographics represent a further factor. Difference in population age structure or the living area influences the proportion of susceptible individuals. In China, for example, people 65 years of age will outnumber those under 15 by 2050, therefore increasing the burden of chronic diseases brought by air pollution. By 2030 the urban Chinese population will overtake the rural population, thereby increasing the exposure to risk factors in the urban environment, due to new city dwellers and related additional sources of pollution (Health Effects Institute, 2004).

Clean water and sanitation

In poor countries or in deprived areas in more industrialized countries (US and Europe), the traditional risk factors, such as the indoor air pollution from solid fuel use or limited access to clean water and sanitation, are compounded by the modern risk factors such as tobacco smoking, referred to as "healthy risk overlap". The comparison between industrial and poor countries shows the different susceptibility reported by the WHO. While HIV (9%), lower respiratory infections (8,2%), diarrhoeal diseases (6,3%), childhood cluster diseases (5%) are disease categories reported in poor countries, ischemic heart disease (9,4%), uni-polar depressive disorders (7,2%), cerebral-vascular disease (6%), alcohol and drug disorders (3,5%) are categories reported in Industrialized countries (WHO, 2002).

Occupational diseases and air pollutants

On the World Day for Safety and Health (28 April) ILO presents data on occupational diseases. An occupational disease is a disease contracted as a result of exposure to risk factors arising from work. An estimated 2 billion workers breathe dangerous levels of air, 160 million workers suffer from related diseases and there are an estimated 270 million fatal and non-fatal work related accidents per year. An estimated 2.5 million workers die each year from work-related diseases.

There are not statistics on the impact of air pollution on work-related accidents. Notwithstanding this, sound concerns have been expressed regarding relationships between air pollution and work-related accidents (mutagens). Millions of workers continue to be at risk of pneumoconiosis, especially silicosis, coal-workers' pneumoconiosis and asbestos-related diseases due to widespread exposures to particulate matter (PM) emitted by construction and manufacturing processes. Their associated illnesses, such as chronic obstructive pulmonary disease, cause permanent disability or premature death. (ILO, 2013). Though some traditional risks (like asbestos) have declined due to improved safety, technological advances and better regulation, they continue to take an unacceptably heavy toll on workers' health. In parallel, new forms of occupational disease are increasing without adequate preventive, protective and control measures. Emerging risks include poor air composition and its interaction with socio-economics conditions, with particular emphasis in rural areas, small and medium sized companies and in the informal economy. According to ILO statistics, the issue of air pollution should be included in the Occupational Safety and Health Convention (Nr 155/1981), Occupational Health Service Convention (161/1985) and the Promotional Framework for Occupational Safety and Health Convention (187/2006). Yet, the relationship between air pollution and health effects should go beyond the EU legal framework and be included as a permanent theme in the EU policy debate.

2. Exposure

General framework

Human exposure is determined by the amount of air pollution in the environments (microenvironments) where people spend their time and by the amount of time spent there. Space, time and pollutants determine the "microenvironments". (W.R. Ott, 1982).

According to these criteria, the world is classified into four micro environments as outlined in the following scheme:

	Industrialised Countries		Non Industrialised Countries	
	Rural	Urban	Rural	Urban
Indoor				
Outdoor				

This classification can be applied both to industrialised and non-industrialised countries leading to 8 microenvironments.

Human exposure is when a person comes into contact with a pollutant of a certain concentration during a certain period of time. Cumulative exposure is the most common indicator to measure exposure used in occupational epidemiology (T.J. Smith, 1992). It is the result of concentration (or intensity) multiplied by duration. Its utility in describing exposure-effects relationships is based on several interlocking assumptions about processes related exposure to tissue dose and tissue dose to adverse effects.

Concentration and dose

Exposure is distinguished from concentration, the quantitative amount of a pollutant within a given environmental, and from the dose, the amount of pollution actually entering the respiratory system. The dose includes a wide range of factors specific to the pollutant, such as solubility or pattern of deposition in the lungs, or physiological factors (personal level of activity, skin condition, health status, etc). Exposure studies are focused on respiratory and interrelated cardiovascular effects following inhalation. Needless to say information on people's time is used in conjunction with data on air concentration in the related microenvironments. The most important microenvironments for air pollution exposure are those where people spend the majority of their time and those likely to contain the highest concentration of air pollutants, including workplaces, home and traffic routes.

The assessment of exposure

Exposure assessment is used by Health institutions and scientists to estimate people's risk caused by air pollutants. In general, a four-step process is adopted so as to identify pollutants in the air (phase 1), to estimate the amounts of these pollutants released from different sources (phase 2), and related concentration (phase 3), to provide estimates of the number of people who breathe air containing reported pollutants (phase 4) (US EPA, 1991).

Exposure assessment takes into account the appropriate time average since a large proportion of daily exposure occurs in only a few hours. If a heavy metal is observed, a simple calculation of long-term average is provided by adding the total personal exposure averaged over each micro-environment. On the other hand, sulphur dioxide requires just a few minutes for the exposure calculation. Exposure effectiveness is defined as the fraction of pollutant that actually enters a person's breathing zone: the amount of material actually inhaled, ingested or absorbed by an individual. The potential for a pollutant to affect human health is determined by its exposure effectiveness.

Cigarettes as a key pollutant.

Studies suggest that although benzene emission from cigarette smoke is only a small fraction of the emissions from vehicles, cigarettes can have an intake fraction up to a few hundred times more than outdoor emissions (D.H. Bennett, 2002). Since people spend most of their time indoors, most of the exposure to pollution of outdoor origin takes place indoors, where exposure can be modified by the building and its equipment such as air conditioning.

The issue is particularly aggravated when the indoor area in question is an industrial plant. Here, after the emission takes place, inert pollutants such as carbon monoxide disperse but for chemically reactive pollutants such as nitric oxide, a higher concentration indoor and outdoor develops.

Workers affected by primary and secondary pollutants.

The formation of secondary pollutants, in contrast, develops as a large-scale phenomenon with a uniform spatial distribution. As a result, workers who are vulnerable, suffer double effect: the spatial distribution of secondary pollutants and the concentration gradient related to the first pollutants. Particulate matter has a different spatial variability. Fine particles have a small spatial variability while ultra-fine and coarse particles have a much wider spatial variability. Specific components such as elemental carbon (diesel soot) and nitrogen dioxide concentrations show quite strong spatial variability owing to the distribution of local emission sources (vehicles). On the contrary, the spatial variability of ozone is reported very low across larger areas. The interaction of multiple pollutants between outdoors and industrial plants depends on the so-called penetration coefficient, the ventilation rate and the decay rate (W.E. Wilson, 2000; L. Wallace, cit).

The Interaction effect

The problem of interaction for multiple pollutants requires data on differences between measured and actual pollution levels for each pollutant and information about differences in correlations across pollutants (J. Schwartz, 2004). Particles flying in outdoor air penetrate to indoor air. Ozone, for example is a highly reactive component and reacts quickly with surfaces when penetrating indoors developing further chemical reactions. Ozone concentrations are generally high during sunny weather, conditions under which windows are open. The same applies for nitrogen dioxide and sulphur dioxide concentration of which is reported high notwithstanding the absence of sources in the indoor air. Workers in non-decent working conditions, particularly those working in less protected structures have less control over their respiratory system. The flux of air pollution penetrating industrial plants increases with ventilation rate which is higher when it is windier outside, when the temperature difference between indoor and outdoor air is higher and when the windows are open for a longer period. Several epidemiological studies provide evidence of different levels of toxic concentration in different outdoor-indoor interactions. (J.A. Sarnat, 2000; D.T Mage, 2001).

Knowledge about health effects yet to be implemented

It remains unclear whether the observed association between nitrogen dioxide and health is due to the nitrogen dioxide itself or whether nitrogen dioxide is an indicator of other correlated pollutants, such as ultra-fine particles emitted by other outdoor sources. For acute effect it would be interesting to investigate whether the exposure of workers followed from day to day varies with the respective day-to-day variation in outdoor air pollution. Although the association between indoor and outdoor air pollution has shown variations from worker to worker on a company population level, this correlation is considered to be sufficiently high to justify the use of outdoor concentration as a measure of exposure.

It is worth noting that for pollutants with low effective penetration from outdoor to indoor environments such as ozone, significant correlations have been found only for outdoor workers or during warm weather (M.S. O'Neill, 2003). Epidemiological studies on the relationship between indoor-outdoor air pollution has been conducted in Europe and North America and little knowledge is available in other parts of the worlds. Studies also report different impacts for susceptible workers, such as roadside vending resulting in obviously higher exposure.

Air Pollution Forecasts

Levels of air pollution are measured by Air Quality Indexes. For example in US the Air Quality Index is adopted while in UK the Daily Air Quality Index (DAQI) is used. The air quality indices indicate how clean or unhealthy the air is and the associated health effects. Therefore, these indices focus on health effects one can experience within a few hours or days after breathing unhealthy air and are calculated depending on the air pollutants chosen. For example in US, ground level ozone, particle pollution, carbon monoxide and sulphur dioxide are measured, while in UK the DAQI is determined by the highest concentration of fine pollutants: Nitrogen Dioxide, Sulphur Dioxide, Ozone, Particulate Matter (PM 2.5 and PM 10). These tools measure air pollutants concentration but provide no information about individual reaction to air pollutants, which could be different and worse from the index's advice. They provide health advice in the form of recommended actions to be taken, according to the level of air pollution. In general, air pollution indices are numbered (1-10 UK or 1-500 US) and accompanied by a colour showing the related risk which can be Low, Moderate, High or Very High.

According to the Air Pollution Forecast, one can take simple actions to reduce one's own exposure to unhealthy air by avoiding prolonged (outdoor activity done intermittently for several hours) or heavy (outdoor activity causing to breathe hard) exertion. Regrettably, for some workers' categories, reducing working activity might be impossible.

3. Sources of air pollution.

Definitions

Air pollution is defined as the existence of certain pollutants in the atmosphere at levels that adversely affect (European Environment Agency, 2013):
-
- human health
- environment
- cultural heritage (buildings, monuments and materials).

In its turn, the definition of pollutants is the following (Mukesh Sharma, 2008):
Presence of any substance, in some concentration, in the atmosphere that may or may tend to be injurious to human, plants, property and the atmosphere itself. This substance is called a pollutant.
The different between the two definitions refers to the impact on the atmosphere itself. This is quite important since pollutants originate chemical reactions in the atmosphere which are difficult to measure.

Air pollutants come from man-made sources and natural phenomena such as volcanic eruptions, forest fires or sand storms. Pollutants consist of dust particles travelling in the atmosphere due to winds and clouds and taking part in chemical reactions.

Air composition

The air includes solid, liquid and gaseous mass and assumes different density and different chemical composition depending on the altitude, pressure and temperature.
While the liquid part of air (vapour) varies depending on weather conditions, its main part, the gaseous one, contains 78% of Nitrogen (N2), 21% of Oxygen (O2) and 1% of other gases called trace gases (EEA, 2012).

Trace gases include:

Argon (Ar), Carbon dioxide (CO2), Neon (Ne), Helium (He), Kryptom (Ke), Xenon (Xe), Hydrogen (H2), Nitrous oxide (N_2O), Ozone (O_3) Methane (CH_4), Sulphur dioxide (SO_2), Nitrogen dioxide (NO_2), Ammonia (NH_3), Carbon monoxide (CO), Iodine (I_2), Benzene (C6H6). Primary pollutants include Sulphur Oxides (SOx), Nitrogen Oxides (NOx), Carbon Monoxide CO), Particulates, Metals (mercury and lead),

Chlorofluorocarbons (CFCs), Ammonia and Volatile Organic Compounds (VOCs). Secondary Pollutants include Ground Level Ozone (O3), Nitrates and Particulates. Thousands of other solid particles, including soot and metals influence the air composition of the atmosphere up to an altitude of 17 kilometres.

Volatile Organic Compounds

According to US Environmental Protection Agency (EPA, 2012) Volatile organic compounds (VOCs) are gases emitted from certain solids or liquids. VOCs include a variety of chemicals and are consistently higher indoors (up to ten times higher) than outdoors. VOCs are emitted by a wide array of products numbering in the thousands including paints and lacquers, paint strippers, cleaning supplies, pesticides, building materials and furnishings, office equipment such as copiers and printers, correction fluids and carbonless copy paper, graphics and craft materials including glues and adhesives, permanent markers, and photographic solutions. Organic chemicals are widely used as ingredients in household products releasing organic compounds while using them, and, to some degree, when they are stored.

EPA found levels of about a dozen common organic pollutants to be 2 to 5 times higher inside the home than outside, regardless of whether the homes were located in rural or highly industrial areas. EPA's studies indicated that while people are using products containing organic chemicals, they expose themselves and others to very high pollutant levels, and elevated concentrations can persist in the air long after the activity is completed. Chemical components of paints are solvent (Ethyl acetate and acetone) while cleaning products and refrigerants emit Chlorofluorocarbons. Benzene is a chemical found in environmental tobacco smoke and methylene chloride is in adhesive removers and aerosol sprays. When absorbed in the human body, methylene chloride is converted into carbon monoxide. Perchloroethylene is another volatile organic compound emitted during dry cleaning. Formaldeyde is emitted by old buildings especially when humidity and temperatures are high.

Respiratory system

Together with air composition it is worth adding the respiratory exchange ratio since 11 m3 are required every 24 hours. (Kirk Smith, 2011)

The Respiratory exchange ratio is:

R= Rate of CO_2 Produced / Rate of O_2 Consumed = CO_2/O_2.
As standard, CO_2 is produced at rate of 200 mil / minute while O_2 is consumed at 250 mil per minute. Hence, the respiratory exchange ratio is 200/250 = 0.80
Since respiratory exchange ratio changes under certain conditions, air pollution interacts with an individual's vulnerability affecting individual health in different ways.

When air is polluted, the respiratory exchange ratio is higher, and impact of the pollutants on the human body is more severe.

Dynamic nature of air and secondary pollutants.

The state of the air is highly dynamic since substances react and interact with other substances due to the function of heat as a catalyst, forming what is called Secondary Pollutants, more harmful to human health and nature. Some trace gases are defined as long-lived or inert gases because they do not react readily in the air, like carbon dioxide, nitrous oxide or nitrogen. Other trace gases have a variable status because they react so quickly and are referred to as short-lived gases (Sulphur dioxide SO_2, ammonia NH_3, ozone O_3). They are toxic to human health and vegetation, move slowly and can be detected in industrialized areas. Trace gases are transformed by the sun's energy into new chemical compounds. Nitrogen dioxide NO_2, for example, produced by industrial plants or combustion processes, when exposed to sunlight, is split into nitric oxide and atomic oxygen.

Further chemical reactions

The chemical process continues with other reactions (John Seinfel, 2005). Atomic oxygen, reacts with molecular oxygen (O_2) forming ozone (O_3), a powerful oxidant, one of the most important pollutants in industrialized areas. Europe, US, China, India, Japan due to vehicles and industrial plant emissions ozone precursor gases, suffer from ozone impact on health and nature. Sulphur, emitted as sulphur dioxide, is another example. Once in the air it is transformed into particles of sulphate which reacts with ammonia becoming ammonium sulphate which interact with nitric acid producing ammonium nitrate a very volatile and toxic particulate leading to enhanced nitrous oxide emissions a threat for the human genetic structure.

Particulate Matter

Many of the pollutants emitted by human activity are gases and once in the atmosphere they interact with other gases and are transformed into particles. This phenomenon is defined by chemists "aerosols" (not really as the sea spray we enjoy during windy day at beach), and particles are called Particulate Matter. Particulates can be solid or liquid and, depending on their chemical composition, they become droplets in the moist air, returning to solid particles as the air dries. Looking at the statistics, areas with high rate of Aerosols are associated with high human mortality. Science has proven the health effects of particulate matter and ozone, another pollutant associated with high mortality rate. Sulphur is emitted as Sulphur dioxide SO_2 and Nitrogen as Nitrogen dioxide NO_2. These gases interact with other gases as previously said, becoming other toxic gases. SO_2, for instance, becomes Ammonium sulphate when ammonia NH_3 is in the air, which is created through the interaction between Nitrogen and hydrogen atoms. (D. Fowler, 2013). Combustion in general and car exhaust fumes change the form of many substances releasing a variety of other air pollutants which have short and long-term effects on human health. Some of them cause more serious illness like benzene which damages cells' genetic structure causing cancer.

To sum up, the air composition is continuously changing, pollutants persist for years and migrate around the troposphere exposing different populations, in different countries at different times.

4. Indoor air pollutants

According to research (D.Brooks, 1992), the exposure of pollutants is five times higher indoors than outdoors. Therefore air contaminants in buildings cause serious effects on human health. Although outside pollutants enter in buildings, health and safety managers must also face almost 1000 indoor air contaminants which are intensified by doses, concentration rates, humidity, temperature and lighting. Indoors air pollutants are classified in the following groups: asbestos, radon, biological contaminants, second hand smoke, formaldehyde, lead, sick building syndrome, organic chemical, stove and heaters.

Asbestos is a mineral fiber used in building construction materials, found in older plants, insulation materials, textured paints and other floor tiles. Asbestos exposure causes lung cancer and mesothelioma a rare form of cancer and debilitation of respiratory system. Radon is a radioactive gas produced when uranium breaks down. This process occurs in every building since uranium is a component of the buildings foundations.

The exposure to radon (breathing) affects lungs health leading to lung cancer. Biological contaminants refer to building dust, bacteria and pollen. These contaminants trigger allergic reactions, rhinitis and asthma. Second hand smoking depends on the interaction between the burning end of cigarettes and air compounds. It includes more than 4000 compounds which are strong irritants, some of them are known to cause cancer. Formaldehyde is a chemical used to manufacture building materials and industrial products. In combination with other chemicals it is used in numerous manufactured products, such as in the textile industry or chemical industries. Formaldehyde causes watery eyes, nausea and breathing difficulties. Lead is found in the air, drinking water, water pipes, food, deteriorating paint and again dust. Lead affects all body organs causing convulsion, coma and death. Lower levels of it affect the brain, blood cells, kidneys and the nervous system. Sick building syndrome refers to the deterioration of building and includes air pollution sources and poor maintenance. Office furnishings, paints, adhesives, copy machines, printers, also contribute to indoor air pollution. Symptoms include eyes irritation, as well as nose and throat, skin dryness, headaches and nausea. Sick Building Syndrome influences also the organisational climate and human relations. Organic chemicals refer to paint, varnishes and wax, solvents. They are very toxic and affect eyes and respiratory system, headaches, visual disorders, memory impairment and other chronic illnesses causing cancer. Stove and heaters are additional sources of pollutants due to the combustion process. Kerosene and gas space heaters release carbon monoxide, nitrogen dioxide and particulate matter affecting workers' health through direct and indirect indoor air pollution.

5. Health effects of air pollution

Scientific evidence

Evidence connecting human health to air pollution comes from toxicology and epidemiology and occupational epidemiology. The above-mentioned effects of pollutants on human health are just a few examples. Occupational epidemiology offers an exhaustive list of relationships between air pollution and workers' health. A common health effect reported by WHO occurs in the respiratory system. WHO has identified a broad range of adverse respiratory diseases associated with air pollution ranging from death to reduced quality of life, including some irreversible changes in the physiological functions (D.B. Peden, 2005; H. Gong, 2004).

New epidemiological studies show that exposure to air pollutants during pregnancy are linked to intrauterine growth restriction and pre-term delivery (M Maisonet, 2004). Sub-clinical effects, such as temporary deficits in lung function or pulmonary inflammation occur in most of those exposed while mortality occurs in a few. The total impact of air pollution is likely to exceed that contributed by less frequent but severe outcomes. Premature mortality is the tip of the iceberg, representing a small fraction of all effects associated with air pollution (WHO, 2005).

Short and long term effects

Relationships between pollutants and workers' health should be understood correctly, so as to identify both acute and chronic effects of air pollution. Studies, both in Europe and The United States, suggest that the exposure-response relationship between particulate pollution and mortality is essential linear (increasing exposures=increasing effects frequency). The effects of pollutants occur even at very low levels, explaining why a large proportion of the population is affected by air pollution.

Besides the high frequency of less severe effects, it is important to consider the chronic effects brought about by less severe effects later in life (C.A. Pope, 2000). The combination between the proportion of population affected and the severity of health effects, shows that after premature mortality we can rank hospital admissions, emergency visits, restricted activity or reduced performance, medication use, physiological changes in pulmonary or cardiovascular functions, impaired pulmonary function, sub-clinical effects.

The influence of susceptibility

The broad array of health effects is explained by differential susceptibilities to pollutants, depending on both host (age, health status, diet, genetics) and environmental factors (housing, workplace and neighbourhood conditions). As previously stated, a key determinant of susceptibility is the socioeconomic status. A growing body of occupational epidemiology suggests that economically disadvantaged population groups may experience a disproportionately higher health burden caused by air pollution (M. O'Neill, 2000). The understanding of the biological mechanism through which air pollution exerts its effects has evolved quite rapidly over the last decade. Evidence suggests that the PM effect manifests itself through several interrelated pathways involving oxidative stress and inflammation.

Inhalation of PM triggers inflammation in the smaller airways, leading to an exacerbation of asthma and chronic bronchitis, airway obstruction and decreased breathing. PM also interfere with the clearance and inactivation of bacteria in lung tissue, epithelial permeability and macrophage function acting as an immunosuppressor by undermining normal pulmonary antimicrobial defence mechanism (J.T. Zelikoff, 2003). The cardiovascular system is also affected by inflammatory response which induces transient hypercoagulability, progression of atheroscleroris and increased vulnerability to plaque rupture. Evidence has been accumulated on cardiac control, since air pollution leads to changes in heart rate variability and arrhythmia in susceptible individuals. (H.C. Routledge,2003; T. Suwa, 2002; A. Peters, 1999; A. Seaton, 2002).

Risk assessment

Risk assessment and relations between air pollution and air effects are provided by WHO for Particulate matter, Ozone, Nitrogen dioxide, Sulphur dioxide (WHO, 2005). Health effects of air pollution are classified according to short-term exposure (Daily mortality, Respiratory and cardiovascular hospital admissions, primary care visits or medication, days of restricted activity, work absenteeism, physiological changes) and long-term exposure (Mortality, chronic respiratory disease, lung cancer, chronic cardiovascular disease, Intrauterine growth restriction). Notwithstanding the extensive application of risk assessment in epidemiological studies, the investigation on the impact of air pollutants on workers' health, beyond current scientific modus operandi has yet to be implemented.

6. Air pollutants as Mutagens.

Mutagenicity

Atmospheric emissions spread over long distances, permeate into the water, soil and living organisms. Most air pollution is gasses while particulate matter are the second pollutant group forming a mixture of organic and inorganic substances. Human breath is exposed to both air pollutants and secondary pollutants which cause a mutagenic effect. If the quantity of daily breath (11 m3 of air every 24 hours) is exposed to polluted air, the probability of disease occurs.

Epigenetic science has proved that air pollution effects include changes in the human genetic structure (DNA). Since DNA is formed by a nitrogen basis, each pollutant reacting with this chemical composition of DNA leads to a genetic change and related diseases such as cancers and leukaemia.

The harmfulness of particulates to DNA depends on the particulate diameter. Air containing particles smaller than 2.5 micrometer (-10 meter) is the most harmful pollutant to human and animals since it penetrates the respiratory tract settling on the surface of alveoli and therefore processes within the blood system. The complexity of pollutant composition and reaction once emitted impede the epidemiological observation on air mutagenicity.

Chemical compound and consequences.

A huge number of compounds representing different chemical classes can be found in polluted air and those compounds form complex mixtures of unknown biological consequences (K. Piekarska, 2009). Studies show that the nitro-amino-oxy PHA derivatives are classified as "mutagens". Considering that mentioned compounds have a synergistic effect, their isolation and the identification or their "reaction" is vital for human health. Mutagens are physical or chemical agents which change the genetic structure (DNA) leading to cell mutation and subsequent death. As mutations cause cancer, mutagens are therefore likely to be carcinogens. It is worth noting that not all mutations are caused by mutagens. Occupational epidemiology shows how different mutagens act on the DNA differently. Powerful mutagens result in chromosomal instability or modify the DNA sequence. In particular, changes in nucleic acid sequences by mutations include substitution of nucleotide base-pairs and insertions and deletions of one or more nucleotides in DNA sequence. Images of DNA changes by mutagens generated by tobacco smoke (benzo(a)pyrene), are quite impressive.

Many metals, such as arsenic, cadmium, chromium, nickel and their compounds may be mutagenic but they are also associated with the production of other chemical reactions leading to death.

The Latin meaning of mutagen is origin of change. Hippocrates, Paracelsus, John Hill, Percivall, Pott, Herman Muller, Charlotte Auerbach among others provided evidence on different mutagens and their serious effect on health. The industrial revolution, being the origin of the change of western society brought mutagens up to the current economy based on continuous accumulation and growth (J. Evans, Modeling of Air Pollution Impact, Harvard University Press, 1996). The watershed of development is entrenched in the will and capacity to prevent mutagens by taking the sustainability as the imperative to be followed by economic and social actors.

7. Understanding Air Pollution Prevention.

The general framework

Literature on Prevention (US EPA, 2003) includes three areas following the cycle of pollutants: sources, transportation and receptors. At source, emission ratios and type of pollutants are studied within other physics variables such as height, temperature, pressure and the speed of exit. The transportation issue includes wind speed, moisture, temperature, physical transportation and chemical reaction, the atmospheric chemistry and physics. The meteorology variables such as rain, dry dispersion, influence the pollution dynamic but are not part of a prevention programme. Receptors, in their turn, include sea, earth, humans, animals, monuments, buildings and the atmosphere itself. While air pollution prevention cannot be applied in the Transportation phase, Prevention at source and at receptors is feasible. Needless to say Prevention at Receptors is seen as the last resort, achieved by Air quality standards, Air Quality Goal and Guidelines. Since Air Quality Standards are country specific and depending on policy makers sustainability culture, air prevention at source is the preferable solution. The prevention policy is based on knowledge of pollutants and the emission context. For instance, PM sources are identified in Construction sector, Agriculture, Waste and Cigarette smoke, CO sources are caused by incomplete combustion in the energy, transportation and Industry sectors, SO2 sources are identified in burning coal and oil from Industry, transportation and energy sectors, NO2 sources from industrial processes, car exhausts, VOC sources from industrial processes, waste and transportation, lead sources, again from industrial processes and transportation. As far as secondary pollutants are concerned, SO2 Sulphur dioxide becomes the source of H2SO4, NO Nitrogen Oxides are the source of Nitrogen dioxide NO2 and HNO3 Nitric acid, whereas NO and VOC Volatile Organic Compound (paints and lacquers, paint strippers, cleaning supplies, pesticides, building materials and furnishings, office equipment such as copiers and printers, correction fluids and carbonless copy paper, graphics and craft materials including glues and adhesives, permanent markers, and photographic solutions) form Ozone O3.

Aims of Air pollution Prevention

The aims of air pollution prevention are to reduce the quantity and the hazardous character of pollutants. (OECD, 2000). Related activities are applicable on a life-cycle basis and articulated into three types: strict avoidance, reduction at source, product re-use. Subsequent processes, such as Recycling, Incineration, Land-filling belong to Waste Disposal. According to the OECD definition, Strict avoidance involves the "complete" prevention of waste generation by virtual elimination of hazardous substances or by reducing material or energy intensity in production, consumption and distribution. As far as reduction is concerned, reduction at source involves minimising use of toxic or harmful substances and minimising material or energy consumption.

Product re-use involves the multiple use of a product in its original form, for its original or alternative purpose with or without reconditioning. As a result, air pollution prevention occurs before pollutants are emitted or products are identified as waste. It is worth noting the difference between air pollution prevention addressed to relative reductions pollutants and other activities and programmes focused on absolute pollutants reduction.

The combination of prevention and recycling.

While air pollution prevention will never make recycling obsolete, the application of both prevention and recycling will have a greater influence on overall waste prevention than the individual application of one or the other. (see OECD Manual, Strategic waste prevention, 2000). In fact, high rates of prevention result in fewer materials being recycled. In its turn, recycling appears as the only solution in the case of toxic and dangerous substances. Since recycling and prevention are to be substituted, the increase of recycling waste acts as a disincentive to waste prevention. Depending on circumstances, specific characteristics of industries, products or materials lead to the decision to recycle rather than treat as a prevention issue. The recycling industry could be negatively influenced by prevention programmes. Therefore, the choice between recycling and prevention should be taken after a thorough evaluation on multiple factors including both technical and social.

The most important difference between strategic waste prevention and recycling is the ultimate focus. Strategic waste prevention, addressed to materials, contributes to a cleaner air encouraging Eco-efficiency policy, Industrial ecology, Integrated pollution prevention and control, extended producer responsibility and integrated product policy. Strategic waste prevention is closer to the green economy and its rational is often drawn by the specification of what, how, when and who complemented by two other prevention concepts like why and where to finalise prevention policy. Waste prevention is (in its most basic sense) an old behaviour pattern. The use of material in a frugal manner concerns any survival goal. Repairing a damaged item rather than buying a new one, saving used materials for re-use, producing objects and tools that maximize efficient use of raw materials are part of a society based on the principles of green economics. Pressure to grow and to accumulate is in contrast with the waste prevention habit impeding the practice of producing the same product with far fewer materials. Consuming less, excluding toxic materials are not commonplace in the liberalistic economy and in people's minds convinced by a bombardment of marketing. Waste production, due to materials, complements waste emissions leading to a huge toxic waste and related health impact. This is why prevention programmes based on relative reductions in waste generation (per unit output) are not enough. Absolute waste reduction should be broadened, overcoming barriers associated with inadequate information, lack of system analysis and lack of environmental sensitivity.

8. European policy on prevention

Since the EU Council Directive 78/176 on waste, a number of substantial changes have been made in European legislation concerning air pollution prevention. Several sectoral directives lay down specific minimum requirements including emission limit values for certain industrial activities such as large combustion plants, waste incineration, activities using organic solvents. The Directive on Industrial Emission (IED) 2010/75/EU replaces the IPPC Directive (Integrated Pollution Prevention and Control, 2008/1/EC) and summaries the European Union's work on Prevention strategy. The European Strategy on Air Pollution was published in 2005 through the Communication 2005/446. Following the Communication on the Clean Air for Europe (CAFÉ) the Strategy includes the assessment of health impact of pollution. Ground level ozone and particulate matter are considered pollutants of the most concern, leading to premature mortality. Ozone is not emitted directly but formed through the reaction of volatile organic compounds and Nitrogen oxides in the presence of sunlight. Particulate matter, in its turn is emitted directly (primary particles) but it is also formed in the atmosphere as secondary particles from gases such as sulphur dioxide, Nitrogen oxides and Ammonia.

In 2013 a loss in statistical life expectancy of over 8 months due to 2,5 PM in air was reported. This is equivalent to 3.6 million life years lost annually and 340.000 premature deaths. In monetary terms, the damage to human health is estimated at between 190bn euro and 610bn euro per annum. The latest science also shows that some environmental impacts of air pollution, such as acidification and eutrophication are more serious than expected. The EU Strategy points out that in view of these costs taking further action is not an option. As a result, the Strategy had the objective to achieve levels of air quality that do not give rise to significant negative impact on and risk to human health and the environment, through two means: simplification of air quality legislation and control measures. The Directive on industrial emission 2010/75/EU can be considered a first result towards air quality prevention and related abatement of SO_2, NOx, VOCs, NH_3 emission levels.

The IED Directive (84 articles and X annexes) covers definitions, general principles and prevention obligations, best available technologies, emission limit values, installations requirements, environmental inspections, controls of emissions and monitoring and special provisions for installations and activities using organic solvents. Technical issues are presented in Annexes. The European Pollutant Release and Transfer Register is the new Europe-wide register providing data reported annually by some 28.000 industrial facilities covering 65 economic activities. This register is a remarkable instrument for prevention since it contributes to transparency and public participation in environmental decision-making.

The decision to designate 2013 as the Year of Air reflects the concern about the impact of pollutants on human health. The European Environment Agency plays an important role in prevention policy. Air Quality in Europe Reports provide data on sources and effects of Particulate Matter, Ozone, Nitrogen Dioxide, Sulphur Dioxide, carbon Monoxide, heavy Metals and Benzene.

9. Strategic air pollution prevention

Green technologies.

Air pollution Prevention or its abatement is expensive and it is perceived as a part of business costs and an inevitable cost of growth which can be passed on to consumer price. Costs of compliance with all environmental regulations go beyond the capital investment of control equipment and include engineering costs, tender and bidding costs, operational costs, costs for training dedicated staff, costs associated to monitoring and statistics and laboratory costs. Due to the aforementioned costs, investment in green technologies as a way to prevent air pollution in same circumstances is not feasible. The green technology is a technology which achieves a cleaner less polluting production. A usual case, often mentioned, refers to the conversion of a coal-fired electricity plant to a natural gas technology which cut unburned hydrocarbons (UHC), lowered carbon dioxide (CO_2), mercury, PM, NO_2, and sulphur dioxides. In addition, gas fired plants are cheaper to build. Another example is the case of US Air Force which decided in 2003 to destroy material rather than incinerate it. Disintegrators provide an alternative to incineration. In this case, the reengineering of destruction processes costs less than incineration costs.

Prevention programmes

Pollution Prevention programmes applied to enterprises (called P2) are demanding and not always practical. (N. P.Cheremisnoff, 2001).

Needs analysis is the initial phase aimed at gathering information for a baseline description of operations and their pollution impact. Environmental performance and financial performance are taken into account. In plant assessment the next phase is followed by the third and conclusive phase devoted to corrective action formulation. Monitoring of gaseous emissions is not always detectable and measurable and thus it is an indirect estimation. Several relationships are measured such those between odours and unit operations, vapours and employee irritations, gaseous emissions and respiratory problems among workers and so on. In essence, the environmental impact and human health are considered in a whole assessment document containing recommendations on production process changes, equipment to be changed, changes in process control, use of dispersion in place of solvents, the revision of raw materials flows, raw material substitution, process substitution with cleaner technology. Economic evaluation, which is of considerable importance for the company, accompanies the final assessment together with the full cost accounting.

The choice of Air Pollution Prevention.

The 1990 US Clean Air and Pollution Prevention Act shifted the control and measurement strategy to the Pollution Prevention Strategy emphasising the reduction or elimination of waste production "before" it is emitted into the environment (L. Theodore, 1992, T.E. Higgins, 1995). At industrial, commercial or household sites, Pollution Prevention requires the substitution of a process that is less hazardous to human health and the environment. Pollution Prevention also foresees innovative solutions to the process, equipment or plant operating practices towards the elimination or reduction air pollution. More efficient maintenance procedures or conservation of energy at the source methods are also part of the P2. Effective air pollution prevention steps include the source reduction, recycling, waste treatment and disposal, as a last resort. Regarding Source reduction, material substitution and source control are the most useful methods applied. The former occurs when a fuel source or raw material is replaced by a less toxic component which is equally suitable for manufacturing, as in the case of the replacement of chlorofluorocarbons with hydro chlorofluorocarbons. A typical example of material substitution refers to coal and other ores before subjecting them to the manufacturing process. Source control involves changes in the equipment and operational settings of a plant or segregating toxic chemicals from one another to reduce the number of dangerous events to public health.

When other at source reduction techniques are not possible Recycling appears to be the option. In this case a waste product is used as a fuel resource to power a manufacturing process. Since waste exchange between industries is based on economic convenience, when this is not the case recycling is not pursued. Recycling also involves the chain between factory and consumer. In this case, the financial variable is added by the ecological spirit of the consumer, which is culture-based. When a chemical composition or hazardous material cannot be reduced, substituted or recycled, its treatment is the last resort and includes incineration, chemical alteration or physical treatment.

Treatment refers to pollutants that cannot be reduced or recycled or transformed into less toxic chemical components and includes incineration - either biological, physical or chemical. The aim of incineration is to reduce the amount of toxicity of a pollutant. When treatment is not feasible, the last resort is disposal the least attractive option. Disposal is carried out through land farming, deep well injection, land filling and ocean dumping. Regrettably, these systems produce pollutants and are not the right response.

10. Role of education towards sustainable mindset

Cooperation among science, industry and educational institutions.

Emissions from Industry, public and private buildings, transportation and other combustion-based human activities are threatening not only climate patterns or the environmental balance but they also impact on human health leading to diseases and premature death. Reducing and Preventing air pollution are two different strategies of two opposing ways to address development and growth. In this effort, close to the development approach and far from business as usual cynicism, cooperation among researchers, industry, general public and educational institutions is the imperative. Foundations for a sustainable society depend on the preventive principle. Since the preventive paradigm must be learnt, strategic education should be organised so that this goal can be achieved as soon as possible.

Sustainability science

Rather than emphasize a sustainability concept based on the World Commission on Environment and Development, (satisfy current needs without compromising the ability of future generations to meet their own needs) sustainability science as a discipline that unifies global, social and human systems, should be strengthened (H. Komiyama, 2011). The "global system" includes the geosphere, atmosphere, hydrosphere and biosphere. The Earth provides natural resources, energy and a supportive system. The "social system" comprises the economic, political, industrial and the societal base for a fulfilling human existence. In this realm, for instance, the declining birth rate is interpreted as the unsustainability of the family. In its turn, the "human system" is connected to the social system and affects directly the health and survival of human beings.

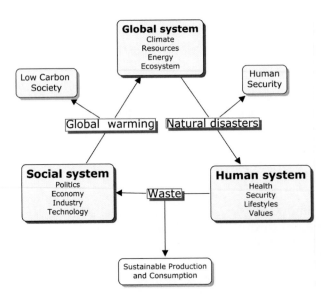

Poverty, hunger, disease, lack of housing and exclusion, religious tensions or wars are part of the human system. Relationships between the above-mentioned domains define problems humanity must face. The interaction between the social system and global system leads to global warming whereas the links between the social system and human system causes mass production and therefore waste. The links between human system and global system leads to poverty, hunger and diseases. As a result, a low carbon society is the response to global warming, sustainable production and consumption the response to waste and the human security the answer to poverty and hunger.

Sustainability science refers to the comprehensive and holistic view underlined by the aforementioned interactions. It would be beneficial to shift the focus from the definition outlined in the Brundtland Report towards a more useful framework drafted by sustainability science.
Two obstacles impede progress towards sustainability science:
- the complexity of the problems;
- the specialisation of science that seeks to address the problems.
Multiple factors behind the sustainability crisis are not faced by an overarching strategy. Rather, the compartmentalization of disciplines means that the analysis takes a highly restricted perspective. The period of explosive expansion started in the 1950s and not arrested by the economic crisis of 2008-2013 coincides with the severe period of air pollution. What is worse is the "mobility" of pollution generated in one part of the world but impacting on humans' health in entirely different areas. In addition, the attempt to provide uniform solutions to different, even if global concerns, is another part of the problem. Yet, dialogue and consensus, crucial factors towards sustainability science, are not so widespread among experts and academics, therefore aggravating the identification of innovative and trans-disciplinary solutions.

The need for a comprehensive view

Segmentation and specialisation of knowledge is due to the massive flood of information from libraries and on line source. For example, over 3000 articles were published in 2010 alone (Y. Kajikawa, 2010) on sustainability and this number is growing exponentially. Needless to say Knowledge advances society and prosperity, but the problem lies in the lack of a comprehensive view. Scientists are trained to produce specialized bricks of knowledge without looking at the whole building. Regarding sustainability, there is a general agreement about its meaning as the ability to sustain a certain state or level.

However, when the World Commission on Environment and Development relates sustainability to development as "a development that meets the needs of the present without compromising the ability of future generations to meet their own needs (WCED, 1987)" some doubts are raised by green economists. The current generation concept, in fact, is not a "neutral" concept but entails differences among current population cohorts and their needs. Who decides what needs should be met, those of industrialized countries or those of others? The second difference regards the nature of needs, often assimilated to physical goods measured with money rather than other kinds of goods, such as health, education or spiritual needs. It is difficult to accept that 1,3 billion people who live on 2 dollars a day could think about future generation needs and can afford the cost of the polluter-pay principle. Yet, the treatment of future generations seems difficult as they cannot express their needs and wishes nor enter negotiations. Furthermore, ethical issues are involved when the efficiency principle is considered. Since pollution is part of human activity and could not be eliminated (Laws of thermodynamics) and pollution is often a by-product of beneficial processes (health care), setting pollution targets requires the evaluation of cost and benefits in monetary terms. This might be judged unethical. As a result, an economically efficient pollution target may not be socially optimal (P. Singh, 2007).

Transdisciplinary

The UN University **a**nalysed the academic landscape of sustainability through a citation network analysis of 29.391 papers including the concepts as sustainability. Regrettably, results showing 15 main domains (Agricolture, Forestry,Business, Soil, Energy, Water, Wildlife, Health, etc) do not include Air. This is an example that data and information are not enough. Knowledge is identified through modelling and modelling is a process that replaces the part of reality with an abstract representation of the world that has a similar but simpler structure (Y. Kajikawa, 2011). This is why researchers are building a common modelling framework for sustainability science. Forecasting science is another example in that it includes Goal-settings, indicators design and measurement, casual chain analysis, problem-solution framework. Since forecasting is not based on data, backcasting is needed to use available data, but backcasting has no change options. In conclusion, sustainability science needs both backcasting and forecasting, overcoming the separation of disciplines toward a multidisciplinary and trans-disciplinary approach. This effort combines engineering and psychology, economics and governance, in short science and humanities.

A collective action towards prevention.

Concomitant to the comprehensive perspective goes the need for effectiveness of action. It is said that knowledge without action cannot change a situation and action without knowledge leads to uncertain results (G.D. Brewer, 2007). Action-knowledge is a key relationship in the design of collective action indispensable to transform current society into a sustainable community. The collective action points out that a single action has a limited impact on sustainability. Without an orchestration towards sustainability, all activities by numerous actors have a marginal effect. This collective action should be built through a first stage of decomposition and analysis of unit action, followed by a second stage relating to the integration of multiple actions into a new and innovative action which will be the collective action after the promotion and agreement of common goals. Collective action needs transparent flows of information between actors and requires a network of networks so that knowledge promotion, mutual learning, trust and strong social capital are achieved. By strengthening a network of networks, knowledge is shared, leaning processes become mutual, skills and resources are used in a complementary way, innovation is breathed collectively. These relational activities have the capacity to overcome the tendency to apply a single solution, even if it were powerful, to many problems, allowing plausible solutions to meet temporal and spatial factors. To this end, a partnership-building approach is needed to involve stakeholders, organise responsibilities, reach credible commitment and legitimacy of the collective action. In short, everyone should`in the words of Wangari Maathai be a hummingbird and do the best they can.

References

J. F. Bach, The effect of infections on susceptibility to autoimmune and allergic diseases, New England Journal of Medicine, Nr 347, 2002

P. Brimblecombe, The big smoke, London, 1987

D.H. Bennett, Defining intake fraction, Environmental Science and Technology, Nr 36, 2002

G.D. Brewer, Inventing the future, Sustainability science, Nr 2, 2007

D.Brooks, Understanding indoor air quality, Lewis Publisher, London 1992

N. P.Cheremisnoff, Green Profits: Pollution Prevention, Butterworth, Mass. 2001

J. Evans, Modelling of Air Pollution Impact, Harvard University Press, 1996

F. Eyraud, The evolving world of work in the enlarged EU, ILO, 2007)

European Environment Agency, Every breath we take, 2013

EEA, Air Quality Report, 2012EPA, Introduction to Air Quality, 2012

J. Hardin, Science Vol 162, 1968

D. Fowler, Every breath we take, 2013

H. Gong, Exposures of elderly with chronic obstructive pulmonary disease COPD to concentrated particulate pollution, Inhalation Toxicology, Nr 16 2004

Health Effects Institute, Report on Health effects of outdoor air pollution in developing countries, Boston, 2004

ILO, The prevention of occupational diseases, 2013

Y. Kajikawa, The structuring of knowledge, UN University press, 2010

H. Komiyama, Sustainability science, UN University Press, 2011

Y. Kajikawa, The structure of sustainability science 2011

D. Peden, The epidemiology and genetics of asthma risk associated with air pollution, Journal of Allergy and Clinical Immunology, Nr 115, 2005

D.T Mage, A procedure for use in estimating human exposure to particulate matter of ambient origin, Journal of Air and Waste Management Association, Nr 51, 2001

M. Maisonet A review of the literature on the effects of ambient air pollution on fetal growth, Environmental Research, Nr 95, 2004

M.S. O'Neill, Ozone exposure among Mexico City outdoor workers, Journal of the Air and Waste Management Association, Nr 53, 2003

M.S. O'Neill, Health, wealth and air pollutions, Environmental Health Perspectives, Nr 111, 2003

W.R. Ott, Concepts of human exposure to air pollution, Environment International, Nr 7, 1982

K. Piekarska, Mutagenic effects of main group of organic pollutants absorbed on suspended particulate matter, Environment protection engineering, Vol 35, N. 1 2009

A. Peters, Increases in heart rate during an air pollution episode, American Journal of Epidemiology, Nr 150, 1999

C.A. Pope, Particulate matter-mortality exposure-response relation and threshold, American Journal of Epidemiology, Nr 152, 2000

H.C. Routledge, Why cardiologists should be interested in air pollution, Heart, Nr 83, 2003

J. Schwartz, Control for confounding in the presence of measurement error in hierarchical models, Biostatistics, Nr 4, 2004

J.A. Sarnat, Assessing the relationship between particulate and gaseous exposure in Baltimore, Journal of Air and Waste Management Association, Nr 50, 2000.

Mukesh Sharma, Air Pollution, Kanpur University, 2008

OECD Manual, Strategic waste prevention, 2000

OECD, Working Party on Pollution Prevention and Control, 2000

Kirk Smith, Air Pollution, University of California, 2011

John Seinfel, Air composition, California Institute of Technology, 2005

John Spengler, Air Pollution: a public health perspective, Science, 22, 1983

A. Seaton Particulate air pollution and health, Lancet, Nr 360, 2002

P. Singh, Pollution Control, IJGE, Vol 1, Nos 3/4, 2007

T.J. Smith, Occupational exposure and dose over time, American Journal of Industrial medicine, Vol 21, 1992

T. Suwa, Particulate air pollution induces progression of atherosclerosis, Journal of the American College of Cardiologists, Nr 39, 2002

L. Theodore, Pollution Prevention, Van Nostrand Reinhold, 1992, T.E. Higgins, Pollution Prevention handbook, Boca Raton Ed., 1995

United States Environmental Protection Agency, Principles and practices of air pollution control, 2003

US EPA, Principles and Practice of air pollution control, 2003

US EPA, Evaluating Exposures to toxic air pollutant, 1991

WCED, 1987

WHO, Air Quality Guidelines, 2005

UNCED 1992

WHO, Air Quality Guidelines, 2005

K. Vahakangas, Molecular epidemiology of human cancer risk and gene-environment interactions, Methods in Molecular Medicine, Nr 59, 2003

WHO, Top 10 diseases categories, 2002

W.E. Wilson, Estimating separately personal exposure to ambient and non ambient particulate matter for epidemiology and risk assessment, Journal of the Air and Waste Management Association, Nr 50 2000

WHO, Air Quality Guidelines, 2005

J.T. Zelikoff, Effects of inhaled ambient particulate matter on pulmonary antimicrobial immune defence, Inhalation Toxicology, Nr 15, 2003

2.2 Agricultural Greening: Organic Production And Chernobyl Contaminated Areas

By Vyacheslav Potapenko

According to the calculations of United Nations experts, the production of foodstuffs on the planet should be increased by 70 % up to 2050 to meet the demands of the Earth's population. Most of the lands in Europe and Northern America have been exhausted, and only 5 countries have great potential for increasing their volumes of agriculture production output. These are Brazil, Russia, India, China and Ukraine.

Agriculture is the most promising branch of the primary sector of the economy in Ukraine. About 40 % of the territory of Ukraine consists of potentially fertile chernozem soils in the forest-steppe and steppe zones in the centre, south and east of the country. Allowing for rather high content of humus (4.9 %) and loamy mechanical composition, chernozems provide for high fertility, especially of cereals and oil-bearing plants under bogharic (dry-land) agriculture. Watering, ploughing and fertilizing, other agrotechnical and agrochemical arrangements permit increasing essentially the crop capacity.

The farming lands in the territory of Ukraine have been utilized for thousands of years. Ukrainian chernozems were actively used in the 20th century that resulted in the highest soil ploughing in Europe (79 % of the total area of agriculture lands). Considerable areas of farm lands suffered from the accident at the Chernobyl NPP and from negative effect of other technogenic factors.

However, the population employment in agricultural production in Ukraine (18 % of employed population) is still the highest one in Europe. A sharp decrease of investments in agriculture during the crisis 90's of the 20th century, degeneration of land ownership and other factors made farmers to give up the broad use of agrotechnical means of plant protection and nutrition. Partial conversion to small natural economy, rebirth of traditional agrotechnologies, use of horse traction and manure in cultivation of land, etc., became a common practice. This situation, which was considered economically dangerous in the period of industrial development, is a favorable one in conditions of current tendencies of production greening, realization of the principles of "green economy" and formation of the demand for production of organic agriculture. The organic agriculture can become a locomotive of reformation of Ukrainian economy in accordance with the world standards, environmental in particular.

Ukraine has special advantages as to potentialities proposed by the balanced and organic agriculture. They are determined by low level of the use of pesticides and chemical fertilizers, by a considerable share of small farms and accessibility of agricultural manpower. There is also export attractiveness – the neighborhood with European Union, the second in the world market of organic food products which grows at a high pace.

According to the data of the Federation of Organic Movement in Ukraine 121 producers of organic farm products were certified in Ukraine by the early 2010; there are 145 enterprises which produce and process organic products in total. The producers which have received the corresponding certificate can mark their production as organic in Ukraine.

According to experts' calculations the predicted volume of sales of Ukrainian organic production will be $ 35 000 000 in 2015, and Ukrainian market of this segment will grow to $ 139 000 000. Producers of organic dairy products occupy about 3 % of Ukrainian market. Lack of large trade lots of raw products is one of the causes which restrains the increase of the market of organic products in Ukraine.

Allowing for the fact that organic foodstuffs are more expensive than ordinary products, they are considered products for the rich, and the demand for them depends directly on consumers' financial position. The volumes of sales of organic production increased swiftly in Ukraine during 1993-2008, and they have reached by some positions 26 % a year, but already in early 2009 this index dropped to 7.5 %. In so doing the rates of the increase of the share of organic market are still twice as high as those of the common foodstuffs market.

This production is not almost promoted in retail trade because of the decrease of purchasing capacity of the overwhelming majority of citizens which cannot spend additional money for organics. But even those Ukrainian consumers which want and can pay for the organic products have to buy imported analogs which, owing to marketing and logistic expenditures, are more expensive than common products by 300 %.

About 1 % of all agricultural lands of the country from about one third of lands fit for farming are occupied by organic cultures; mainly cereals and oil-producing crops grow on these lands. Investigations in the middle 1990's confirmed that up to 90 % of arable land in Ukraine underwent various degrees of degradation. About 35.8 % of lands were eroded, 25.6 % possess high acidity, 9.7 % are salted and alkaline, and 8.9 % are water-logged and swamped. On the other hand, as a result of economic crisis, because of the lack of current assets in particular, the use of mineral fertilizers, pesticides and other chemicals has been considerably decreased in the recent years. Thus the loss of natural fertility of soils has paused. There are considerable areas of uncontaminated chernozems which may be converted to organic agriculture during relatively short period.

The EU countries are the basic sales market of organic products because of low demand for organics on the part of home consumers. The financial-economic crisis has slowed down the development of organic market, which increased by 10 % annually mainly at the expense of EU countries, and reduced the demand for organic production because of its high prices. This has deprived Ukrainian producers of the only sales channel. According to the data of the Centre of Environmental Safety of Consumers, Ukrainian companies, which produce organic food-stuffs, did not export any products, despite the available agreements, and that was because of fall in demand in 2009.

A traditional sales channel – through traders – proved to be the only one that remained accessible for businessmen which had lost the specialized market. But traders bought organic products as common cultures at prices equal to those on cereals market (rather low today – about 1000 UAH/t of food wheat). Such a way may be profitable, allowing for inconsiderable expenditures for organic cultivation compared with traditional methods – owing to saving of mineral fertilizers, etc.

When vegetables and fruits are grown by the organic method, crop capacity sharply decreases, sometimes two-four times. It is rather difficult to grow vegetables by the organic method. Projects of organic agriculture are realized for growing mainly cereals and oil-producing plants. If cereals and oil-producing plants make thousands and tens of thousands hectares for one project, vegetables – only 0.5-3.0 ha. When growing cereals and oil-producing plants, crop capacity may be even increased; at the same time the expenditures for their growing may be decreased. In so doing, if grain crop cannot be sold as organic, it may be always sold as common without special expenditures. On the other hand, the companies which are specialized producers of organics had to pay for certification according to international standards, and it was difficult to compensate such expenditures when crops were sold as inorganic production.

The profitability of "organic" business all over the world depends badly on the level of state support. In EU countries with a lot of adherents of organic products and state support of this trend the producers can venture to keep prices at a comparatively high level: organic products in Europe are more expensive than common ones by 20-40 %. Prices could beat least twice as high without state subsidies. There are no laws which regulate the market of organic products in Ukraine, but their drafts exist, the law *About Organic Agriculture* in particular.

One of the basic problems in introduction of technologies of organic agriculture in Ukraine is the low level of knowledge of population and producers concerning organic agriculture (comprehension of the basic characteristics and peculiarities of these technologies, the advantages of their use and possible problems in the process of introduction). The other weighty problem is the low level of environmental consciousness of population (first of all rural) and low technological culture of agriculture production of all levels – from personal farm to great agrarian associations. This group of problems is caused by the absence of the corresponding education courses in the theory and practice of managing organic agriculture at educational institutions of various levels of accreditation.

Besides the lack of appropriate education and environmental consciousness, one can observe the unwillingness to change obsolete views, which have been formed for a long period of agriculture intensification, and low level of innovational activity of managers and administrative structures. Mention should be made of complicated demographic situation in the country-side (depopulation, age structure) and low living standard of rural population. Put in conditions of a necessity to survive, people meet everything new with distrust and prejudice, and they do not want to risk their property.

The range of institutional and legal problems of introduction of organic agriculture in Ukraine is as follows:

- lack of corresponding legal and normative basis, first of all the basic law about the organic agriculture and certification of organic production coordinated with requirements of international law;

- lack of the efficient national system of certification and control of organic farms and their production;
- lack of the corresponding internal infrastructure (associations/unions/centres for producers of organic stuff;
- absence of state support in providing access to foreign markets of organic production;
- lack of the proper information support (popularization of technologies of organic agriculture, environmental education of population and producers of organic foodstuffs, advice support of producers, special trainings for the farm chiefs and workers).

"Greening" of agriculture will allow providing with foodstuffs the evergrowing population of the world, without undermining the reserves of natural resources.
Foodstuffs contaminated with radionuclides (first of all, with cesium and strontium) are the major danger after the catastrophe at the Chernobyl NPP. The penetration of these radioactive elements to human organism occurs mainly as a result of their transfer from soil to plants and then to plant-growing and cattle-breeding products. About 8.400 000 ha of agriculture lands of Ukraine have been contaminated with radionuclides as a result of the catastrophe at the Chernobyl NPP, and it is the obtaining of radiation-safe farm products that is the key instant of preventing negative consequences of the Chernobyl catastrophe.

The total number of persons living in contaminated territories, where they can receive a dose of additional irradiation of about 0.5 mSv/yr at the expense of Chernobyl discharges, is approximately 320 000 (Table 1), rather than 2 200 000 persons, that corresponds to legislative and sublegislative acts in force.

Table 1
The number of people living in the territories contaminated with radiation as a result of catastrophe at the Chernobyl NPP

Average dose a year	Total number	Children to 18 years old
D ≥ 5 мSv/year	986	319
1 мSv/year ≤ D <5 мSv/year	135621	32758
0.5 мSv/year ≤ D < 1 мSv/year	179874	54909

All completeness of aid and privileges granted by law was confirmed in Constitution of Ukraine. Articles 16 and 22 of the Constitution jointly make the benefits and privileges granted by law to the persons, victims of the Chernobyl catastrophe, irreversible; this gives scope for the easy and highly efficient political demagogy without respect to financial restrictions of the state.

Law of Ukraine *On the Status and Social Defense of Citizens Which Were Victims of the Chernobyl Catastrophe* foresees about one hundred kinds of privileges, compensation payments, extra payments and aids for citizens which were the catastrophe victims; above fifty of these benefits require financial security. The number of invalids permanently increases: there were about 2 000 disabled persons in 1991, their number is 113 000 today, including 3 000 children.

The exclusive circle of unreal payments and irreversible liabilities gives no chance for efficient overcoming both economic consequences of the Chernobyl catastrophe and, that is no less important, its social consequences.

The conception of the UNO Chernobyl program of revival and development consists in lending support to population initiatives concerning the renascence of communities-victims by self-organization into self-governing structures based on the community and own leadership in planning, managing and introduction of their social, economic and environmental renascence and development into life.

International aid was received permanently by Ukraine for liquidation of after-effects of the Chernobyl catastrophe. Ukraine has received $ 2.6 billion of international aid since 1986 and till the Chernobyl NPP close down in 2000.

The economic and social renascence of the territories which have suffered from the catastrophe at the Chernobyl NPP proceeds in fact, bypassing the law in force. About 10 000 people live in the second zone of unconditional settling-out, in the Narodychi settlement where approximately 500 000 more families are waiting for settling-out. In spite of the legislative ban for development of production and building, and restriction of farming activities, all these trends of activity are realized, with attraction of foreign investments as well. For example, they grow rape for biodiesel production in the Zhytomyr Region in the territories referred by law to radiation-contaminated ones. The agricultural production is performed on all lands of the Rivne Region, where radiational situation is better; with attraction of investors' assets in particular. Both the officials and deputies, businessmen and local residents want to annul the ban for economic activities in the fourth, third, and even second zones.

All local officials and deputies take changes in the borders of zones as a necessity which cannot be put off, first of all for economic reasons. The local authorities consider it necessary to make total radiological examination or introduction of passport system of the territory with following abolition of zones in all settlements, except for those with high radiation background. However, both the officials and deputies think it necessary to preserve privileges for all categories of ChNPP accident victims, the persons born after the accident in the corresponding territories in particular.

So, the specific territory has been actually formed on the northern border of Ukraine, the subsidies, restrictions for nature management and rights for resources as well as human population in the state of depression being its features. The use of the principles of environmentally safe "green" economy can become an approach to economic and later to social renascence of the territories which have suffered from the accident at the Chernobyl NPP.

The ratio between the content of a certain radioisotope in a plant and its content in soil, called the conversion factor, is used to estimate the level of arrival of radionuclides from soil to farm production. It depends both on the type of soil and a kind of farm culture.

The highest conversion factors are characteristic of soddy-podzolic sandy loam and and loamy soils, they decrease in soddy-podzolic clayey loam soils and grey sandy and loamy soils. For example, for pea, the culture which considerably absorbs ^{137}Cs, the absorption row looks as follows: soddy-podzolic sandy loam soils 34 (Bq/kg) – soddy-podzolic loamy 24 (Bq/kg) – soddy-podzolic clayey loam 15 (Bq/kg) – grey sandy 15 (Bq/kg) – grey loamy 15 (Bq/kg) [170]. Dependence of the factor of radionuclide conversion to plant on the culture type in certain soil looks as follows. There is the absorption row of ^{137}Cs for soddy-podzolic sandy loam soils: pea 34 (Bq/kg) – oats13 (Bq/kg) – potato 11 (Bq/kg) – winter rye 11 (Bq/kg) – maize for silage 7 (Bq/kg). An analogous absorption row with other absolute values is characteristic of all types of soils of Ukrainian Polissia, which most territory consists of radiation-contaminated lands.

The sustainable development of radiation-contaminated territories is based on the system of administrative decisions directed to rehabilitation of these territories with the aim of their economic use. Radiation-contaminated agricultural lands are subject to rehabilitation based on the use of countermeasures.

Administrative decisions in rehabilitation of radiation-contaminated territories foresee: elimination of the territory from nature management and settling-out of residents, change of the type of land use, territory rehabilitation without changing the type of land use, treatment, propaganda of determining the expedient types of the use.

In the first case the territory is completely excluded from the practical use as it was with the 30-km zone of ChNPP or the territory with ^{137}Cs contamination level of 5.0-15.0 C/km^2. Another type of the decision foresees a radical change in land use type, for example, the exclusion of lands of agricultural use (their planting with forest or creation of artificial reservoirs or even creation of industrial enterprises on the plots with a considerable level of radiation contamination), settling-out of residents of settlements, etc. The decisions on the radical change of land use are made at a high managerial level. In accordance with the third type of decisions the territory is completely rehabilitated with preservation of land use type but with the change of technologies. Thus the system of countermeasures is used on the farm lands contaminated as a result of ChNPP accident; it allows obtaining environmentally pure products.

The efficient rehabilitation of radiation contaminated territories of agrarian use foresees the correspondence of farm products quality to environmental standards at economic efficiency of agricultural production under the conditions of stable functioning of agroenvironment system of economy.

Rehabilitation of agricultural lands includes a set of measures directed to obtaining of plant-growing and cattle-breeding products corresponding to radiologic standards. This complex consists of four groups of arrangements – organizational, agrotechnical, agrochemical and technological.

Organizational arrangements foresee:
- inventory of lands by the levels of radiation contamination, mapping; analysis of soils, contamination level of agricultural lands;
- prediction of radionuclides content in crop, reactiveness of countermeasures, level of crop contamination;
- planning of agriculture works in accordance with prediction results and change of the areas under crops, use of farm production;
- radiation control of farm production.

Agrotechnical arrangements include:
- mechanical withdrawal of radionuclides from the upper layer of soil;
- deep ploughing with turning out of the arable layer that decreases 3-10 times ^{137}Cs arrival to agriculture plants;
- increasing of the areas under cultures with low level of radionuclides accumulation;
- prevention of secondary contamination of plants by decreasing the inter-row cultivation;
- carrying-out of works on humid soil;
- radical and surface improvement of hayfields and pastures.

Agrochemical arrangements are as follows:
- liming of acid soils, which decreases the accumulation of nuclides in plants 2-4 times;
- introduction of high doses of potash fertilizers that decreases the accumulation of radionuclides in plants 2-10 times ;
- introduction of high doses of phosphoric fertilizers that decreases the accumulation of radionuclides in plants 3-10 times;
- introduction of organic fertilizers: manure, peat, sapropel, compost that decreases the accumulation of radionuclides in plants 1.5-3 times;
- introduction of nitric fertilizers;the content of radionuclides
- use of meliorative components in cattle-breeding that decreases considerably the content of contaminants in milk and meat compared with their content in fodder: zeolites – 2 times; humolite – 2-4 times; ferrocene – 2 times.

Technological arrangements foresee:
- washing and cleaning of gathered production;
- use of various methods of cultures gathering;
- processing of products aimed at decreasing the content of radionuclides.

Complex estimation of countermeasures efficiency foresees determination of possible changes of land use type and requires studying agrolandscape structure of the territory with allowance for urgent natural, economic and environmental characteristics of each territory system. The territory nature-economic system (facies), relatively homogeneous by geological structure, geomorphologic and microclimate peculiarities, characteristics of surface and soil waters, soil-forming rocks, soils and by the type of agricultural use is considered by elementary agrolandscape area [225]. Scenarios of using various rehabilitation arrangements are modeled on this basis.

To develop and realize rehabilitation on radiation-contaminated agricultural lands it is necessary to calculate the content of radionuclides in foodstuffs. The available technologies permit calculating the expected content of radioisotopes in cattle-breeding and plant-growing production. The conversion factor, as was noted, depends on numerous factors, and thus, it is calculated depending on the soil type, its physic-chemical characteristics, temperature regime and humidification, level of radionuclides content, biologic characteristics of plants and other parameters.

As was noted above, the structure of information organization during the use of GIS-technologies, necessary for modeling rehabilitation scenarios, foresees generalization of the data according to type landscapes of radiation-contaminated territories. The latter, in its turn, makes it possible to systematize information about main factors affecting the conversion of radionuclides to plants:
- orographic conditions of migration (morphostructure, morphosculpture, exceeding of the local basis of erosion);
- soil characteristics (mineral composition – chemical, granulometric

composition, density, humidity, content and composition of organic substances, acidity, absorption capacity, temperature, concentration and composition of soil solution);
- weather-climatic conditions of migration;
- time of the season temperatures above $0°$ (average annual, seasonal temperatures, annual precipitation quantity, precipitation distribution by seasons).

When plants are grown under similar landscape conditions, the difference of absolute values of the conversion factor is determined by biologic peculiarities of various cultures only. Different types of countermeasures influence the conversion factor and, thus, the content of radionuclides in production, as well as the yield of farm cultures [224].

Information about the kinds and efficiency of a certain type of rehabilitation countermeasure can be systematized for each type of landscape, and a fragment representing the matrix structure – for each agricultural culture (Table 2).

Table 2 – Changes of the conversion factor (F_c), C/km for ^{137}Cs and productivity (c/ha)
A successive matrix analysis permits making a rehabilitation scenario for each

Hilly moraine-outwash plain on boulder loams with soddy podzolic gleyed sandy soils						
	Farm culture					
Countermeasure		pea		Potato		wheat
	F_c	Crop	F_c	Crop	F_c	Crop
No countermeasures	0.152	10.0	0.054	100.0	0.38	14.2
Liming (6 t/ha)	0.072	10.2	0.024	102.3	0.32	13.9
Potash fertilizers (C/m²)	0.025	10.5	0.010	108.0	0.16	15.4

radionuclide and certain type of landscape, i.e., creating successively an optimal set of farm cultures and countermeasures, which will provide their correspondence to ecologic standards and economic production efficiency.

The use of countermeasures is necessary in most type landscapes of Polissia in contrast to the forest-steppe zone of Ukraine. The type forest-steppe landscapes with fertile soils, high potential yield keep well radionuclides and permit growing relatively pure production. The landscapes, typical of Polissia, with poor infertile soils are characterized by the essential conversion factors of radionuclides; these landscapes are dangerous for use in agriculture under radiation contamination, thus they, certainly, require the use of countermeasures up to the change of land use type.
Situation in the territories, which have suffered from the accident at the Chernobyl NPP, is dangerous and catastrophic to certain extent. But from the viewpoint of introduction of new environmental-economic principles – the principles of "green"

economy and sustainable development – the established conditions proved to be favorable. The industrial base of the region has been practically ruined, the experienced personnel has departed, reached the pensionable age or lost qualification. This allows developing economy, big industrial and agrarian production of the region in particular, from the very beginning, attracting labor resources, interested in development of "green" technologies, from all Ukraine and other states of the world.

The outdated infrastructure created in the 70-80's is kept operating that, on the one hand, permits developing new economic projects based on modern "green" technologies. Close-down of the Chernobyl NPP in 2000 on demand of EU countries causes the deficit of electric power that forms the unique favorable conditions for development of alternative power industry, especially in the territories of Polissia with low population density, long distances between settlements and bad roads. Direct legislative prohibition on introduction of chemicals for plant protection and nutrition [220] has created unique conditions for development of organic agriculture in these territories. The "elementary" organic agriculture, which is supported by the experience of traditional farming and is adequate in conditions of the lack of current assets and complicated credit receipt, is characteristic of small (about 10 ha) peasant farms in Ukraine. The mushroom and berry gathering is traditionally developed in the region. In spite of the excessive radiation background, they meet the radiation requirements of EU countries and are successfully exported through agents, mainly Polish, to European countries.

"Green" tourism is one of the most promising trends of development of "green economy" in the territories referred to those which have suffered from the accident at the Chernobyl NPP. Big forests, numerous bogs, lakes and rivers, meadows and fields were not spoilt for more than two decades. They have passed through the stage of natural renovation without anthropogenic pressure. Thus a unique natural resource has been formed, which is the underestimated natural capital for development of "green" tourism.

So, practical realization of the principles of "green economy" will permit creating a new strategy of rehabilitation for the territories which have suffered from the Chernobyl accident and for the whole region.

Photo Miriam Kennet. The Old Apple Tree

2.3 Heathrow's hidden health costs

By Ryte Mamacuvite

After exploring the effects of an incinerator in the neighbourhood and its effect on us, we have unfortunately come across another Deadly Neighbour. I expect it is not a big surprise for readers to find out that this title will be dedicated for Heathrow airport. Heathrow airport is one of the busiest airports in all over the world using its capacity nearly 100%. It handles over 67million passengers per year using over 90 different airlines. Besides that, due to its historical reasons, it is also ranked as one of the most poorly sited airports on earth. It was built in a heavily populated area and it is surrounded by houses on three sides. Generally, particularly in the UK aviation plays an important role as an environmental issue contributing as much as 13% of all greenhouse gases. And even half of this 13% is actually caused by Heathrow airport. So, this means that Heathrow airport is responsible for 6.5% of the country's entire climate impact.

And you may be aware that it seems the effects are destined to be even greater in the future. Instead of addressing and solving climate issues and improving its effects, Heathrow airport aims to be expanded. From around 2014 onwards, once the redevelopment and construction of the five terminals are completed, it will be able to handle 95 million passengers a year, which means an expansion of nearly 40%. And here comes the essential question: can an expanded Heathrow airport ever meet its environmental targets?

The UK Government's climate change law requires an 80 per cent reduction in UK greenhouse gas emissions by 2050, based on 1990 levels. According to the claims of Heathrow airports owners, this target could be met even along with the expansion of the airport, relying on new planes producing less emissions and new technology reducing the levels of carbon produced by vehicles. But unfortunately scientists and researchers are not as optimistic. Indeed most of them are opposed and heavily in doubt about the country's ability to meet these targets if Heathrow airport does expand. The government says the emissions from aviation can rise if other sectors compensate by cutting their emissions even more, but until now this has not ever been achieved.

In addition to the common UK environmental targets, it is worth mentioning that Heathrow airport already breaches the EU and UK legal limits for nitrogen dioxide. This legal limit has been specified because of this pollutant's impact on human health. Now, let's imagine Heathrow airport does expand. What happens? Simple. More flights mean more pollution. The extra flights also mean more people using the airport, which will lead to increased traffic, meaning more emissions from cars. So, without any doubt, considering Heathrow airport expansion legal limit for nitrogen dioxide would be further devastated and should also be involved in our consideration that other limits like particulates 2.5 and 10 could be overstepped. So, all things considered it concludes with an even higher risk to local communities' health.

Specific health factors.

So what are these risk factors? Some investigations were carried out in order to find out the impact on communities' health of having airports in the neighbourhood. The results seemed to be rather shocking. Alarming statistics resulted in:

- a 57% higher asthma rate
- a 28% higher pneumonia/influenza rate
- a 26% higher respiratory disease rate
- an 83% higher pregnancy complication rate
- a 50% higher infant mortality rate
- genetic diseases are statistically higher
- 48% higher for all causes of death mortality rates

One more investigation took place by proving airport's impact to a particularly vulnerable group of people, the local children. The effects of aircraft noise exposure on children's health and cognition around London Heathrow airport were examined. The noise was associated with high levels of annoyance and perceived stress, poorer reading and mathematics performance, sustained attention as well as social deprivation and main language spoken.

So, you can ask me what are the arguments for Heathrow airport expansion? People who are in favour of expanding Heathrow airport claim that expansion is necessary in order to boost the economy out of recession because the airport generates a lot of international flights to economically important destinations such as China, India, Brazil. There is no doubt that so far Heathrow airport has benefited the economy of West London, London as a whole and, indeed, the UK. But that is not what is in dispute. Disputable is the calculation that expansion at Heathrow will bring economic benefits of £5 billion over 70 years. Overestimated numbers are highly debatable due to the low figures of the tax-breaks and environmental costs and the subsidies which skew these calculations.

If readers are sitting here and asking themselves, what can they do to help? There are several ways to express your own point of view. You can say locally NO by writing your local councillor, you can say nationally NO by writing to your local member of Parliament at the House of Commons. Or you can so NO in your own unique way by making a poster and displaying it in your own window. Before finishing, I will add one more incentive especially for Windsor residents. It is estimated that under the scenario if Heathrow airport expansion is avoided, due to improvements in aircraft technologies Windsor will drop out of the 'annoyance' envelope and redidents health will be improved by 2030.

Photo Miriam Kennet. In the pharmacy

2.4 Health and well being in a polluted environment: a case study of chronic obstructive pulmonary diseases (COPDs) in selected cities in England and Wales

By Lawrence Sappor

1. Background of the study

The United Nations Environment Programme (UNEP – 2011) describes a green economy as "one that results in improved human well-being and social equity, while significantly reducing environmental risks and ecological scarcities". In other words, we can think of a green economy as an economic environment that achieves low carbon and pollutant emissions, while resources are efficiently used to promote societal inclusion and prevent loss of biodiversity and ecosystem services. However population health and the ecosystem are being affected with emission being released into the atmosphere from industry, transportation and waste disposal. This research will assess an association between Chronic Obstructive Pulmonary Diseases (COPDs) and health as a result of environment pollution emitted from transport and waste disposal system (Sunyer et al 1997; Sonia et al 2005) using GIS and remote sensing technology.

I was inspired to take on this research after participating in a forum with the lung suffers society on the topic, "Air Pollution and Lung Diseases in Slough – Windsor". I realised GIS can be used to assess COPDs patients suffering from fumes or gases emissions from tobacco smoking and link cases of COPD infection or spread of pollution using an overlay of wind data. Also, geo spatial analysis can be used to illustrate why pollutants from the fumes are recognized as the most common chronic respiratory diseases worldwide, including the United Kingdom, with an increasing prevalence of morbidity and mortality higher than bowel cancer, breast cancer or prostate cancer (Mckeown 2007; Chauhan and Johnston 2003; US EPA 2011; WHO 20011: 2008). The lung suffers society members present were excited that I want to carry out a research into COPDs using the GIS concept, and are prepared to offer support. The study will examine efforts being undertaken to prevent people getting COPDs, promote population understanding of the risks of having poor lung health, support improvements to the diagnosis of, and care of people with the disease. Having already undertaken a study into HIV/AIDS using the GIS concept and interest in green economics, I will implore similar approach to air pollution and its impact on COPDs.

Concepts of what constitutes a quality life have been a controversial issue since Aristotle's theory to Maslow's hierarchical theory of needs (Nordenfelt 1993). These concepts have enabled a definition described as 'wellbeing' to be introduced by the local government act 2000, which seek to promote a safe economic, social and environmental economy. Wellbeing is also described by the UK Government Whitehall working group in 2006 as "a positive physical, social and mental state, not just the absence of pain, discomfort and incapacitation", which includes good health and attractive environment (Steuer and Marks 2008; DEFRA 2012; UNCSD 2012; Huitt 2007). Thus, attractive environment and combined effect of policies will enable people have reasonable access to social, economic and environmental resources to attain personal goals and participate in society (Welsh Government; Hunter and Killoran 2004).

One of the greatest challenges that will face health systems globally in the twenty-first century will be the increasing burden of non – communicable chronic diseases such as COPDs (WHO 2002). Since the early 1960s, emerging respiratory diseases has been attributed to tobacco smoking. However, significant proportion of fossil fuel emissions by vehicles, industry and energy production has been recognised as potential collaborator to COPDs.

2. Aim

Arguably two main strands in quantitative spatial techniques and experimental theory will focusing on the possibilities and potentials between air pollution and COPDs

Firstly, papers which outline or analyse fundamental conceptual approach to air pollution from transport, industry and waste disposal will be reviewed from multi-disciplinary basis using GIS techniques. For example, published reports and research only target some of the pollutants such as the particulates (PM10 and PM2.5), nitrogen oxides, carbon monoxide and sometimes sulphur dioxide. Conversely, ignored pollutants found in smaller quantities become harmful toxins, are detected mainly in patients during hospital visit (the guardian 2012; scientific America 2012; WHO, HELI 2004). The pollutants in small quantities are known to be more toxic and cause severe health problems than the larger emitted pollutants. Although the European law has helped cut down some of these toxins from exhaust fumes and chimneys, other harmful pollutants are still found at dangerous levels in Europe (such as benzene, 1, 3 - butadiene, lead, ozone, ammonia and polycyclic aromatic hydrocarbons). The guardian 2012 environmental report based on a European Environmental Agency (EEA) report indicated that 30% of city-dwellers are exposed to a complex mixture of air pollutants particularly hazardous to health above a yearly EU target level. These pollutants mix together with existing atmospheric elements create new chemical compounds, some of which become toxic. Understanding the 'state' of and key trends influencing air quality in Europe (UK) is a critical first step in dealing with COPDs.

The second part of the research will assess the welfare of COPD patients through assistance received and how policies ensure that the green economic agenda is being accomplished. Influential papers indicate that many, who live with the condition usually over age of 35 can constitute economic burden associated with long-term medical management and disability. Telehealth solutions, a patient-focused health cost reduction company estimates the direct cost of COPD to the UK healthcare system to be between £810 million and £930 million a year, with certain regions being worse affected than others.

3. Objectives

The purpose of this study is to explore a multidisciplinary approach in examining collected data in selected cities in England and Wales on people suffering from any chronic obstructive pulmonary disease. GIS would be used to express a visualised data that indicates endemic areas, while a time series analysis will indicate changes over a period. GIS and Remote Sensing will assist to indicate how behavioural changes are distressing the possibility of effectively controlling or reducing air pollution effects on health.

Analyses and interpretation will validate international data from such surveys as well as investigate the subjective phenomenon as described by the patient. The study will also use well-being measurement to examine assistance COPDs patients receive, as appropriate support, to live longer, happier and healthy life. It will also examine policies that are implemented to ensure green economic issues are attained.

4. Relevance of the study

The study will create a narrative literature that allows for flexible and resourceful presentation of interpretive findings, while demanding adherence to sound interpretive research. With limited resources and budget constrain, escalating health research such as COPDs can cause a drain on the economy. However, this study will demonstrate the use of limited resources available to engineer awareness into controlling increasing COPDs infections.

Different techniques have been used in campaign awareness programmes, including the media (Television, Radio, and newsprints), books, schools, churches, parents/relatives, workshops etc, yet there is increasing reports of COPDs. A geo spatial inclusion to data, allows clear visualisation of relevant information and scope of COPDs, indicating population areas prone to infection from air pollution.

It is also likely to support monitoring activity of reported cases from clinical view, societies, councils, environmental agencies and government institutions such as the *United Nations Environment Programme (UNEP)* and World Health Organisation (WHO). The WHO vision a 2008- 2013 Action Plan themed: "The Global Strategy for the Prevention and Control of Non- Communicable Diseases". Also developed by Ghana as a Medium-Term National Development Policy Framework on the pathway to green economy under the theme: Ghana Shared Growth and Development Agenda 2010-2013.

The UK Department of Health /Medical Directorate/Respiratory constituted a team in February 2010 to advice how "local communities can prevent people from getting

COPDs, understand the risks of having poor lung health, secure improvements to the diagnosis and care of people with the disease, and reduce health inequalities". The UK Department of health estimates around *835,000 people have been diagnosed,* however over 3 million undiagnosed people have the disease, with one person dying every 20 minutes from COPDs in England and Wales, about 25,000 people a year (NHS 2012; BLF 2012; NHS and NICE 2010).

Also based on the UNEP-led green economy initiative launched in late 2008, this research will use GIS to achieve aspects of the three main activities: analyse sustainability; provide advisory services on ways to move towards a green economy and to engage a wide range of research, non-governmental and business institutions. The conclusions will add to existing knowledge, support the green revolution and medical interventions by health professionals to improve health issues as a result or air pollution.

It is hoped that the themes revealed in this study will generate additional understanding and insight for future ground-breaking research.

5. Method

The theoretical literature will review work done by known individuals, groups or organisations through recognised discussions, books, presentations, journals and magazines. The empirical study will process and integrate health data with geographical area data in GIS analytical software (ESRI – ArcGIS, ERDAS Imagine or MapInfo software). Many processes such as overlay analysis, buffer analysis, network inter linkages, data query, statistical analysis, interpolation or extrapolation. Then a multi – disciplinary approach will be implored in perspective to produce maps that will justify the theoretical literature and created maps in relation to COPD cases, especially in regions with incinerators, airports and heavy vehicular traffic environments.

The result will be analysed in terms of the education, data collection, monitoring and evaluation of COPD infections. As used by David B. et al in mapping air pollution, this research will implore the regression method to analyse COPDs and represent the result in a GIS map form.

Data will be obtainable from the lung society, department of health and city councils for the selected areas. Also unstructured interviews will capture detailed patient experiences verbatim. This study will be discussed in line with the economic, socio-cultural as well as environmental impacts on the population.

Recommendations will be based on awareness activities that had been effective and the idea of COPDs as observed during the study. It may track progress budget allocation and local change with emphasis on the Comprehensive Area Assessment reports.

6. Collaborations

As data is a key instrument in this study, however, the lung society has indicated to provide the research with available data. This research will also be under close observation and collaboration between the Birmingham City University and the Green Economics Institute.

7. Results and Conclusions

Getting the analysis right is a good starting point but not sufficient for achieving environmentally efficient outcomes. Continued research such as this and other policy interventions are often necessary to complement environmental and health issues.

Interviews will reveal valuable insights from a patient's or family perspective, into the impact of chronic obstructive pulmonary disease on their daily lives. The brief interaction with the lung society at Windsor hospital, participants described feelings of frustration, tired of breathlessness and loss of social activity.

This research will provide valuable insights into the increasing socio-economic impact of air pollution on society; how suffers view the overall impact and subsequent degree of coping with chronic obstructive pulmonary disease from day to day.

References:

Anderson, H.R., Spix, C., Medina, S., Schouten, J.P., Castellsague, J., Ross, G., Zmirou, D., Touloumi, G., Wojtyniak, B., Ponka, A., Bacharova, L., Schwartz, J., Katsouyanni, K., 1997, "Air pollution and daily admissions for chronic obstructive pulmonary disease in 6 European cities: results from the APHEA project" from the European Respiratory Journal website: http://erj.ersjournals.com/content/10/5/1064.full.pdf+html [accessed October 2012]

British Lung Foundation (BLF), 2012, "Lung Health" from the website: http://www.blf.org.uk/Conditions/Detail/COPD [accessed October 2012]

Chauhan, A. J., Johnston, S. L. (2003), "Air pollution and infection in respiratory illness" obtained from the British Medical Bulletin website: http://bmb.oxfordjournals.org/content/68/1/95.full and accessed October 2012 [accessed October 2012]

David, J.B., Collins, S., Elliot., Fischer, P., Kingham, S., Lebret, E., Pyrl, K., Van Reeuwijk, H., Smallbone, K., Van Der Veen, A., 2001, " Mapping Urban Air Pollution Using GIS Regression – Based Approach" obtained from the International Journal of Geographical Information Science magazine from the Taylor and Francis website: http://www.tandfonline.com/doi/abs/10.1080/136588197242158 [accessed October 2012]

Defra National Statistics Release, February, 2012, "Emissions of air pollutants in the

UK, 1970 to 2010 – Supplementary" from the website of DEFRA (Department for Environment, Food and Rural Affairs): http://www.defra.gov.uk/statistics/files/National-Statistical-Release-AIR-supplementary.pdf [accessed October 2012]

Huitt, W. (2007), "Maslow's hierarchy of needs", an Educational Psychology *Interactive* from Valdosta State University: http://www.edpsycinteractive.org/topics/regsys/maslow.html Retrieved [October 2012]

Hunter, D.J., and Killoran, A., 2004, "Tackling health inequalities: turning policy into practice?" obtained from the NHS Health Development Agency website: http://www.who.int/rpc/meetings/Hunter_Killoran_Report.pdf [accessed October 2012]

McKeown, D., 2007, "Air Pollution Burden of Illness from Traffic in Toronto – Problems and Solutions" obtained from the Public Health website, Toronto Canada: http://www.toronto.ca/health/hphe/pdf/air_pollution_burden.pdf and accessed October 2012

National Health Service (NHS) – National Institute for health and clinical Excellence (NICE), 2010, "CHRONIC OBSTRUCTIVE PULMONARY DISEASE – Management of chronic obstructive pulmonary disease in adults in primary and secondary care (partial update)" This guideline partially updates and replaces NICE clinical guideline 12 obtained from: http://www.nice.org.uk/nicemedia/live/13029/49397/49397.pdf [accessed October 2012]

National Health Service (NHS), 2012, "Chronic obstructive pulmonary disease" from the website: Open University book edited by Nolte, E., McKee, M., 2005, "Caring for people with chronic conditions - A health system perspective", obtained from the World Health Organisation International website: http://www.euro.who.int/__data/assets/pdf_file/0006/96468/E91878.pdf, accessed October 2012

Nordenfelt, L., 1993, "Quality of Life, Health and Happiness" from the website: http://sh.diva- portal.org/smash/get/diva2:17056/FULLTEXT01 [Accessed October 2012]

Scientific American, 2012, "Breathing European air shortens lives -report" from the magazine website: http://www.scientificamerican.com/article.cfm?id=breathing-european-air-shortens-liv and accessed October 2012

Sonia, B. A., Vollmer, W. M., Sullivan, S. D., Weiss, K. B., Lee, T. A., Menezes, A. M. B., Crapo, R. O., Jensen, R. L., and Burney P. G. J., 2005, "The Burden of Obstructive Lung Disease Initiative (BOLD): Rationale and Design" from the informa healthcare website: http://informahealthcare.com/doi/abs/10.1081/COPD-57610, accessed October 2012

Steuer, N. And Marks, N., 2008, "Local wellbeing: Can we Measure It?" from the website:

http://www.youngfoundation.org/files/images/YF_wellbeing_measurement_web.pdf [accessed October 2012]

Sunyer, J. , Kogevinas, M., Kromhout, H., Antó, J.M., Roca, J., Tobias, A., Vermeulen, R., Payo, F., Maldonado, J.A., Martinez-Moratalla, J., Muniozguren and the Spanish Group of the European Community Respiratory Health, 1997 "Pulmonary Ventilatory Defects and Occupational Exposures in a Population-based Study in Spain" obtained from the American Journal of Respiratory and Critical Care Medicine website: http://ajrccm.atsjournals.org/content/157/2/512.short, accessed September, 2012

The Guardian 2012, "Air Pollution still at Dangerous Levels in Europe" reports from the website: http://www.guardian.co.uk/environment/2012/sep/24/air-pollution-dangerous-levels-europe [accessed October 2012]

United Nations Conference on Sustainable Development (UNCSD Rio+20) and Share the Worlds Resources, 2012, "Happiness and Well-being: Defining a New Economic Paradigm" from the website: http://www.stwr.org/economic-sharing-alternatives/happiness-and-well-being-defining-a- new-economic-paradigm.html and http://www.uncsd2012.org/rio20/content/documents/690Bhutan.pdf [accessed October 2012]

United Nations Environment Programme (UNEP) 2011, "Green Economy - About GEI" from the UNEP website: http://www.unep.org/greeneconomy/AboutGEI/WhatisGEI/tabid/29784/Default.asp x, accessed October 2012

United Nations Environment Programme (UNEP), Advisory Services 2010, "Ghana's Pathway to Green Economy" from the UNEP website: http://www.unep.org/greeneconomy/AboutGEI/WhatisGEI/tabid/29784/Default.asp x, accessed October 2012

United States Environmental Protection Agency, advisory services report 2011, "Ghana's Pathway to a Green Economy" obtained from the US EPA website: http://www.unep.org/greeneconomy/AdvisoryServices/Ghana/tabid/56355/Default.a spx [accessed October 2012]

Welsh Government, 2011, "Environment – Protection and Quality" from the Welsh Government website: http://wales.gov.uk/topics/environmentcountryside/epq/airqualitypollution/?lang=en [accessed October 2012]

WHO 2010, "Global Status Report on non-communicable diseases" obtained from the WHO website: http://www.who.int/nmh/publications/ncd_report_full_en.pdf [accessed October 2012]

WHO, 2004, "Health and Environment Linkages Initiative" obtained from the Health and Environment Linkages initiative (HELI) site: http://www.who.int/heli/en/ and accessed October 2012

Wikipedia 2012, "Third Industrial Revolution" from the website: http://en.wikipedia.org/wiki/The_Third_Industrial_Revolution#First_and_Second_Industrial_Revolutions [accessed October 2012]

World Health Organisation (WHO) 2002, *"Innovative Care for Chronic Conditions: Building Blocks for Action" obtained from the* World Health Organization website: http://www.who.int/diabetes/publications/iccc_exec_summary_eng.pdf, accessed October 2012.

World Health Organisation (WHO) 2008, "Outdoor Air Pollution - Children's Health and the Environment" a WHO Training Package for the Health Sector of the World Health Organization, *obtained from the* World Health Organization website: http://www.who.int/ceh/capacity/Outdoor_air_pollution.pdf, accessed october 2012

World Health Organisation (WHO) factsheet (media centre) 2011, "Chronic obstructive pulmonary disease (COPD)" *obtained from the* World Health Organization website: http://www.who.int/mediacentre/factsheets/fs315/en/index.html, accessed october 2012

Part 3: Health, Wealth, and Poverty – Social Justice

3.1 Global Green Human Being: concepts and main issues

By Kristina Jociute

Introduction

The world faces such problems such as climate change, poverty and income inequality. Though major efforts and a lot of discussions are taking place, 25.19 % of the population (according to 2005 data) still lives in households with consumption or income per person below the poverty line (World Bank, 2005). Only 20 per cent of the world's population has adequate social security coverage and more than half lack any coverage at all (ILO). Overall warming since the mid-19th century totals ~0.8°C (almost 1.5°F), with most of the increase occurring since 1970 (MacCracken, M.C., 2009). These striking pieces of data force us to give pause to the thought that something is wrong with the way we are living. This work will try to examine where we are going wrong, what the consequences are and what should be done if we wish not to ruin the Planet but to solve the problems which the World faces.

Misguided economics management concentration

Local and global government authorities take responsibility of their own states economic management. As the world becomes more global and economies more open, countries are faced with global as well as national issues such as unemployment, inflation, downturns, etc. Both for local as well as for global authorities relevant indicators are GDP, unemployment and price indexes. Considering those indicators and their prognosis authorities take relevant decisions which influence the population, its welfare and such essential issues as climate change. The prevailing macroeconomic indicator is Gross Domestic Product (GDP), which is derived from Keynes.

"In a series of three articles published in The Times of London, Nov. 1939, economist John Maynard Keynes noted that in World War I, excessive money creation stemming from defense spending led to inflation, which greatly hurt the working classes. Can we avoid this in World War II? asked Keynes. We can. But how? First by calculating "the maximum current output we are capable of organizing from our resources" (i.e. GDP). Next, "by estimating how fast we can safely draw on our foreign reserves by importing more than we export" (i.e. Imports minus Exports). Next, by estimating the minimum necessary capital formation needed to

maintain plant and buildings (Gross Capital Formation). Next, by estimating how much will be required by our war effort" (Public Defense Consumption). What is left is "the size of the cake which will be left for civilian consumption" [i.e. both personal and public]. Keynes recommended using taxation and compulsory saving to ensure that consumption spending did not exceed that 'cake,' so that demand-pull inflation should not emerge." (Maital, Sh., 2009).

In macroeconomics, science and global economies GDP, and more specifically its growth, is a central feature. GDP information influences all agents in the economy: consumers, savers, investors, banks, stock and option markets, private companies, the government, central banks and international organizations (Bergh, J.C.J.M., 2007).

The main GDP calculation is: $GDP = C + G + I + NEX$, where C – consumption, G – government expenditures, I – private and public investment and NEX – net export (export – import). In the past as well as now, governments make announcements that X economy is experiencing a downturn as its GDP has declined by Z % or Y economy is expected to revive as its GDP is now stabilizing and not declining. As well as this fixation with GDP at a macro level the same is also true at a micro level with companies, as the main indicator used is profit rate. However, we must not lose sight of the fact that all of this, both at a micro and macro level, is based purely on calculations.

Therefore GDP used as an indicator to measure countries wealth level has been created for robots existing in a mechanical planet. The purpose of GDP according to Keynes was to calculate and manage countries' wealth. However, it ignores each person as an individual / personality, and all the Earth as the whole of those individuals interacting between each other and the entire surrounding environment. It also ignores the quality of all these interaction processes as well as damage done to the environment, including the ineffective and reckless exploitation of natural and non renewable resources.

For more than half a century discussions have centered on the notion that GDP is not the most suitable indicator in terms of identifying the real state of a country and its society's welfare situation. Furthermore, GDP doesn't indicate sustainable development processes: i.e. to what extent a country's development is environmentally friendly and takes account of future generations as well as equally for all the Earth's population without any exceptions.

It should be clearly possible to focus on the true final goals of the economy and to incorporate all ecological issues simultaneously. This means an end to tweaking growth into ever different purposes which are not in line with the most important objective of the economy of providing people with a higher quality of life (Heinemann, V. and Kennet, M., 2008). While analyzing and seeking well-being and equality for society and all the planet, opportunities to act for ALL the planet's people, accessibility to those opportunities and protection from external negative factors should be taken into account as well as care about environmentally friendly processes. Economic growth at any price is dangerous for every individual, as well as the whole of society and the entire Planet.

Negative consequences of unlimited human needs satisfaction and inequality

Mainstream economics is still too bound up with concerns of price, profit, economic growth and the perspective of the owners of production versus the workers (Kennet, M. and Heinemann, V., 2006). Mainstream economics deals with how to satisfy unlimited human needs with limited resources. It is concerned mainly with human needs. However, this is quite dangerous as humans, after they reach a certain level of income and consumption level (the one that they had targeted to reach), start to want to achieve higher and higher levels. This has created a consumer society with over-consumption, over-exploitation and profit seeking issues.

Maslow posited a hierarchy of human needs based on two groupings: deficiency needs and growth needs. Within the deficiency needs, each lower need must be met before moving to the next higher level. Once each of these needs has been satisfied, if at some future time a deficiency is detected, the individual will act to remove the deficiency. The first four levels are (Huitt, W. , 2007):

> 1. Physiological: hunger, thirst, bodily comforts, etc.;
>
> 2. Safety/security: out of danger;
>
> 3. Belongingness and Love: affiliate with others, be accepted; and
>
> 4. Esteem: to achieve, be competent, gain approval and recognition.

According to Maslow, an individual is ready to act upon the growth needs if and only if the deficiency needs are met. The growth needs are as below:

> 1. Cognitive: to know, to understand, and explore;
>
> 2. Aesthetic: symmetry, order, and beauty;
>
> 3. Self-actualization: to find self-fulfilment and realize one's potential; and
>
> 4. Self-transcendence: to connect to something beyond the ego or to help others find self-fulfilment and realize their potential.

A significant proportion of the world's population is not able to satisfy the first of these (physiological needs) so they can hardly try to satisfy the fifth need, which is mostly related with the education level of that society. Ideologies offer different ways to live, and hence different ways to use resources. As the effects of globalization are creating further disparities and inequalities, around the world we are seeing an increase in violence and human rights abuses as disputes about territories, food and water are spilling into wars and internal conflicts. People are fighting for basic needs (Shah, A., 2001).

Mainstream economics seeks GDP growth, i.e. seeks growth in consumption - often without any concern about consumption quality and responsibility. Consumption was specifically encouraged in order to stimulate markets, rather than to meet people's needs, and this ignored the limits or requirements of other species or the planet

(Heinemann, V. and Kennet, M., 2008). In addition, concern just about GDP growth means we overlook the need for consumption equality among all the global population. In "super-size-me" land, Americans gobble up more than 120 kilograms of meat a year per person, compared to just 6 kilos in India, for instance (Pearce, F., 2009). The true facts about global consumption inequality is mainly due to income inequality, and it can be seen that the poorest 20% of the population consume just 1.5 % of the world's private consumption, whereas the richest 20% of the population consume 76.6 % of the world's private consumption (in 2005). There is a huge private consumption gap that exists between the poorest 10% of the population and the richest 10%. This shocking situation is based mainly on income inequality consequences.

In order to demonstrate real facts, the weekly food expenditure of families from different countries is now displayed (Halberg, T. and Halberg, Ch., 2007):

1. Italy: The Manzo family of Sicily: Food expenditure for one week: 214.36 Euros or $260.11

2. Germany: The Melander family of Bargteheide: Food expenditure for one week: 375.39 Euros or $500.07

3. United States: The Revis family of North Carolina: Food expenditure for one week $341.98

4. Mexico: The Casales family of Cuernavaca: Food expenditure for one week: 1,862.78 Mexican Pesos or $189.09

5. Poland: The Sobczynscy family of Konstancin-Jeziorna: Food expenditure for one week: 582.48 Zlotys or $151.27

6. Ecuador: The Ayme family of Tingo: Food expenditure for one week: $31.55

7. Bhutan: The Namgay family of Shingkhey Village: Food expenditure for one week: 224.93 ngultrum or $5.03

8. Chad: The Aboubakar family of Breidjing Camp: Food expenditure for one week: 685 CFA Francs or $1.23

Such an outcome happens not because of different human needs. Mainly it occurs, as has been mentioned previously, because of income inequality and created consumerism as the authorities seek GDP growth, which is possible by consumption encouragement. The major problem occurs as GDP is not concerned about basis consumption in order to satisfy basic needs as well as environmentally friendly consumption. Such consumption inequality reveals tender global issues such as poverty.

> *"Eradicating extreme poverty continues to be one of the main challenges of our time, and is a major concern of the international community."*
>
> – United Nations Secretary-General BAN Ki-moon

–

The fact that people in employment still suffer from poverty is further proof of failing mainstream economic processes. The share of the extreme working poor in total employment was 21.2 per cent in 2008, representing a total of 633 million workers living with their families on less than USD 1.25 a day. In the case of the USD 2 a day working poor, 39.7 per cent of all workers were in this category, equal to 1,183 million workers around the world (ILO).

According to macroeconomics' schemas, possibly used by authorities, GDP growth influences unemployment reduction in the sense that as production volume grows employers demand more labour to satisfy increased demand for goods and services. However the main global issues still remain unsolved and it is a most relevant fact that GDP does not care about damage done to the environment. Despite strong economic growth that produced millions of new jobs since the early 1990s, income inequality grew dramatically in most regions of the world and is expected to increase due to the current global financial crisis. Global employment rose by 30 per cent between the early 1990s and 2007, but the income gap between richer and poorer households widened significantly at the same time (ILO).

Under existing poverty a major part of the population is starving and suffers from undernourishment, which is defined by the Food and Agriculture Organization (FAO) as the status of persons whose food intake regularly provides less than their minimum energy requirements. Hunger has increased not as a result of poor harvests but because of high domestic food prices, lower incomes and increasing unemployment due to the current global economic crisis. Many poor people cannot afford to buy the food they need. Most hungry people live in Asia and the Pacific (642 millions) and Sub-Saharan Africa (265 millions), with not such high volumes in Latin America and the Caribbean (53 million), Near East and North Africa (42 million) and in developed countries (15 millions) (FAO).

Over the timeframe in question the percentage of undernourished persons has decreased but the total volume of undernourished persons has varied and during 2004-2006 was almost the same as in 1969–1971. The FAO estimates that 1.02 billion people were undernourished worldwide in 2009. Thus there are now more hungry people that at any time since 1970, the earliest year for which comparable statistics are available. It is most interesting that GDP during the same period has notably increased.

These facts provide further evidence that mainstream economic counting and management processes do not work. The FAO claims that the world currently produces enough food for everybody, but many people do not have access to it. During 1979-1981, 1989-1991 and 2000-2003 daily consumed calories per capita were respectively 2549, 2704 and 2738, while the average minimum energy requirement per person is about 1800 kcal per day. Taking into account the fact that 13-19% of the world population do not consume even 1800 kcal daily per capita it gives us a striking conclusion that the remaining part of the population has been over-consuming food.

Under overconsumerism a major part of the world's population consumes more food than it needs, taking those used natural and non-renewable resources from future generations, whilst leaving one part of the population to starve.

If humans could be rational (unfortunately they are often not) then there would be enough food for ALL the Earth's population and even food production and consumption could be lower. Unfortunately, by chasing GDP growth and consumption growth this problem is left unsolved.

For as long as GDP, profit and consumption growth indicators remain central to our way of thinking, the Earth will continue to be damaged and poverty and inequality issues will remain unsolved.

Human overconsumption shows that we are an unconscious species. Most people are aware and take account just about seeable threats which directly impact them, such as illness, financial problems, the death of a sibling, theft from them etc. Still they are not thinking about the subsequences of those threats and disasters. So most humans don't think about how their every action influences others and nature, and are not aware about climate change problems.

Before humans emerged on the Earth, the ecosystem circulated and acted in its own way. After humans evolved there was a period - in which they lived in harmony with the entire ecosystem. However, later we started to intervene in the ecosystem and brought chaos which influenced climate change processes and harmed the Earth through a rise in global sea levels, a change in vegetation zones, an increase in disease levels, and a change in ecosystems (UKECN).

Some factors such as distance from the sea, Ocean currents, direction of prevailing winds, relief, proximity to the Equator and the El Nino phenomenon, affect the climate naturally. However, it is human activity that has mostly influenced climate change processes. Global temperatures have risen by 0.6 degrees Celsius during 1860 – 1990 (UKECN). Often humans don't take account of the fact that their actions affect climate change, various cataclysms and biodiversity loss. Biodiversity provides many benefits for humans including fresh air, clean water, rich soils, medicines, natural beauty, and more. However biodiversity is diminishing in the face of several threats, including climate change, pollution, overpopulation, environmental degradation overexploitation and consumption, and invasive species (Earth Council Geneva).

Inequality exists not just in terms of social and income issues, but also from an environmental perspective. First of all humans tend to think of themselves as superior to nature, even if it is vice-versa in reality as humans are not able to manage environmental process such as hurricanes, rains, etc. Secondly, poor people damage Earth less than rich ones. However, the effects of climate change, which will have dramatic consequences in many cases, will more rapidly and intensely impact the poor and indigenous peoples because they have fewer resources for proactive adaptation (MacCracken, M.C., 2009).

Stephen Pacala, director of the Princeton Environment Institute, calculates that the world's richest half-billion people - that's about 7 percent of the global population - are responsible for 50 percent of the world's carbon dioxide emissions. Meanwhile the poorest 50 percent are responsible for just 7 percent of emissions. The carbon emissions of one American today are equivalent to those of around four Chinese, 20 Indians, 30 Pakistanis, 40 Nigerians, or 250 Ethiopians" (Pearce, F., 2009).

Such figures are really quite astonishing. It is possible here to notice that some countries do not care about human equality and keep overconsuming and overpolluting. The result is that they are indirectly destroying ecosystem balances and overexploiting resources, which negatively impacts other countries' citizens as well as their own.

Green being schema concept

It is desperately necessary to analyse economics not through a "quantitative prism" but rather by taking into account environmental issues, the health of individuals and other qualitative indicators. Though considering qualitative economic development an important role goes to human consciousness and effective consumption of resources without any overconsumption. All of this should be done for both us and future generations.

There are two alternative ways of humans acting and managing the economy:

1. Concentrate on needs satisfaction at any price. Take account just on GDP growth as well as production, consumption and profits growth.

2. Concentrate on quality and "green" relations between economic agents (government, human, companies, NGOs) as well as "green" ways of acting, i.e. think about green economics. Green Economics and its development is in fact one of the most holistic and multidisciplinary economics the world has ever seen. The aim of Green Economics is to create a new discipline that works for the benefit of all people eveywhere, for the planet, the biosphere, non-human species, nature, and other life forms (Kennet, M. and Heinemann, V. 2006).

It should be realized that the Earth consists of renewable and non-renewable resources as well as a wide spectrum of biodiversity which provides humans with many benefits. Humans should think in a mainstream economic way, i.e. how to use all the resources in a better way in order to produce more. It is not the way to over-exploit the resources and only then think about the future possibilities. It is necessary to think with a long-term perspective and about how to survive with the usage of far fewer resources and minimal damage to nature. All human activity processes should be "green" and sustainable. "Green" contains equality, quality and environmentally friendly processes.

Mainstream economics should be changed by taking a Green Economics approach. From my point of view, Green Economics is to be based on the Human Green Being (HGB) concept which is based on green consumption, green production, education, health and work which interact between each other. The interaction between these four factors and all processes are based on three pivotal values: environmentally friendly action, quality and equality.

Every human action, impact upon nature or damage to any of these 3 values has feedback in either the short run or long run. Most relevant feedback occurs when humans neglect the environmentally friendly value. Everything shouldn't be concerned with how to achieve happiness as it is really not precise and is a subjective concept. Everything should be concerned with the human green being, i.e. how to live and act in a "green" way and what influences this "green" being.

Humans will then live in the right way as their consumption and production will be "green", i.e. no overconsumption, no overexploitation of resources, being responsible while consuming and producing. Education as well is included in the HGB as it helps to raise the quality of work, and to spread knowledge about global environmental, social and economic processes and their sustainable relations. The most important factor for any human is their health as upon this depends their quality of life, and their ability to study and work. All these factors are influenced by nature and the ecosystem as humans do not live in a vacuum.

Due to environmentally friendly factor feedback to humans they should change their thinking about consumption, production and finance. In addition, there should exist equality between nature and human, social, incomes and consumption equality. Above all, the most important factor is the quality of all the human action processes.

Conclusions

Economic growth at any price is dangerous for every individual, as well as the whole of society and the entire Planet. The Global Economy has grown notably over past century, i.e. GDP has grown. However relevant issues such as poverty, inequality and negative climate change results caused by the irresponsible action of humans have deepened. The poorest 20% of the population consumed just 1.5 % of the world's private consumption, whereas the richest 20% of the population consumed 76.6 % of the world's private consumption (in 2005).

The number of undernourished people worldwide reached 1.02 billion in 2009. However, per capita daily consumption of calories exceeded the minimum required rate (1800kcal per day). This data shows over consumerism under which a major part of the world's population consumes more food than it needs, taking those used natural and non-renewable resources from future generations, whilst leaving one part of the population to starve. Irresponsible human activity has also damaged nature and resulted in the over-exploitation of non-renewable resources, a rise in global sea levels, a change in vegetation zones, an increase in disease levels, and a change in ecosystems.

Therefore it is time for humans to stop and think about their green being on Earth. The Human green being concept is based on green consumption, green production, education, health and work under such values as quality, equality and environmentally friendly being. Under this HGB conception negative feedback will be avoided, thus helping to preserve the only living planet we have.

A version of this chapter was first published in the Proceedings of the 5ᵗʰ Annual Green Economics Institute Conference at Mansfield College, Oxford University, held in July 2010, published by the Green Economics Institute.

References:

Amin, A.A. (2009). Economic Growth and Human Development with Capabilities Expansion. Available at: http://www-3.unipv.it/deontica/sen/papers/Amin.pdf (last accessed 17/07/2010).

Bergh, J.C.J.M. (2007). Abolishing GDP. Vrije Universiteit Amsterdam, and Tinbergen Institute. Available at http://www.tinbergen.nl/discussionpapers/07019.pdf (last accessed 16/07/2010).

Earth Council Geneva (ECG) (2007). Biodiversity. Available at: http://earthcouncil.com/ecgsite/content/view/44/1/ (last accessed 18/07/2010).

Food and Agriculture Organization of The United Nations (FAO), Statistics Division (2006), Food and Agriculture Statistics Global Outlook. Available at:

http://faostat.fao.org/Portals/_Faostat/documents/pdf/world.pdf (last accessed 17/07/2010).

Food and Agriculture Organization of The United Nations (FAO), (2010). Hunger. Available at:

http://www.fao.org/hunger/hunger-home/en/ (last accessed 17/07/2010).

Halberg, T. And Halberg, Ch. (2007), Average weekly food consumption of families around the world. Avalable at: http://blog.halbergphotographers.com/2007/12/11/average-weekly-food-consumption-of-families-around-the-world/ (last accessed 17/07/2010).

Heinemann, V. and Kennet, M., (2006) „Green Economics: setting the scene. Aims, context, and philosophical underpinning of the distinctive new solutions offered by Green Economics", Int. J. Green Economics, Vol. 1, Nos. ½, pp.68-102.

Heinemann, V. and Kennet, M., (2008). Framework Paper for the Sustainable Development Commission. The Green Economics Institute. Available at: http://www.sd-commission.org.uk/publications/downloads/Miriam_Kennet_thinkpiece.pdf (last accessed 16/07/2010)

Huitt, W. (2007). Maslow's hierarchy of needs. *Educational Psychology Interactive*. Valdosta, GA: Valdosta State University. Available at http://www.edpsycinteractive.org/topics/regsys/maslow.html (last accessed 18/07/2010)

International Labour Organization (ILO), (2010). Social security. Available at:

http://www.ilo.org/global/Themes/Social_Security/lang--en/index.htm (last accessed 18/07/2010).

International Labour Organization (ILO) (2008), World of Work Report 2008 - Global income inequality gap is vast and growing. Available at:

http://www.ilo.org/global/About_the_ILO/Media_and_public_information/Press_releases/lang--en/WCMS_099406/index.htm (last accessed 17/07/2010).

International Labour Organization (ILO) (2010), Global Empoyment Trends. Available at: http://www.ilo.org/wcmsp5/groups/public/---ed_emp/---emp_elm/---trends/documents/publication/wcms_120471.pdf (last accessed 18/07/2010).

MacCracken, M.C. (2009), Climate Science in Six Well-Documented Findings. Available at: http://www.climate.org/topics/climate-change/science-in-six-findings.html (last accessed 17/07/2010).

Maital, Sh. (2009), The Man Who Invented GDP. Available at: http://timnovate.wordpress.com/2009/02/22/the-man-who-invented-gdp/ (last accessed 18/07/2010).

Pearce, F. (2009), Overconsumption Dwarfs Population As Main Environmental Threat. Yale Environment 360. Available at:

http://www.organicconsumers.org/articles/article_17573.cfm (last accessed 17/07/2010).

Shah, A. (2001). Effects of Over-Consumption and Increasing Populations. Available at: http://www.globalissues.org/article/216/effects-of-over-consumption-and-increasing-populations (last accessed 17/07/2010).

Shah, A. (2008), Consumption and Consumerism. Available at: http://www.globalissues.org/issue/235/consumption-and-consumerism (last accessed 16/07/2010).

The United Kingdom Environmental Change Network (UKECN) (2000). Climate change. Available at:

http://www.ecn.ac.uk/Education/climate_change.htm (last accessed 18/07/2010)

United Nations Secretary-General BAN Ki-moon, United Nations (2002). Available at:

http://www.un.org/millenniumgoals/bkgd.shtml (last accessed 18/07/2010).

World Bank (2007). Replicate the World Bank's regional aggregation. Available at:

http://iresearch.worldbank.org/PovcalNet/povDuplic.html (last accession 18/07/2010).

3.2 Women Doctors at St. Mary's Hospital in Paddington, London: A History

By Dr. Katherine Kennet, MBBS BSC.

Introducing women into the medical profession was far more significant than just allowing a few well educated, strong willed and kooky women to enter a traditionally masculine career, it had huge political repercussions, rocking the foundations of British society. It was clear from the outset of the women's movement that women doctors would redefine the essence of women and what gender roles would be. This made the argument over female physicians highly political and controversial.

What were the ideas about gender prior to the First World War?

In the 19th century it was commonly accepted that men and women operated in separate spheres[1] ;men were the logical and intellectual ones, and women were closer to nature, and it was their natural destiny to reproduce. Doctors were therefore exclusively male and the male's dominion over scientific knowledge gave them power over women, and particularly in medicine (Kent 98).

Views of women doctors have certainly have come a long way in the past 150 years; the editorial from the Lancet in August 1878 offers an insight into the opinion of the medical profession on this subject and it is clear that the editors believe not only do women doctors "revolt against the reign of natural law"[2] but their existence will also cause women to "abandon rearing and tending of the young"[3]. These dramatic views were considered mainstream within the medical profession until Jex-Blake and her Contemporaries fought their way onto the scene.

But it wasn't just some determined women who began changing attitudes to women doctors; Kent explores the area of abuse of women at the hand of male doctors. Many found the speculum (a tool overused for even the simplest of female health complaint) not just hurtful, violating and injuring to their modesty, but also, most worryingly, medically unnecessary. The speculum also united women of all classes in the battle against the male medical profession's violation of their bodies, giving really force to the feminist movement. This clear abuse coupled with an inability of male doctors to talk frankly with women patients about their symptoms resulted in reluctance in women to seek medical care. This reluctance led to the neglect of early symptoms and Ethel Snowden[4] commented that "tens of thousands of women have neglected to consult a physician when there was a real need for such a consultation". Jex-Blake argued that a woman physician could "far more fully appreciate her state, both of mind and body, than any medical man would be likely to do"[5]. Jex-Blake saw the woman physician's role as a doctor to women, replacing the lustful motives of men with the genuine concern for the woman's best interest which women doctors would provide. (Kent 98)

The Contagious Diseases Acts were a clear example of men and women being treated very differently for the same diseases: any woman could be stopped and subjected to a violating and degrading gynaecological exam in a bid to stop venereal disease but men were under no such obligation. Kent describes this physical violation of women as "the logical outcome of an ideology that defined women in terms of sex and in relation only to male sexuality".[6] These acts were eventually repealed after much protest from the public but this clear example of double standards put fire into the women's movement. For feminists, the contagious diseases act demonstrated that medical men were not motivated by the quest for scientific truth, but the love of power and of dominating women. Butler went as far as to describe the fight to repeal the Acts as a "deadly fight for our bodies".[7] this gives an indication of the extent to which women felt their rights were being denied.

Co-educational verses Single Sex medical education

By the 1860s only Britain and Russia remained against co-education in medicine in Europe. This created a control on the numbers of women who could enter into medical degrees, as they could only attend special women-only medical schools. "Separate but equal" was the idea behind this philosophy but a double standard soon developed as is inevitable when separation from the mainstream occurs. Jacobi wrote in 1890 that "co-education in medicine is essential to the real and permanent success of women in medicine".[8] This resistance of Britain to coeducational teaching made Britain far more conservative that America, where co-education had been tried and considered to be a success.[8] It was clear that equality between the sexes in medical education would not come to Britain without a big external push.

The woman doctor in the hospital before the First World War

Views of women in the hospital changed dramatically with the advent of the First World War. Initially the London medical schools were seen as no place for young ladies, aside from the anatomy (it was seen as inappropriate for a women to dissect, particularly in the same session as men) there was also the issue of the male medical students: Garner (1998), describes the medical school environment as "the elder brother of the Edwardian public school"[9], with boxing, drinking and rugby the main pastimes of many student, it was seen as a totally inappropriate environment for young ladies of good upbringing. There was an alternative for the dedicated female physician: In 1972, Dr Elizabeth Garrett opened the New Hospital for Women, staffed by medical women, designed to treat women and children, and was the first of its kind[10]. It was these Women's hospitals aim not just to provide medical care for women's otherwise unmet health needs, but also to provide an place for young women doctor's clinical training before such a thing was commonplace in traditional hospitals.[10] These hospitals, as more were set up around the country, provided a network of support between practicing women doctors, which provided an alternative to the old boy's club of mainstream medicine.

The woman doctor in the hospital during and after the First World War

After the outbreak of the First World War, the drain on the numbers of nurses who volunteered for military service caused a shortage of nurses at home. This void was filled by many volunteering upper and middle class women (including Princess Arthur of Connaught a member of the royal family, who volunteered at St Mary's Hospital) (Garner 1998). This had a large impact on traditional views of women's delicate femininity- demonstrating that women could care for the unwell without sacrificing their respectability. Of course, it was not just nurses who volunteered for service; many doctors (including the majority of the housemen at many London hospitals) also wished to serve their country by treating those injured in the war. The shortage was so severe that in some hospitals medical students were called into fill the place of the doctors. There was also a shortage of both medical students and applications to medical school (many young me had abandoned their studies in favour of serving their country in the military). This situation provided a unique opportunity for female physicians and I shall use Garner's case study of St Mary's Hospital to illustrate how these crucial year's in the fight for women doctor's unfolded. This new predicament put St Mary's in a very different position to that which it had enjoyed before the war, far from the luxury of choice over who was admitted as students, the medical school was now struggling to get enough students to keep the school out of bankruptcy. While opening its doors to women may now seem like an elegant solution, at the time the opposition to this idea was so strong, the medical school chose to introduce several non-practical solutions first. The first of which was in 1915, the height of the war, a non-naturalised German was admitted to the medical school in preference to women, and another answer to their funding crisis was a compulsory £20 donation from the medical school staff, which was far from sustainable or professional. By 1916 St Mary's medical school saw that admitting the female students from the London School of Medicine for Women to complete their clinical training was the only way out of their financial troubles. The women were treated on the same terms as the men and far outstripped the men academically. By 1918 the dean had announced the admission of female students "a great success". In fact, the daily mail printed a headline reading "women doctors making good :a promising career".[11] This great step forward for the cause of women doctors should, and indeed could, have begun a transition into the equality in education that we see today, and this success at St Mary's certainly inspired the other London medical schools to admit women, however the freedom of education in the medical schools changed drastically when the war was over.

In 1920 the dean of St Mary's was superseded by man with a less favourable view of female doctors. Dean Charles McMoran Wilson was keen to reverse the intake of student to rugby playing, public school educated young men. He might not have succeeded in putting an end to women medical student admission had the feeling amongst the male students not also changed since the war; the male students returning from combat did not take kindly to the new profile of medical student permitted to join St Mary's, struggling to take authority from the female house who had risen to house officers and demonstrated and hostility towards the women increased until 1924, when ninety six students signed a petition demanding the cessation of women admission to the medical school (Garner 1998). This reversal to pre-war conditions must have felt like a massive step backwards for the women's movement, as this post war backlash was happening simultaneously in all the London medical schools, with some stopping the intake of women medical student altogether and others strictly limiting the numbers admitted. This left those women who were still studying or working in an awkward and embarrassing position (C Dyhouse 98).

Conclusion

Ideas about gender clearly changed greatly between the Victorian era and the advent of the Second World War in many aspects of life, particularly medicine. Although not treated as equal to male doctors by 1939, women had come a significant distance from 1873, when Elizabeth Garret Anderson was the only woman on the BMA's register, to the 6300 doctors on the register by 1939.[12] It seems absurd that after the great step forward during the first world war, where women doctors proved themselves equally professional and capable of the job, the situation practically reverted back to its pre-war position. The change from the Victorian view of women as the illogical and weaker sex may not have completely diminished by the First World War, but women were at least starting to be taken seriously as doctors, even if it was mainly in women's hospitals. It seems a shame and a pity that despite the First World War providing the boost that women doctors needed for entering the coeducational medical schools and, consequently, the mainstream medical profession, it transpired to be inevitable the war's end brought the reign of women doctors to, if not an end, then a certain temporary dip in acceptability.

Bibliography

1.   Dr A Woods (2011) *Women in medicine*, History of medicine module iBsc, Imperial College London, 18th March 2011.

2.   'Women as doctors and women as nurses', *The Lancet*, 17 August 1878, p226-7. In D. Brunton, *Health, disease and society in Europe 1800-1930: a sourcebook* (Manchester University Press, Manchester 2004), p119

3.   'Women as doctors and women as nurses', *The Lancet*, 17 August 1878, p226-7. In D. Brunton, *Health, disease and society in Europe 1800-1930: a sourcebook* (Manchester University Press, Manchester 2004), p. 118

4.   S Kent, *Sex and suffrage in Britain, 1860-1914* (Routledge, London) ch 4, pg. 129

5.   S Kent, *Sex and suffrage in Britain, 1860-1914* (Routledge, London) ch 4, pg. 132

6.   S Kent, *Sex and suffrage in Britain, 1860-1914* (Routledge, London) ch 4, pg. 119

7.   S Kent, *Sex and suffrage in Britain, 1860-1914* (Routledge, London) ch 4, pg. 120

8.   T Bonner, *To the ends of the earth: Women's search for education in medicine* (Harvard University Press, London, 1992), ch 6, 120-37.

9.   JS Garner, 'The great experiment: The admission of women students to St Mary's hospital medical school, 1916-25', *Medical History* 42 (1998), 68-88

10. Mary Ann Elston, "'Run by Women (Mainly) for Women': Medical Women's Hospitals in Britain, 1866-1948," in Lawrence Conrad and Anne Hardy (eds), *Women and Modern Medicine*, Clio Medica 61, 2001, pp. 73-90 only

11. C Dyhouse, 'Driving ambitions: women in pursuit of a medical education, 1890-1939, *Women's History Review* (1998), 321-343, pg. 333

12. C Dyhouse, 'Driving ambitions: women in pursuit of a medical education, 1890-1939, *Women's History Review* (1998), 321-343, pg. 321

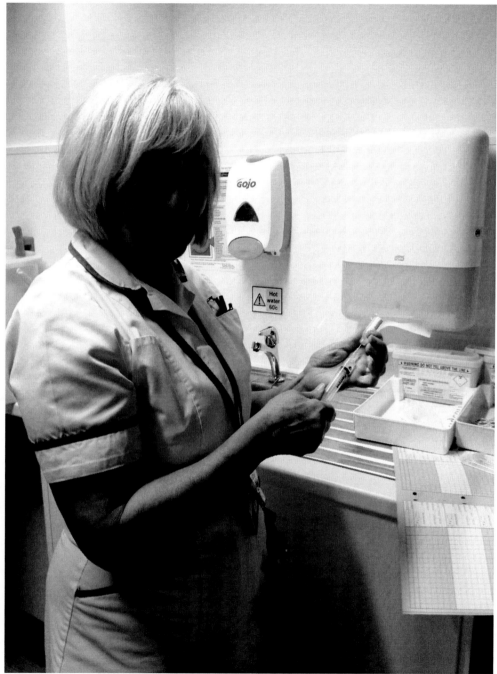

Photo Katherine Kennet. Today's hospital

3.3 Indian Maternal Health and Welfare Outcomes

By Dr. Katherine Kennet, MBBS BSC.

Maternal health is an issue that strikes at the heart of every family; every minute of every day a woman dies of a child-birth related cause[1] and the majority of these deaths are preventable. In a country with a birth rate as high as India's (the birth rate in 2010 is 21.34, calculated by births during a year per 1,000 persons in the population at midyear[2]) it is no surprise that this is a key issue, in fact, a quarter of the world's reported maternal deaths are in India[3]. What I find particularly interesting is how in India, a country currently booming economically, the maternal health remains so poor, in fact, the maternal mortality ratio for India was worse in 2005 (450) than in 2004 (440)[4]. In this chapter I shall attempt to answer the question of why so many women are dying of these preventable diseases, what current strategies are in place to reduce the numbers and what the future holds for India's women.

Setting the epidemiological scene of India

India is a massive country with a population of 1140 million people, it is hardly surprising that there are huge variations in all areas of life, especially health, across the vastly different geographical areas. India is split into 28 states[5] of which the northern states tend to have the worst health indicator figures. For example, the maternal mortality ratio for Rajasthan (in the north) is 445, where as the maternal mortality ratio for Tamil Nadu (a southern state) is 134. This huge variability is what makes India so interesting and is reflected across all areas of Indian life.[3]

When looking at India as a whole it is hard to gauge its position on the global stage; on one hand it has large areas of devastating poverty and until very recently was considered a "third world" country, but in recent years it has undergone massive economic change, economic growth and development (India's GDP has gone from 5.5 in 1998 to 9.1 in 2007)[6]. when it comes to basic needs you only have to look at *Figure 1* to see that not only does India have a long way to go to reach the standards of the west, it also has massive inequality between rural and urban areas.

This urban to rural inequality is mirrored in many aspects of maternal health, with 75% of India's births occurring in rural areas[7] (see *Figure 2)* it is clear to see that addressing the rural maternal health needs will go a long way in changing the maternal health profile of India.

India's Gross national income per capita is $2930. This is well below the global average of $10307 and a fraction of the UK's at $36240. This massive disparity is reflected in the countries' total expenditure on health per capita: $109[8] in India and $2784 in the UK.[9] This enormous difference puts the challenges faced by India's government into perspective and I shall discus their policies to tackle maternal mortality later.

Kerala: an unusual state

As I have already said, there is a huge variety in health indicators across India, not just between rural and urban areas, but also between states. It would therefore be incomplete to talk about India's epidemiology without mentioning Kerala: Kerala is a costal state in the south west of India and it is an anomaly when it comes to all parts of life. Kerala has a rich history of trade dating back five thousand years and is governed by the Left Democratic Front, a part of the communist party of India (an Indian Marxist political party).[10] Its health indicators are so different to the rest of the country it is hard to believe it is an Indian state: life expectancy in Kerala is 74 (and expected to grow further in the next 10 years to 77 years) which is well above the national value of 64, and significantly higher than its neighbouring states of Tamil Nadu and Karnataka, which are at 66.2 years and 65.3 years respectively.

This trend is followed when it comes to maternal health: the maternal mortality ratio in Kerala is 95 compared to India's 254 [11]. It is no coincidence that in 2008 the percentage of women in Kerala giving birth in a medical facility was 99.4%, of which 99.3% were in rural areas and 99.9% in urban areas[12]. This equality is what makes Kerala so successful when it comes to health indicators. These figures are not as surprising when you look at the proportion living below the poverty line; Kerala only has 12.72% in comparison to India's 26.10[11] and the state's female literacy rate of 87.8% (this is the highest in India and well above the national average of 53.7%).

Why is maternal mortality important and how is it measured?

Maternal mortality is considered to be such a significant global issue that it is the fifth millennium development to reduce maternal mortality by 75% between 1990 and 2015[13]. A maternal death affects far more than the family involved (although this alone has massive implications with children who have lost their mothers being up to ten times more likely to die prematurely[13]) there is also an economic loss to the country as a whole; According to the United Nations Population Fund (UNFPA) women's unpaid work on the farm and at home account for one-third of the world's GDP[14] this loss has a massive impact on the country's wealth.

It is measured by maternal mortality ratio: Maternal mortality ratio is the maternal death per 100,000 live births in one year (where maternal death is defined the "death of a woman while pregnant or within 42 days of termination of pregnancy, irrespective of the duration and site of the pregnancy, from any cause related to or aggravated by the pregnancy or its management but not from accidental or incidental causes"[5]. Unfortunately, good quality data on maternal mortality is not available as many women who die due to pregnancy or birth die at home in rural areas where their deaths are not recorded. This lack of reliable data alone is an obstacle in tackling maternal health in India.

Why is pregnancy so dangerous in India?

There is no question that women in India have a lower status than those in the west. There are many reasons for this and to cover them all would require another chapter but the main factors are that in Indian society men are more revered and respected. Men are far more likely to have been to school and to have been to school for a longer period of time. There are a number of reasons for this; despite free schooling being a constitutional right in India it costs a family to send a daughter to school in the hours lost in housework (it is normal in for the girls of the family to help around the house)[15], also there is very little chance that an education will lead to a job, especially in the poorer and more rural areas where the employment for women tends to agricultural or domestic.[16] Another key cultural factor keeping women at a lower status than men is the issue of marriage. Traditionally, when an Indian woman gets married she moves in with her in-laws and comes with a "dowry". This dowry was originally a wedding gift from the bride's family to her new family to help with the cost of the wedding and to act as insurance in case she was mistreated[17] more recently though, and despite anti-dowry legislation being in place since 1961's dowry prohibition act[18] its usual for the dowry to consists of goods and cash payments to the groom's family. If this dowry is not forthcoming or not considered enough the groom's family commonly torture and harass the bride, often escalating to murder. These "dowry killings" and both under reported and so commonplace in India, that Delhi's main prison has an entire "mother-in-law's block" for the perpetrators[19]. In 2008 alone there were 195856 cases of crimes against women including 81344 cases of cruelty by husbands or relatives[20]. This demonstrates the shocking inequality between the sexes in India and shows how at risk the female population of India, even before the added medical dangers of pregnancy and childbirth.

Another key factor linked strongly with poor maternal outcome is the age of the mother when delivering her first child. One study[21] found that women under the age of 20 were at a two and a half higher risk of death. This is particularly significant when you consider that in India the cultural norm is for women to get married at a young age (in Rajasthan, one of the northern states, where two thirds of all maternal deaths occur, the average age for a woman to marry is 16.05 years) and subsequently have their first child young (in Rajasthan the average for a first time mother is 17)[21].

Then of course there is the birth itself. Often said to be one of the most high risk times in a woman's life, pregnancy is intrinsically full of potential threats to the mother's health, but if so much of the danger is biological, why are so many more women dying in India than other areas of the world? In answering this question we must look at where these deaths are happening: the majority of maternal death occurs out of the hospital or health-centre environment and the main causes are postpartum haemorrhage (around a fourth of maternal deaths in India)[21], puerperal sepsis, eclampsia, severe anaemia and obstructed labour[21] (see *Figure 3*). Most of these causes are preventable with the correct medical resources and assistance both antenatal and during the birth itself. With such a large proportion of the population living in rural areas there is no underestimating the part physical access to maternal health care plays in preventing maternal death: if a woman develops problems during labour and the nearest hospital is two days walk away, her chances of survival are going to be significantly lower than a woman living in a city, moments from a health centre (see *Figure 4*). There is also an issue of women not using the maternal health facilities that they have access too; *Figures 5 and 6* demonstrate key determinants in maternal health, namely the educational and economic status of women. As these graphs demonstrate the wealthier and more educated a woman in India is, the more likely she is to use maternal health facilities. This demonstrates that the bulk of India's maternal mortality is in the poorer sectors of society.

What are the Indian government doing to address the problem of maternal health?

One of the Governments recent initiatives was the Janani Surakash Yojana[22] (which translates as safe motherhood scheme) known as JSY, is a conditional cash transfer scheme to incentivise women of low socioeconomic status to give birth in a health facility. (The idea being that fewer births outside medical facilities would lead to a lower maternal mortality rate). The scheme targeted the women most at risk of death from maternal causes by offering bigger cash incentives (up to 1400 rupees, which equates to $31.1) in rural areas and in high risk states. The scheme is implemented by community-level health workers who also aim to give all pregnant women at least three antenatal care visits. This scheme is the biggest of its kind in the world and provides cash to 9.5 million of the 26 million pregnant women in India this year. In a recent analysis of the schemes effectiveness researchers found that the more socially disadvantaged castes were far more likely to participate in the scheme. They also found that women with more years in education (up to 12 years) were far more likely to participate than those with fewer years of education, or those with no education at all. Other findings included that although distance from a health facility did have a slight impact (i.e. the further the distance to travel, the fewer women attended), a far more significant relationship was found in the age of the mother: the younger the mother, the more likely she was to participate.[22] These findings clearly show that the government's initiatives are having an impact, but is it enough? India clearly has issues regarding its large rural population, with one of the key problems being women living too far from the health centres. There has been much thought to address this by training up members of the community to act as health workers in rural areas. This prevents the potentially fatal delay between health issues occurring and getting to a health professional.

One study[23] I looked into assessed the effects of women's groups in two of India's poorest and most rural areas: Jharkhand and Orissa. 40% of their combined population lives below the poverty line, an estimated 63% of the women who live here are illiterate and the female life expectancy is 60 years. The maternal mortality ratio in both these states is well above the country's average of 254 at 371 in Jharkhand and 358 in Orissa. The women's groups here met monthly and were lead by a local woman who was given 7 days residential training and supported through fortnightly meetings with district coordinators. Each of these local women ran many meetings a month in different rural locations to reach as many people as possible. The groups gave information about safe delivery practices and care seeking behaviour through discussion of case studies, picture-card games, role play and story-telling. The outcomes of this study were striking with large reductions in not just maternal mortality but also neonatal mortality and moderate depression in new mothers. The latter was thought to be due to the support network created by these groups. Women's groups cannot replace trained medical care but I believe they certainly have a key role in maternal health in rural areas, providing simple information on topics such as hygiene and creating invaluable support networks at extremely low financial cost. There is no doubt over the cost effectiveness of training members of the community to run women's groups.

Conclusion

While writing this chapter I have been shocked time and time again by the staggeringly large numbers of women affected by poor maternal health in India. This alone should be reason enough for India's government to prioritise maternal health in the years to come, and continue investing in schemes such as JSY and women's groups. I hope I have demonstrated that this is an important and complex issue, with key cultural issues right at its core, but, as the state of Kerala shows, pregnancy in India doesn't have to equate to life threatening danger. I believe that women's health is so intricately linked with their education, wealth and their position in society that to make strides in decreasing maternal mortality all these issues must be addressed. This may sound like a tall order but ultimately, there can be no justification for preventable and unnecessary deaths and I dearly hope India's government keeps that in mind.

Graphs and figures

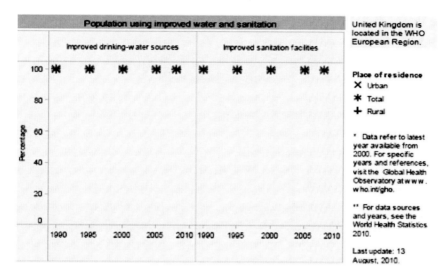

Figure 1: Graph to show percentage of the rural, urban and total population using improved water and sanitation in the UK[24] (top) and India[25] (bottom)

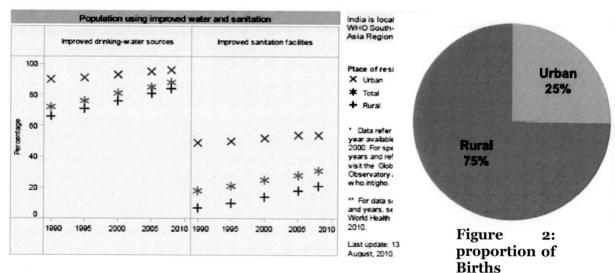

Figure 2: proportion of Births

occurring in urban and rural area

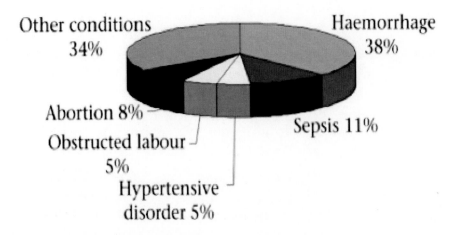

Figure 3: Causes of maternal death in India in 2003

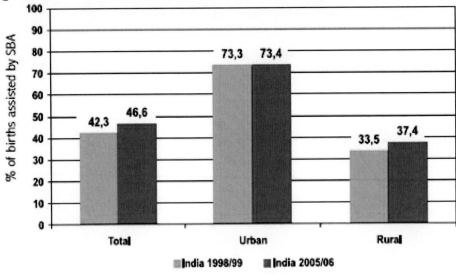

Figure 4: Percentage of births assisted by skilled birth attendants in India in 1998/99 and 2005/06 in urban, rural and all areas

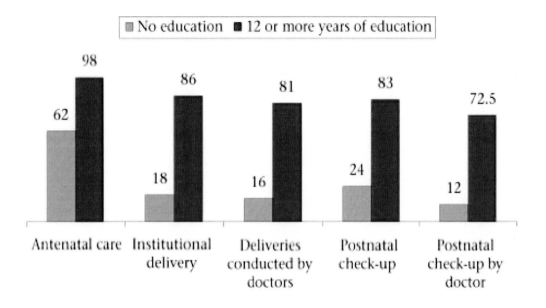

Figure 5: Access to maternal healthcare according to maternal education in 2005/06

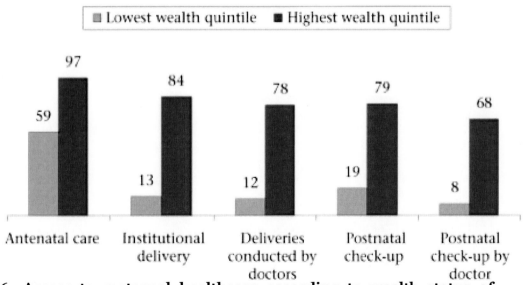

Figure 6: Access to maternal healthcare according to wealth status of pregnant women 2005/06[3]

References

World Health Organisation. *Why do so Many Women Still Die in Pregnancy or Childbirth?* [Online]. Available from: http://www.who.int/features/qa/12/en/index.html [Accessed 8th December 2010]

. Index Mundi. *India Birth rate.* [Online]. Available from: http://www.indexmundi.com/india/birth_rate.html [Accessed 8th December 2010]

Vora, K., Mavalankar, D., Ramani, K., Upadhyaya, M., Sharma, B., Iyengar, S., Gupta, V., Iyengar,K. Maternal Health Situation in India: A Case Study. *Journal of Health, Population and Nutrition* 2009;27(2).

United Nations Development Program. *Tracking the Millennium development goals.* [Online]. Available from: http://www.mdgmonitor.org/map.cfm?goal=4&indicator=0&cd= [Accessed 2nd December 2010]

World Health Organisation. *Maternal Mortality ratio* . [Online]. Available from: http://www.who.int/healthinfo/statistics/indmaternalmortality/en/index.html [Accessed 3rd December 2010]

World Bank. *India at a glance.* [Online] Available from: http://devdata.worldbank.org/aag/ind_aag.pdf [accessed 3rd December 2010]

World Health Organisation Department of Making Pregnancy Safer. *India: Country Profile.* [Online]. Available from: http://www.who.int/making_pregnancy_safer/countries/ind.pdf [Accessed 3rd December 2010]

World Health Organisation. *India.* [Online]. Available from: http://www.who.int/countries/ind/en/ [Accessed 3rd December 2010]

World Health Organisation. *United Kingdom* [Online]. Available from: http://www.who.int/countries/gbr/en/ [Accessed 3rd December 2010]

The Communist Party of India (Marxist). *The Communist party Of India (Marxist): About Us.* [Online]. Available from: http://www.cpim.org/content/about-us [Accessed 7th December 2010

Government of India, Ministry Of Health and Welfare. *Kerala.* [Online]. Available from:http://www.mohfw.nic.in/NRHM/State%20Files/kerala.htm [Accessed 3rd December 2010]

Government of India, Ministry of Health and Family Welfare. *District Level Household and Facility Survey* [Online]. Available from: http://www.jsk.gov.in/dlhs3/kerala.pdf [Accessed 7th December 2010]

United Nations. *Goal 5: Improve maternal Health Fact Sheet.* [Online]. Available from: http://www.un.org/millenniumgoals/pdf/MDG_FS_5_EN_new.pdf [Accessed 7th December 2010]

Maternal Health Task Force. *The Impact of Maternal Mortality and Morbidity on Economic Development.* [Online]. Available from: http://maternalhealthtaskforce.org/discuss/wpblog/2010/07/19/the-impact-of-maternal-mortality-and-morbidity-on-economic-development/ [Accessed 7th December 2010]

. The Sociology Guide. *Women's position in India.* [Online]. Available from:

http://www.sociologyguide.com/women-and-society/womens-position-in-india.php [Accessed 7th December 2010]

Ohio University, Global Learning Community. *Current Status of Women in India* [Online]. Available from: http://global_india1.tripod.com/current.htm [Accessed 7th December 2010]

Indian Child. *Dowries in India.* [Online]. Available from: http://www.indianchild.com/dowry_in_india.htm [Accessed 7th December 2010]

.Government of Haryana, Department of Women and Child Development. *The Dowry Prohibition Act, 1961.* [Online]. Available from: http://wcdhry.gov.in/Women_Acts/Dowry_Act.pdf [Accessed 7th December 2010]

Mynott, A. *Fighting India's Dowry Crime.* [Online]. Available from: http://news.bbc.co.uk/1/hi/programmes/correspondent/3259965.stm [Accessed 7th December 2010]

Government of India, Ministry of Home affairs, National Crime Records Bureau. *All India Figures at a Glance 2008* [Online]. Available from: http://ncrb.nic.in/cii2008/cii-2008/figure%20at%20a%20glance.pdf [Accessed 7th December 2010]

Gupta SD, Khanna A, Gupta R, Sharma NK, Sharma ND. Maternal Mortality Ratio and Predictors of Maternal Deaths in Selected Desert Districts in Rajasthan: A Community-Based Survey and Case Control Study. *Women's Health Issues* 2010 2;20(1): pp. 80-85.

Lim SS, Dandona L, Hoisington JA, James SL, Hogan MC, Gakidou E. India's Janani Suraksha Yojana, a conditional cash transfer programme to increase births in health facilities: an impact evaluation. *The Lancet* 2010 6/5;375(9730): pp. 2009-2023.

Tripathy P, Nair N, Barnett S, Mahapatra R, Borghi J, Rath S, et al. Effect of a participatory intervention with women's groups on birth outcomes and maternal depression in Jharkhand and Orissa, India: a cluster-randomised controlled trial. *The Lancet* 2010 4/3;375(9721): pp. 1182-1192.

World Health Organisation. *United Kingdom: health profile.* [Online]. Available from: http://www.who.int/gho/countries/gbr.pdf [Accessed 3rd December 2010]

World Health Organisation. *India: health profile.* [Online]. Available from: http://www.who.int/gho/countries/ind.pdf [Accessed 3rd December 2010]

3.4 Methodologies for Green Economics health analysis: GIS (Geographical Information Systems) and Spatial Methodology

By Lawrence Sappor

Abstract

As energy economics aims at expanding clean energy production, increasing energy efficiency, reducing greenhouse gas emissions, and pollution, conserving water and other natural resources, we shall explore how GIS and geospatial analysis (as a new tool/instrument) in research is making use of data to assist critical decision making. The process of GIS analysis often proceeds in a simple sequence from problem specification to problem outcome or vice versa. In reality this is an over-simplification, as scientific approach is adopted in a broader context for a more iterative and narrative approach. GIS analysis focuses on the relationship between spatial patterns and processes as a guide to a broader understanding of the problem. The objective of the analysis can be presented in the form of a statistical or descriptive data, commentary, general maps, or associated documents. The chapter will explore some of the unique challenges and probability of integrating participatory action research into understanding the technological, social and political constructive issues of life. As well, this approach can foster critical reflection on the impacts of digital spatial data and GIS technologies in research design and methodologies.

GIS analysis

Sustainability and climate change is the forecast of some industries, the need to increase production, compete in the surging economy and increasing profit is affecting the campaign to control emission especially from aviation and road transport systems. Most industries produce and/or use both green and non-green goods and services, so making distinctions is difficult. For example, the transport industry produce green services but make use of non-green goods, a consequence is its effect on the environment and health. This can be measured using the input-output approach. That is, irrespective of a firm's output (input), count the number of green input (output) based on whether the occupational activities of the firm make production greener. To better understand the effect of choosing one approach over another, GIS analysis brings them together and makes you see what is happening to make an informed decision. GIS is a relatively broad term, which refer to a number of technologies, methods and processes attached to many operations in analysing problems related to health, engineering, planning, management, transport, logistics and more. The domain of GIS analysis (sometimes referred as geospatial analysis) which describes an aspect of the earth's topography by providing a distinct perspective of a situation (as a unique lens) through which events, patterns, and processes that operate on or near can be examined.

In many instances the process of spatial analysis follows a number of well-defined (often iterative and interrelated) stages: problem formulation; planning; data gathering; exploratory analysis; hypothesis formulation; modelling and testing; consultation and review; and ultimately final reporting and/or implementation of the findings. The qualitative method investigates the smaller why and how of decision making on an often focused large issues whereas quantitative methods display more than just what, where, when. Both are used to seek empirical support for information on the particular cases studied and any more general conclusions are propositions (informed assertions) such as research hypotheses.

Basic components of a GIS analysis

a.   Basic information - the data which are the subject of analysis are qualitative or quantitative. This data entered into the software represents real objects (such as roads, land use, elevation, trees, waterways, health cases etc.). The data put into the software becomes a digital data which determines the mix between discrete objects (e.g., a house, trees, or roads) and continuous objects (such as rainfall amount, or elevations). Qualitative data such as high-resolution digital terrain images, digitized maps, photographs or aerial imagery and quantitative data such as numbers and letters are edited to remove errors for further processing.

b.   Software tools – Next is the software and computer machine to process the data. This time round there is a varied amount of software so it depends on your knowledge and skills in a particular one. Most known is ESRI (ArcGIS), MapInfo, IDDRISI, Microsoft Office

c.   Structures and arguments – This depends on the amount of research work available from same or similar study or importance of the study and the outcome of the study. Qualitative data such as high-resolution digital terrain images, digitized maps, photographs or aerial imagery and quantitative data such as numbers and letters are edited to remove errors or further processing.

Simply put, the basic components use the concept of uniformitarian to describe the situation and link the relationships between what is happening with what has happened by exploring the present to understand the past. From a clear understanding of a problem and expectations, one can work *back* through the process stages identifying what needs to be included and might be excluded in order to have the best chance of meeting those expectations and requirements within the timescale and resourcing available. This concept of change is a study, gradual and evenly distributed process throughout time and space. For instance, an Idrisi cartographic modeling commentary informs that, "In developing a cartographic model we find it most useful to begin with the final product and proceed backwards in a step-by-step manner towards the existing data. This process guards against the tendency to let the available data shape the final product."

Methodology: Which analytical methodologies or scientific approaches?

The basic components of spatial analysis are the data, software and other structures which provide the essential conceptual framework. As with all scientific disciplines, first identify and formulate the problem to be addressed and developed an outline plan. Then related software tools perform analytical functions by addressing the exploratory analysis on the hypothesis formulated, model and testing, which may be relatively "blunt". This sounds very simple and straightforward. In reality, underlying concepts employed (be it simple, intuitive or advanced, complex mathematical or computational techniques) allow conclusions, recommendations and decisions to be drawn. Ultimately, campaigns to ensure that the air must be cleaner and greener for the health of the population and environment using GIS software portrayal pictorial condition of the situation. The structures and arguments built on the basic information provide the richness of spatial GIS analysis. For instance, indicating why road, aviation and incinerator emissions are the main source of COPDs (Chronic Obstructive Pulmonary Diseases) must be investigated in relation to source of emission, mode of dispersion, area of possible infection, recorded cases, history of patient location and more. Example below is the disability mapping:

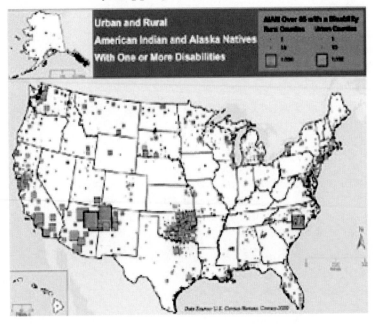

Using GIS in a first national mapping of functional disability among older American Indians and Alaska natives from the 2000 (CDC, September 2006) - courtesy Najafabadi,2009

The first task typically involves obtaining the data, location (indicating the x, y and z –

longitude, latitude and elevation), and narrative literature. This immediately raises many questions that have an important bearing on subsequent stages:

a.   What assumptions have been invoked in order to represent the "real-world" and what are the implications of this for subsequent analysis?

b.   How complete are the data — spatially and temporarily?

c.   How accurate are the data (spatially, temporarily and in terms of measured attributes)?

d.   Are all of the datasets compatible and consistent with one another — what sources are they drawn from and how do they compare in terms of scale, projection, accuracy, modeling, orientation, date of capture and attribute definition?

e.   Are the data adequate to address the problem at hand?

f.   Can the available data be combined and processed with the resources available?

This kind of process can be though lengthy, decision cycles for highly dynamic environments such as COPDs must be taken with care. For example controlling road traffic not mentioning pollution is a serious population health issues. We can think of COPD types and density of pollutants in real time, source of pollution and its future vital implications without being biased. Then this data can be reliable and sought for the study at hand. It is input into the software for a simple mapping, then a more complex and dynamic exploration of the data. Example is the incidence mapping of HIV/AIDS and spread of HIV/AIDS:

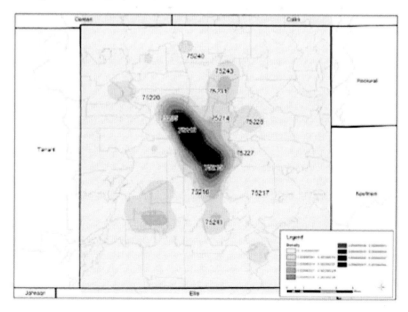

HIV/AIDS Incidence Density among Teens and Youth (13-24) Dallas County 1999-

2003(CDC, 2005) – courtesy Najafabadi,2009

HIV/AIDS PREVALENCE FOR THE YEAR 1994

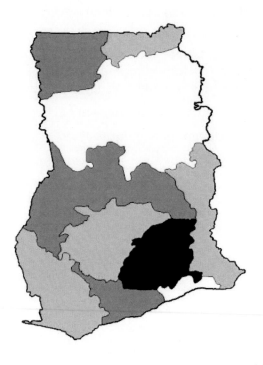

Legend

Regions' prevalence

	5.4% - 5.4%
	5.4% - 7%
	7% - 9.4%
	9.4% - 12.1%
	12.1% - 15.8%
	Country border

0   100   200   300 km

Project map 2
SS/BSS/02/0261
Goe. & Tourism Dept
UCC

HIV/AIDS PREVALENCE FOR 2004

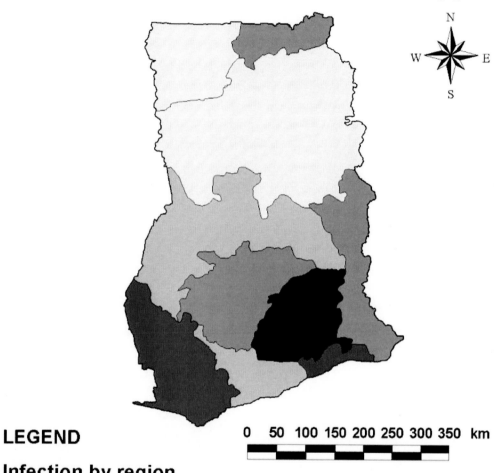

LEGEND

Infection by region

	4% - 4.7%
	4.7% - 9.4%
	9.4% - 11.2%
	11.2% - 12.8%
	12.8% - 15.2%
	Country border

0   50   100 150 200 250 300 350   km

Project Work- SS/BSS/02/0261
Geo. and Tourism Dept.
UCC

Courtesy Lawrence Sappor 2006

The fact involved is that the disease has not come only as a health issue but has other implications. People were scared of undertaking HIV/AIDS test even during marriage counselling, which is a compulsory check, due to Ostracism. Research has revealed a great deal of valuable medical, scientific, and public health information about the Human Immuno-deficiency Virus (HIV) and the Acquired Immune Deficiency Syndrome (AIDS).

A decision support framework can be developed to support decision making. This decision-making can reflect purely academic or commercial, governmental or community interests. Increasingly these involve the use of formal decision-support systems, from simple cost-benefit analysis to more spatial decision support systems (SDSS), Multi-Criteria Evaluation (MCE) and visualization techniques. As timeslots for presentation and decision making become so brief, cases continue to occur while the range and experience of users continue to grow, decision based on visualization presents the best alternative.

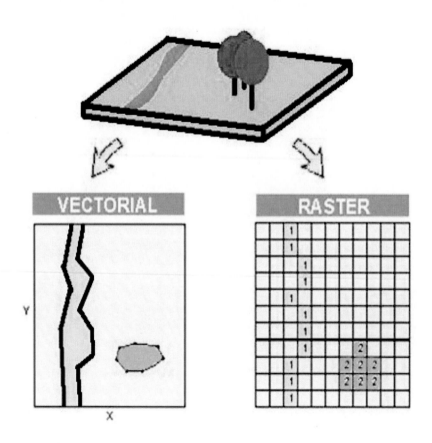

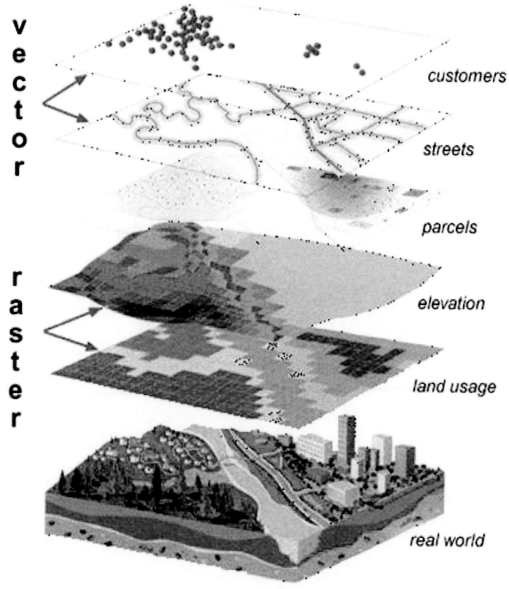

customers

streets

parcels

elevation

land usage

real world

Courtesy of Stueve

Simple GIS graphical model

Methods of spatial analysis are robust and capable of operating over a range of spatial and temporal scales. Increasingly, to reflect this trend, GIS developers have developed tools to facilitate processing GIS data in the form of a rater or vector. While the vector presentation is similar to an amateur drawings in the form of the lines, areas, and points, the raster presentation of the reality in the form of little "squares" or cells comprised of computer codes. There is numerous software to analyze these information but they all depend on leading GIS tool such as ArcGIS, Erdas Imagine, and IDRISI. Currently, lots of other programs are linked to these technologies.

GIS uncertainties and Data

Powerful computers and web technology are changing the quality, utility, and expectations of GIS though accuracy of some data is uncertain. Wherever the data source depends on how it is encoded, referenced and related to other layers of data to visualise a phenomenon. Data obtained in a qualitative and quantitative form are edited to remove errors for further processing in the software and analysed in relation with other research activity. These data are traditionally stored in a GIS for abstractions mapping references as raster and vector data. At this point, the processes of hypothesis testing, modelling, and analysis are applied to draw up the recommendations and conclusions. For example, it will be difficult to relate pollution data recorded from aviation to transport pollution within a city as a cause of COPDs. However, GIS analysis can be used to depict a link through a two- and three-dimensional layer characteristic in the form of the Earth's surface, subsurface (source of pollution and population density) and atmosphere (pollution presence, wind direction).

When overlapped, they depict or emphasize on the scope of the study, and attempt to identify and draw attention to any obvious weaknesses in the data or methodology. The question for example, can be related to health by indicating the relationship between geometric entities (COPD cases) and pollution, how close are patients from source of infection or pollutants (Proximity), difference between source of emission and point of infection (adjacency) and how did it get that far (containment – by wind). This ideas can be applied to any geometric phenomenon (transport network, utility, planning), hydrological (water bodies), cartography (map), geostatic (archaeology interpolation) and data mining.

Analysis and Conclusions

Many disciplines such as science, government, business, and industry benefit from GIS technology to lower costs and bring continual improvements in real estate, Global climate change, public health, Web mapping, crime, defence, sustainable development, architecture, archaeology, hydrology and coastal management, regional and community planning, transportation and logistics. GIS is also diverging into location-based services which allows GPS-enabled mobile devices to share vital information across the internet (health reports etc), display location in relation to fixed assets (nearest restaurant, gas station, fire hydrant), mobile assets (friends, children, police car) or to relay position back to a central server for display or other processing. These services continue to develop with the increased integration of internet functionality with increasingly powerful mobile electronics (cell phones, PDAs, laptops).

References:

About ESRI from the ESRI website: http://www.esri.com/about-esri/history/history-more

De Smith, M. J., Goodchild, M. F., Longley, P. A., 2009 "Geospatial Analysis – A Comprehensive Guide to Principles, Techniques and Software Tools" third edition from the website: http://www.spatialanalysisonline.com/HandbookExtractV3.pdf

Department of Geography, San Diego State University, 2002 "GeoAgent" from the website: http://map.sdsu.edu/geoagent/gis_intro.htm

Energy economics, 2012, "Energy Economics" from Wikipedia website: http://en.wikipedia.org/wiki/Energy_economics

Forte, F., Strobl, R.O., Pennetta, L.,2006, "A Methodology using GIS, aerial Photos and Remote Sensing for loss estimation and Flood Vulnerability Analysis in the Supersano-Ruffano-Nociglia Graben, Southern Italy" from the SpringerLink website: https://springerlink3.metapress.com/content/1078k1px61625g8k/resource-secured/? target=fulltext.pdf&sid=4ipmtvbkxhajnmeobrtjfn1z&sh=www.springerlink.com

Kennet, M., Heinemann, V., 2006 "Green Economics: setting the scene. Aims, context, and philosophical underpinning of the distinctive new solutions offered by Green Economics" from http://inderscience.metapress.com/content/2atu31k598e85a3u/fulltext.pdf

Najafabadi, A. T., 2009 "Applications of GIS in Health Sciences" from the Shiraz E-Medical Journal, Vol. 10, No. 4 and website: http://semj.sums.ac.ir/vol10/oct2009/87055.htm

Sappor, L.S., 2006 "THE Global Spread Of Hiv/Aids: A Regional Perspective Of Ghana – A Gis Analysis For The Period 1985-2004

Slaper, T. F., Krause, R. A., 2009 "The Green Economy: What Does Green Mean?" From The Indiana University, Indiana Business Review Website: Http://Www.Ibrc.Indiana.Edu/Ibr/2009/Fall/Article3.Html

Stueve, K. M., Introduction To Geographic Information Systems: Basic Principles And Becoming Familiar With Arcmap

3.5 What Opportunity Do Poor People Have To Participate, Or Lead, In The Green Economics Debate?

By Don O'Neal

1.   Introduction

In traditional economics, it has all been the wealthy and the powerful that have defined what economics guides global trade. The poor have had no voice in traditional economics and are casualties of an imbalanced economic order. In 1990, 31% of the population of the developing world lived on less than $1 a day - close to 1.4 billion. (Alexander, 2012).

2.   Rio Summit 1992

In recent decades, there has been a backlash against traditional economics. Five years after the Brundtland Report, the United Nations held a Conference on Environment and Development, in June 1992 at Rio de Janeiro in Brazil. The Rio Earth Summit was the largest environmental conference ever held, attracting over 30,000 people including more than 100 heads of state. Aside from Rio, there have been numerous sessions of the Conference of the Parties (COP 17) to the United Nations Framework Convention on Climate Change (UNFCCC) and other global initiatives such as the Millennium Development Goals. One has to wonder how much the voice of the poor was represented at these negotiations and how much poor people were able to participate. The Rio summit, though, offered hope and real possibility for change. For once it seemed as though the plight of the environment and world development was being put high on the agenda.

3.   Rio+20 in 2012

Twenty years on, one can ask again how much has the voice of the poor been represented at these negotiations and how much poor people were able to participate? How much has changed for the poor of the world? Rio, like Kyoto, and the COP sessions has been a succession of meetings where global leaders and big business have set agendas to satisfy themselves and absolve themselves of doing much at all. Has the past 20 years been a success for poor people? (Box 1. Poverty statistics)

- Still 2.7 billion people struggle to survive on fewer than US$ 2 a day.
- More than 50 per cent of Africans suffer from water-related diseases such as cholera and infant diarrhoea.
- More than 800 million people go to bed hungry every day. 300 million are children.
- More than 2.6 billion people-over 40 per cent of the world's population-do not have basic sanitation, and more than one billion people still use unsafe sources of drinking water.

Source: http://www.unmillenniumproject.org/resources/fastfacts_e.htm [Viewed 27 July 2011]

Bearing the above poverty statistics in mind, what opportunity do poor people have to participate, or lead, in the Green economic debate?

4.   Maslow's hierarchy of needs

The problem for most people living in poverty is that they do not have the luxury to participate in the Green economic debate as they are too busy trying to satisfy their basic needs. American psychologist Abraham Maslow stated that people are motivated to achieve certain needs. When one need is fulfilled a person seeks to fulfil the next one, and so on. The earliest and most widespread version of Maslow's hierarchy of needs includes five motivational needs, often depicted as hierarchical levels within a pyramid. This five stage model can be divided into basic needs (e.g. physiological, safety, love, and esteem) and growth needs (self-actualization) (McLeod, 2007). One must satisfy lower level basic needs before progressing on to meet higher level growth needs. Once these needs have been reasonably satisfied, one may be able to reach the highest level called self-actualization. Every person is capable and has the desire to move up the hierarchy toward a level of self-actualization. Unfortunately, progress is often disrupted by failure to meet lower level needs. (Figure 1. Maslow's hierarchy of needs)

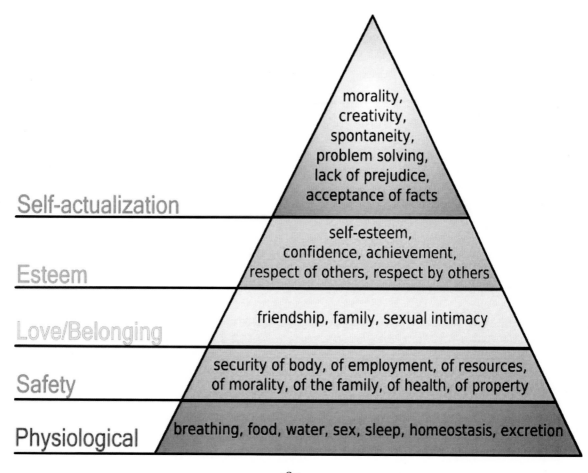

To ponder about Green economics and to participate, or lead, in the Green economics debate, people need to be able to function adequately at the self-actualisation level of Maslow's hierarchy of needs. Most of the world's poor are stuck trying to conquer the lower levels of physiological and safety needs.

Until these lower levels have been overcome, it is difficult for poor people to have opportunities to participate in the Green economics debate.

5.   Example of 'hierarchy of needs' problems and proposed solutions

A real life example of these problems can be illustrated by life in St. Vincent and the Grenadines (SVG). Discussed with these problems are policy ideas of SVG Greens.

5.1   Access to food, water and electricity

Although, some food is grown locally in SVG, a substantial amount is imported. In 2011, £52 million worth of food was imported, which is significant when public debt was £305 million and the SVG Government Budget Estimates 2012 were only £199 million (SVG Government, 2011). SVG Green's policy is to set up farming co-ops and create incentives for supermarkets to substitute foodstuffs they buy from abroad with locally available foods. Imported food is very expensive and by using more locally grown food, food prices will come down and farmers will start to earn a decent living again.

Many households in SVG are not connected to the mains water supply. About 21,600 households were disconnected from the mains water supply during the period 2006 to 2010 (Letter from Central Water and Sewerage Authority - SVG). This is a substantial amount considering the population of the country is only 104,000. SVG Greens' policy is to reduce the cost of water by 50% and to make sure every household is connected to the mains water supply. Also, we intend to make the first 1000 gallons used each month free of charge.

Electricity in SVG is expensive and many households do not have electricity. SVG Green's policy is to reduce the price of electricity by 50% and to make sure every household gets connected. Also, the first 200 KWh would be free. This will be managed by moving away from oil-produced electricity to making SVG 100% reliable on renewable energy sources.

5.2   Access to safety, employment and resources

Crime is a major problem in SVG. In an article entitled 'Is this Caribbean idyll the worst place in the world to be a woman?', it was noted that over the past decade, more than 4,500 refugee claimants — or 4.3 per cent of the tiny Caribbean archipelago's population of an estimated 104,000 – sought asylum in Canada (Yang, 2011). In 2007, SVG had the third-highest rate of reported rapes in the world per capita, according to a UN report. SVG Greens' policy is to reduce crime by strengthening the economy, partly by starting a tuna fishing and canning industry using its deep-sea fish licence. Unemployment is very high in SVG because the economy is on the verge of collapse.

SVG Greens' policy is to strengthen the economy by moving away from tourism and focusing on education and science and technology. Also, we intend to make education free and build a first university for the country.

The internet is very expensive and only a minority of people has access to the internet. SVG Greens' policy is to make internet free in the whole country to encourage innovation and entrepreneurship. Also, provide access to micro-credit schemes to help small businesses and start-ups.

6.   Abolish apartheid

Abolish the apartheid scheme whereby Taiwan and a super-rich minority in Mustique does not pay tax in SVG, whereas everyone else has to pay tax.

7.   Conclusion

If the foundation in people's lives is not there - no food, water, shelter, security and education – then they will fail to participate in Green economics and Green economics may not help them. I believe that Green economics will be richer when more of the poor are involved. We have had the Adam Smith 'trickle down' economics: that has not worked for most of the world. I think that 'trickle down' Green economics will not work either. What's needed is a kind of 'trickle up' economics, to provide more realistic solutions for the poor and empower them to be part of, and benefit from, Green economics, rather than being casualties of Green economics. Stalagmite economics – where the poor are the architects of the solutions and architects of the methods to achieve the solutions. Poor people need to be empowered to participate, or lead, in the Green economics debate.

References

Alexander, R. (2012) *Dollar benchmark: the rise of the $1-a-day statistic.* [Online]. Available from: http://www.bbc.co.uk/news/magazine-17312819

Letter from Central Water and Sewerage Authority, SVG.

McLeod, S. A. (2007). Maslow's Hierarchy of Needs - Simply Psychology. [Online]. Available from: http://www.simplypsychology.org/maslow.html

Millennium Project (2006) Fast Facts: The Faces of Poverty [Online]. Available from: http://www.unmillenniumproject.org/resources/fastfacts_e.htm [Accessed: 20 July 2011]

SVG Government. (2011) SVG Budget Estimates 2012. Kingstown: Government Printer

Sustainable Environment (2012) Earth and man: Action > Rio Earth Summit. [Online]. Available from: http://www.sustainable-environment.org.uk/Action/Earth_Summit.php

Yang, J. (2011) Is this Caribbean idyll the worst place in the world to be a woman? [Online]. Available from: http://www.thestar.com/news/world/2011/11/12/video_is_this_caribbean_idyll _the_worst_place_in_the_world_to_be_a_woman.html

3.6 The Greening of Portugal in a Time of Crisis and Austerity

By Sofia Amaral

Portugal is a small open economy in Western Europe. It recently made headlines due to the European sovereign debt crisis. In 2011, it had to request a bailout because it was no longer able to meet its debt commitments. It is one of the five Eurozone member countries that are under an adjustment process agreed with Troika (tripartite committee formed by IMF, European Commission and European Central Bank). Nowadays, it is struggling to achieve the reforms established in the Memorandum of Understanding with Troika as the economy dips into recession. Most recent data shows that wealth is actually being destroyed (real GDP growth was -3.2% in 2012 according to Eurostat).

Some argue that this is the result of austerity in a time of crisis. Portugal has been implementing measures such as tax increases and public spending cuts, including in health and education sectors. Although Troika has praised these efforts, reality is harsh in Portugal. Domestic demand is falling (it declined by 9% from the start of the financial crisis in 2007 to 2012 according to Eurostat) and unemployment keeps increasing to astounding levels (unemployment rate was 17.8% and youth unemployment rate was 42.5% on April 2013 according to Eurostat).

What are the implications of austerity and the crisis to the development of a green economy in Portugal? This article aims at exploring this issue by first providing a context on the process of greening and its role in a time of crisis. It will further present an overview of the greening of Portugal in recent years and examine the challenges for the future.

Notes on the greening of an economy

Contrarily to what is often believed, the greening of an economy entails more than protecting the environment. Instead, the greening of an economy is a process that aims at improving "human well-being and social equity, while significantly reducing environmental risks and ecological scarcities" (UNEP, 2011). The Green Economics Institute expands the definition by claiming that this process is not only for humans, but all species. A green economy should provide "for all people everywhere, other species, nature, the planet and its systems and always considering that everyone and everything on the planet has economic needs, impacts and responsibilities" (Kennet, 2011).

At its core, a green economy is the ultimate recognition that we are part of very intricate and complex system that we need to nurture. There is more to an economy than production and consumption. An economy is a system that underpins the satisfaction of needs, both social and environmental. Thus, a green economy is one that organises the system in order to promote economic, social and environmental justice. It respects cultural diversity and embraces an intergenerational perspective.

Given the abundant information available about the features of a green economy, this article focuses on three cornerstones of the greening of an economy: low carbon growth, resource efficiency and social inclusivity (UNEP, 2011).

Firstly, low carbon growth means that development is based on economic activities that emit fewer Greenhouse Gas (GHG) emissions. It entails improving energy efficiency and using low-carbon technologies such as renewable energy sources. Besides the environmental benefits that it brings such as mitigation of climate change and less pollution, a low carbon economy offers social and economic benefits such as reduction in external energy dependence for countries that depend on fossil fuels imports, driver for innovation, creation of green jobs, better public health- are few to mention amongst others (By Energy, 2010)

Secondly, using EU's definition, "improving resource efficiency means achieving economic growth using fewer resources" (European Commission, 2013c). It contributes to increase productivity, lower costs, foster innovation and, consequently, boosting competitiveness in a way that is compatible with environmental needs. Furthermore, there are specific areas such as waste and water management that are key to promote resource efficiency. In particular, waste management is a crucial activity to ensure resource efficiency in the sense that it can reduce use of both new resources and energy through recycling. In addition, improving resource efficiency in water management is critical since water is vital for human life and an important component in many economic activities.

Thirdly, social inclusivity implies that economic development is shared by all. There is deep involvement in the process of development so that all people can benefit from it. It requires active participation from the entire society in decision-making.

Therefore, the process of greening the economy will lead to a more efficient and low-carbon economy that provides opportunities for all groups in the society, which will raise the standards of living of the population.

In a context of crisis, some claim that there is a trade-off between economic growth and environmental sustainability, so a country cannot afford to spend resources on dealing with climate change and other ecological crises. However, the greening of an economy can be perceived as an opportunity to overcome the economic crisis. This is because it addresses the triple crises we now face (social-political, economic and ecological). Thus, tackling the ecological crisis can be the driver to eradicate poverty and recover from the economic recession (UNRISD, 2012).

Greening of Portugal in recent years

The greening of the economy has already started in Portugal. The country is working towards a low carbon economy, improving resource efficiency and promoting social inclusivity.

Towards a low carbon economy

Portugal is very committed to reduce GHG emissions. With no sources of fossil energy, the transition to a low carbon economy means not only minimising climate change but also reducing external energy dependence, thereby fostering competitiveness.

One of the first actions Portugal undertook to decarbonise its economy was ratifying the Kyoto Protocol in 2002. This agreement requires Portugal to limit the increase of GHG emissions to 27% of the 1990 level during the period 2008-2012 (Governo de Portugal, 2013).

It seems Portugal will (partly) achieve the target proposed by the Kyoto Protocol, as GHG emissions were 29%, 24%, 17% and 15% compared to 1990 levels from 2008 to 2011, respectively. According to the Portuguese Environmental Agency (2013), this was possible due to the implementation of several measures that contributed to reduce the level of emissions such as "the introduction of natural gas (1997), the installation of new combined cycle thermoelectric plants using natural gas (1999), the progressive installation of co-generation units, the amelioration of energetic and technologic efficiency of industrial processes, the improvement of car efficiency and fuels quality".

Another effective mechanism that contributes to reduce GHG emissions is the EU's Emissions Trading Scheme (ETS), launched in 2005 (European Commission, 2013a). As a EU Member-Country, Portugal participates in this system that aims to limit CO_2 emissions by 20% (compared with 1990 levels) by 2020. This scheme involves key sectors such as heat and power generation, energy-intensive industries and commercial aviation. It involves trading emission quotas among companies, in a way that companies that emit below the target can sell their permits to companies that emit more than the agreed.

Furthermore, in 2008, all EU countries took further action by committing to reduce GHG emissions by 20% (compared to 1990 level), increase the share of renewable energies in energy consumption by 20% and improve energy efficiency by 20% until 2020 (European Commission, 2013b). These are the 20-20-20 targets, part of the Europe 2020 strategy that constitutes a general guideline adapted to each country's reality. For Portugal in particular, the 20-20-20 targets impose a reduction in total primary energy consumption of 25% (compared to 2005 levels), an increase in the share of renewable energy sources in final energy consumption of 31% and limit the increase of GHG emissions to 1% (compared to 2005 levels) for emissions from sectors not included in the ETS, until 2020 (Governo de Portugal, 2013).

Regarding energy efficiency, figure 2 shows annual primary energy consumption as an index based on the 2005 level for Portugal during 2005-2012.

There is a downward trend of primary energy consumption during the period 2005-2010. Consumption declined more each year from 2005, reaching a reduction of 20.69% in 2012. This trend might be the result of the crisis that slowed down the economic activity and in-turn energy consumption. Nevertheless, this means Portugal is approaching the 25% target, but note that the country must still put into place strategies to reduce (or maintain) energy consumption in periods of regular economic activity.

With respect to the renewable energies target, figure 3 illustrates the share of renewable energy in gross final energy consumption for the period 2005-2011 in Portugal and EU27.

The renewable energy sector is very important in Portugal. The share of these sources in final energy consumption has been increasing, from 19.8% in 2005 to 24.9% in 2011. This means Portugal is getting closer to achieve the 31% target in 2020.

Moreover, one can highlight the staggering difference between Portugal and EU27 average, which corroborates the idea that the country is considered to be a world leader in renewable energy. Indeed, Portugal sets the 6th more ambitious target for the total energy consumption supplied by renewable energies (31%), only behind Sweden, Latvia, Finland, Austria and Estonia (EDP, 2013).

Regarding electricity production only, the target is to increase the share of renewables by 60% until 2020. In this case, the numbers are even more impressive.

Focusing on electricity generation, figure 4 shows that renewable energies rose from 14.2% in 2005 to 43.6% in 2011. An interesting fact is that, for a few hours in 2011, electricity was totally produced from renewable energy sources (Ashton, 2012).

This upward trend seems to continue as most recent data indicates that, in the first quarter of 2013, 70% of the electricity produced was supplied by renewable energy sources (Lusa, 2013).

This was possible because Portugal has been investing intensively in this sector. It has one of the biggest solar centrals in the world and one of the biggest wind farms in Europe. Moreover, it has an extensive network of hydro-electric dams (Ashton, 2012). Hydropower and wind energy are the most developed renewable energy sources in the country.

Regarding GHG emissions, Portugal reduced the emissions from sectors not included in the ETS by 6% and 8% in 2010 and 2011, respectively, compared to 2005 levels (Governo de Portugal, 2013).

This progress is, in part, due to different policies and programmes implemented, such as the National Strategy for Energy (ENE 2020), whose goal is to ensure that the 20-

20-20 targets are met, and the National Action Plan for Renewable Energy (PNAER 2020) focusing on setting objectives for the share of energy from renewable sources in several sectors (Naumann, 2013).

All in all, Portugal seems to be on the right track to become a low carbon economy. The investment in renewable energies is not only assisting in this process, but could also contribute to drive the economy out of the crisis. Nevertheless, note that the achievements so far are also a result of the economy's slowdown so effective mechanisms should be implemented to ensure GHG emissions do not increase as soon as the crisis is overcame.

Improving resource efficiency

Portugal's efforts in terms of resource efficiency have been low.

Analysing resource productivity, the evolution of this indicator does not show a clear trend for Portugal. It peaked in 2003 when resource productivity increased by 13% relatively to the 2000 level. However, it decreased until 2008, which means more resources were being used per output produced. Nevertheless, it seems that Portugal is recovering as resource productivity shows an upward trend since 2008. Within EU, Portugal is one of lowest performing countries during the period 2000-2010 as is evidenced by the widening difference between Portugal's and EU 27's resource productivity.

Nonetheless, the country has in place policies to address waste treatment and water management.

Waste treatment can be in the form of landfills, recycling, composting or incineration. As a EU Member-Country, the EU Waste Framework Directive requires Portugal to recycle 50% of its municipal waste by 2020 (European Commission, 2013c). An analysis of the percentage of total waste treatment that is recycled annually in Portugal and the EU27 during the period 2000-2011 leads one to conclude that Portugal has been increasing the proportion of waste that is recycled, from 7% in 2000 to 12% in 2011. This is due to educative campaigns that encourage recycling. However, it is still far from meeting the 50% target. It is also below EU27 average, which was 25% in 2011.

Regarding water management, this is a especially relevant area for Portugal given the mismatch between the availability of water (winter when precipitation is higher) and demand (summer when temperatures are higher). The water exploitation index that relates water availability with demand and the EU defines the sustainability threshold to be 20% (European Commission, 2013c). One can conclude from the evidence that Portugal is below the sustainability threshold, although hydric resources became more pressured since 1990.

Overall, Portugal has not been focused on improving resource efficiency, despite being an essential pillar of greening the economy. In the meantime, it is improving in waste and water management, but it is still far from becoming a circular economy.

Promoting social inclusivity

Social inclusivity is an area of great concern for Portugal given the impact of economic crisis. Table 1 shows some indicators that characterise living standards in Portugal during the period 2000-2012.

Table 1 – Standards of living in Portugal ((a) value refers to 2011), 2000 and 2012

		2000	2012	Variation	EU27 (2012)
Income	GDP/capita	€ 12,500.00	€ 15,600.00	24,80%	25,600.00 €
People	Population	10,225,836	10,557,278 (a)	3,24%	503,011,316 (a)
	Percentage of population living in urban areas	47.80%	48.90% (a)	2.30%	41% (a)
Age	Median Age	37.6	42.3	12.50%	41.5
	Proportion of population aged 0-14 years old	16.20%	14.80%	-8.64%	15.60%
	Proportion of population aged 65 or more	16%	19.40%	21.25%	17.80%
Health	Fertility rate	1.55	1.35	-12.90%	1.57
	Life Expectancy	76.2	80.1 (a)	5.12%	79.7 (a)
Education	Persons with lower secondary (15-64 years old)	78.90%	61.30%	-22.31%	29.20%
	Persons with upper secondary education (15-64 years old)	13.60%	21.90%	61.03%	46.40%
	Persons with tertiary education (15-64 years old)	7.50%	16.80%	124.00%	24.50%
Unemployment	Annual Unemployment Rate	4.50%	15.90%	253.33%	10.50%
	Annual Youth Unemployment	10.50%	37.70%	259.05%	22.80%

In a worldwide perspective, Portugal is a high-income country. Its GDP per capita was 15,600€ in 2012, representing an increase of 24.8% from 2000. But, its level is still lower than EU27 average. With around 10 million inhabitants, it is a relatively small country in EU, representing 2% of EU27 population. The majority of the Portuguese population lives in urban areas, the largest being situated along the coastline.

A clear trend one can extract from table 1 is the ageing of the Portuguese population. Median age of the population increased from 37.6 years old in 2000 to 42.3 years old in 2012, which is reflected in the decrease in the proportion of young people and the increase in the proportion of old people in total population. This trend is related with a fall in the fertility rate and increase in life expectancy.

Moreover, education attainment in Portugal has been improving during the period considered. In 2012, there are more people with upper secondary education and tertiary education than in 2000. However, these levels are still low when compared to EU27 average.

Since 2000, the unemployment rate has been climbing, from 4.5% to 15.9% in 2012. Most recent data indicates that the unemployment rate was 17.8% on April 2013. Note that these numbers are above EU average. The situation is more worrisome when focusing on the group of young people (15-25 years old). The youth unemployment rate has been rising from 10.5% in 2000 to 37.7% in 2012, registering a rate of 42.5% on April 2013.

From this analysis, one can conclude that although living standards seem to have improved in the period considered, given the increase in GDP per capita, educational attainment, life expectancy-amongst others, they are threatened by the current crisis as unemployment is reaching alarming levels. This can lead to situations of material deprivation and social exclusion. In addition, combined with an ageing population and below average educational attainment, it can prevent the population from being involved in the decision-making process essential to the greening the economy.

Table 2 focuses on indicators to assess people at risk of poverty or social exclusion in Portugal since the start of the financial crisis of 2007/2008.

Table 2 – People at risk of poverty or social exclusion in Portugal, 2008-2011 (Source: Eurostat)

	2008	2009	2010	2011
People at risk of poverty or social exclusion (thousand)	2757	2648	2693	2601
Annual variation	104	-109	45	-92
Variation compared to 2008		-109	-64	-156
People at risk of poverty after social transfer (thousand)	1967	1898	1903	1919
Annual variation	49	-69	5	16
Variation compared to 2008		-69	-64	-48
People living in households with very low work intensity (thousand)	517	567	1903	1919
Annual variation	-75	50	133	-34
Variation compared to 2008		50	183	149
People severely materially deprived (thousand)	1029	965	958	881
Annual variation	14	-64	-7	-77
Variation compared to 2008		-64	-71	-148

During the period 2008-2011, the number of people at risk of poverty or social exclusion has been decreasing, except in 2010, when it increased by 45,000 people relatively to the previous year. Yet, since 2008, there are less 156,000 people at the risk of poverty or social exclusion in 2011. However, the number of people at risk of poverty or social exclusion in 2011 still represents 24.4% of total population.

The trend observed in the previous indicator is reflected in the evolution of the number of people severely materially deprived, which has been decreasing each year and relatively to 2008. The share of population in these conditions is 8.3%.

On the other hand, the number of people at the risk of poverty after social transfers is increasing each year after 2010, despite the number decreasing relatively to 2008 level. In 2011, it represented 18% of total population.

In addition, the number of people living in households with very low work intensity has been increasing relatively to 2008 most likely due to the rise in unemployment. In 2011, there were 149,000 more people living under this situation than in 2008. Note, however, a small improvement from 2010 to 2011, when the number of people living in households with very low work intensity decreased by 34,000 people, representing, in 2011, 8.2% of the population.

All in all, although the number of people at risk of poverty or social exclusion seems to be decreasing since 2008, there are more people living in households with very low work intensity relatively to 2008. This results from the explosion in unemployment rates caused by the current economic crisis. This fact, together with an ageing and low-educated population, can undermine the process of greening the economy.

Green development for the future?

Although fairing better in some areas than others, Portugal is transitioning to a green economy. As argued before, this can be the driver to overcome the current economic crisis by developing a more efficient economy based on low-carbon activities, which involves all groups of society in order to provide higher living standards to its population.

One immediate feature of the greening of an economy that can assist Portugal in a time of crisis is the creation of employment, in particular, green jobs. These are not limited to the environmental sector, but concern all activities. According to Prata-Dias et al. (2009), green jobs are "jobs that reduce gradually the environmental and social impacts of the different economic activities, integrating an array of skills and occupations, and encompassing both rural and urban economies. (...) Green jobs should be sustainable jobs from a social, environmental, economic and governance viewpoint."Overall, it seems that green jobs are gaining importance in Portugal

In the period considered, the number of jobs in the environmental goods and services producing sector grew from 29,548 in 2008 to 31,120 in 2011, which represents an increase of 5.32%. Nevertheless, note that there was a decline of 2.39% from 2010 to 2011.

Regarding environmental NGOs, people employed during 2000-2003 fell by 77.56%. Nowadays, the number is increasing but was not yet able to recover to the levels of 2000. After 2003, the number of jobs began to increase and, in 2011, there were 1,896 people employed in environmental NGOs. However, it still corresponds to a decrease of 54.11% relatively to 2000. On the other hand, employment on environmental protection activities has been increasing in the period in analysis, from 875 people in 2006 to 997 people in 2011 (equivalent to an increase of 13.94%), registering only a small decline from 2010 to 2011.

All in all, it seems that green employment has been increasing in Portugal, contrarily to general employment. However, note that in recent years this trend is slowing down, with employment even declining in 2011.

But, future perspectives are bright. According to Prata-Dias et al. (2009 cited in Naumann, 2013), green employment will grow substantially, especially in the renewable energy sector. Table 3 shows estimates for the number of jobs.

Table 3 – Estimated number of direct and indirect jobs per unit of installed capacity in the renewable energy sector, 2020 (Source: Prata-Dias et al. (2009) cited in Nauman, 2013)

	Direct Jobs	Indirect Jobs
Wind energy	19,135	105,066
Solar photovoltaic (centralised)	726	n.a.
Solar photovoltaic (micro-generation)	1815	n.a.
Biomass (including biogas)	302	n.a.
Geothermal energy	37	n.a.
Mini-hydro power	2,779	n.a.
Wave energy	210	n.a.
Total	25,004	> 105,066
Solar thermal energy (target PNAEE 2015)	264	n.a.

According to table 3, the renewable energy sector will create more than 130,000 jobs by 2020. The major drivers will be wind energy, solar photovoltaic (micro-generation) and mini-hydro power.

One important factor that will be determinant to the creation of these jobs is the educational attainment of the population. As shown before, the education level of the population has been increasing, but the development of a green economy requires a set of specific skills. According to Prata-Dias et al. (2009), the number of people pursuing higher education in environment and sustainable development fields is increasing. However, the majority workers in green jobs nowadays have studied only until secondary school. Thus, it is necessary that Portugal create initiatives that foster qualification and formation that is adequate to green employment. Portugal ought to improve vocational training and update qualifications of traditional occupations in line with green skills.

Another factor that can undermine the process of greening are the now common spending cuts that may affect crucial sectors that are mainly provided and/or funded by the state. For now, it seems there is not a disinvestment in these areas. According to QREN (National Strategic Reference Framework) 2007-2013, approved projects in environment interventions accounted for €1.883 billion, representing 17 % of the total approved funding (European Regional Development Fund) (Naumann, 2013). Nevertheless, this is a point that should be taken into account.

Moreover, one main concern that can prevent Portugal from becoming a green economy is the idea that a country cannot combine economic growth with low GHG emissions. However, the National Low Carbon Roadmap proves this rationale wrong. The document concludes that it is not only possible for Portugal to design trajectories leading to 50-60% reduction in GHG emissions compared to 1990 levels, but also that the costs and impacts are reasonable given Portugal's reality (Naumann, 2013). The roadmap suggests these targets can be achieved if there is an improvement in both energy and resource efficiency, together with the introduction of new technologies and development of renewable energy sources.

From all three cornerstone of the greening of an economy, social inclusivity might be the hardest to ensure in Portugal due to the impacts of crisis. However, provided that the process of greening the economy is fully embraced then social inclusivity will arise as a natural consequence. Nevertheless, Portugal should pay special attention to groups at risk such as the population affected by unemployment, because it may lead to situations of poverty and social exclusion. Therefore, stronger income support mechanisms are needed. Another factor that may undermine the establishment of an inclusive economy is the ageing of the population. Nowadays, elderlies are left behind in the countryside while youngsters move to the cities along the coastline where employment opportunities are greater. Thus, the implementation of a network of support to old people is essential.

Furthermore, to fully implement the process of greening the economy, it is necessary to involve the population in decision-making. Portugal has already in place some initiatives that promote participation such as in Environmental Assessment Impact studies and in water management. Further involvement should be undertaken.

Conclusion

In spite of the hard reality it nowadays faces, Portugal shows great potential to fully become a green economy. As the UN claims, "the crisis has opened a window of opportunity" (UNECE, 2013) that Portugal should take advantage of. Continuing investing in renewable energies will not only protect the environment but also create jobs and reduce external energy dependence. This combined with improved resource and energy efficiency will contribute to stimulate the economy and boost competitiveness. Moreover, the resulting lower GHG emissions will provide better quality of life including health improvements. Therefore, Portugal can gain a lot from the greening of its economy.

The greatest challenge is to ensure that Portugal can sustain development with low GHG emissions. Thus, the country will need to improve its resource and energy efficiency to guarantee the GHG level will not revert back to pre-crisis levels when regular pace of economic activity resumes.

Furthermore, education must be in line with new skills that the green economy requires for the process to be successful. In general, education should also raise awareness about the importance of all people participating in this process. Opportunities must be created so that all *groups* of society can be involved in decision-making. This might entail protecting groups at disadvantaged that were particularly hit by the economic crisis or those that have a tendency to be excluded from a rapid changing society (namely, elderlies).

For the future, Portugal should consider as well the benefits of developing a circular economy, where waste is reduced to the maximum and resources are employed to their potential. Then, Portugal can truly become a green economy that respects the surrounding environment and improves people's well-being.

Bibliography:

Ashton, C., 2012. Could Portugal ever run entirely on green energy again?. *BBC*, [online] 22 June. Available at: http://www.bbc.co.uk/news/science-environment-18538813 [Accessed 30 June 2013]

By Energy, 2010. *Estratégia Nacional para a Energia 2020 (ENE 2020)*. [online] By Energy. Available at: http://www.byenergy.pt/estrategia-nacional-para-a-energia/ [Accessed 7 July 2013]

EDP, 2013. *Portugal na liderança das renováveis*. [online] EDP. Available at: http://www.a-nossa-energia.edp.pt/mais_melhor_energia/portugal_lideranca_renovaveis.php [Accessed 30 June 2013]

European Commission, 2013a. *The EU Emissions Trading System (EU ETS)*. [pdf] European Commission. Available at: http://ec.europa.eu/clima/publications/docs/factsheet_ets_2013_en.pdf [Accessed 7 July 2013]

European Commission, 2013b.*The EU climate and energy package*. [pdf] European Commission. Available at: http://ec.europa.eu/clima/policies/package/index_en.htm [Accessed 7 July 2013]

European Commission, 2013c. *Resource Efficiency*. [pdf] European Commission. Available at: http://ec.europa.eu/europe2020/pdf/themes/17_resource_efficiency.pdf [Accessed 7 July 2013]

Governo de Portugal, 2013. *Estratégia Europa 2020 - Ponto de Situação das Metas em Portugal*. [pdf] Available at: http://ec.europa.eu/europe2020/pdf/nd/prgrep2013_portugal_pt.pdf [Accessed 30 June 2013]

Kennet, M., Courea, E., Black, K. , Bouquet, A. and Pipintye, L., 2011. Handbook of Green Economics, A Practitioners Guide. Reading: The Green Economics Institute

Lusa, 2013. Produção renovável abastece 70% do consumo nacional de electricidade no 1.º trimestre. *Público*, [online] 2 April. Available at: http://www.publico.pt/economia/noticia/producao-renovavel-abastece-70-do-consumo-nacional-de-electricidade-no-1%C2%BA-trimestre-1589896 [Accessed 30 June 2013]

Naumann, R., 2013. *EEO Review: Promoting green jobs throughout the crisis, 2013,*

Portugal. [pdf] European Employment Observatory. Available at: http://www.eu-employment-observatory.net/resources/reviews/Portugal-EEO-GJH-2013.pdf [Accessed 7 July 2013]

Portuguese Environmental Agency, 2013. *Portuguese National Inventory Report on Greenhouse Gases, 1990-2000, Submitted under the United Nations Framework Convention on Climate Change and the Kyoto Protocol.* [pdf] Amadora: Portuguese Environmental Agency. Available at: http://www.apambiente.pt/_zdata/DPAAC/INERPA/NIR_20130517.pdf [Accessed 7 July 2013]

Prata-Dias, G., Ramos, T.B., Pipio, A., Fuentes, A. and Valente, S., 2009. *Estudo sobre Empregos Verdes em Portugal.* [pdf] Lisboa: Estudo elaborado pelo CEEETA-ECO e pela Faculdade de Ciências e Tecnologia da Universidade Nova de Lisboa para o Gabinete de Estratégia e Planeamento do Ministério do Trabalho e da Solidariedade Social. Available at: http://blog.rcgoncalves.pt/wp-content/uploads/EstudoEmpregosVerdes.pdf [Accessed 7 July 2013]

UNECE, 2013. *Green Economy.* [online] UNECE. Available at: http://www.unece.org/env/greeneconomy/welcome.html [Accessed 7 July 2013]

UNEP, 2011. *Towards a Green Economy: Pathways to Sustainable Development and Poverty Eradication.* [pdf] UNEP. Available at: http://www.unep.org/greeneconomy/Portals/88/documents/ger/ger_final_dec_2011/Green%20EconomyReport_Final_Dec2011.pdf [Accessed 7 July 2013]

UNRISD, 2012. *Green Economy and Sustainable Development: Bringing Back the Social.* [video online] Available at: http://www.youtube.com/watch?v=O5lBwrJcUOk [Accessed 30 June 2013]

A fuller more complete version of this chapter is available in our book

The Greening of the Global Economy, *edited by Sofia Amaral and available from the Green Economics Institute.* greeneconomicsinstitute@yahoo.com

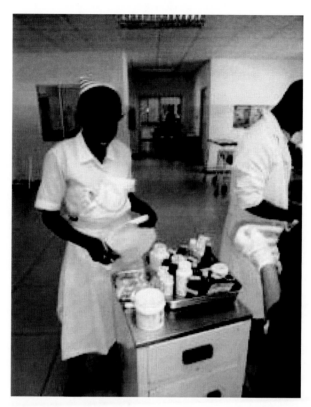

Photo Tone Hedvig Berg and Aase Seeberg. Healthcare in Zambia

3.7 Greening of the Economy: An Indian Perspective

By Kanupriya Bhagat

As the world faces grave economic, social and environmental challenges, Green Economy is widely promoted as the solution to such problems. "Green Economics is one of the fastest growing global movements for change, which has been taken up by many governments and NGOs and is having a huge influence on the worldwide social and economic landscape. It seeks to reform the very concept of economics itself by creating an entirely new discipline which is designed to help all people everywhere, prevent poverty as a given assumption, consider other species, nature and the planet and its systems" (Kennet).

Not only does it prove to be beneficial for the environment, but also holds the power to provide businesses with a "win-win" situation, cutting down on the cost, while simultaneously giving them a competitive edge over their competitors. Two major components of Green Economy are resource and energy efficiencies, which to a certain extent forces us to "rethink how we build our communities, move people and goods around, provide energy and use scarce resources" (Weaver& Michael 2011).

The definition of a "Green Economy" is very subjective to ones perspective. For some "green" could mean using more energy efficient technology, while for the other going "green" may simply mean cutting carbon emissions by any means necessary. Every industry has a different outlook towards "going green" and it is simply impossible to pin point exactly what a "Green Economy" comprises of. However, for the sake of this chapter, I will use the definition developed by UNEP, which states, "Green economy is one that results in improved human well-being and social equity, while significantly reducing environmental risks and ecological scarcities. In its simplest expression, a green economy can be thought of as one which is low carbon, resource efficient and socially inclusive". Moreover, it also suggests "a green economy is one whose growth in income and employment is driven by public and private investments that reduce carbon emissions and pollution, enhance energy and resource efficiency, and prevent the loss of biodiversity and ecosystem services. These investments need to be catalyzed and supported by targeted public expenditure, policy reforms and regulation changes. This development path should maintain, enhance and, where necessary, rebuild natural capital as a critical economic asset and source of public benefits, especially for poor people whose livelihoods and security depend strongly on nature". Another approach towards looking at Green Economics is that of a holistic approach that brings core drivers of economics such as ecology, equity, social and environmental justice together.

In the recent times, India is being looked as a center for research and development due to its innovation in technology, traditional knowledge, cheap manufacturing, labor power and processes. Moreover, after investing over $10 billion to green energy in the year 2011, India has become largest investor towards green technology amongst all major economies. Additionally, with India being the worlds largest democracy and with the growing concerns about the population, poverty, unemployment, waste, pollution, economy and climate change etc. it is highly significant it takes certain steps to ensure a secure future. If India invests now towards the potential of its green economy, not only will it promote a sustainable and clearer environment, but also the economy will see a generation of thousands of jobs. As India already on path of growth, yet to invest in infrastructure and public services, it is a perfect time to change its direction; if they choose to incorporate environmental and social sustainability in their business practices. Even though their initially cost will be higher but they will sustain their business in the long run as it is inevitable giving them a competitive advantage in the short run.

Furthermore, "Climate Disclosure Project says that the business as usual scenario on climate change shows that by 2100 India's GDP growth will be around negative 9-13% due to the impacts of climate change affecting business, livelihood and hence the economy". While, 2100 is very far away and it is highly unlikely that the business practices will remain as usual but this is not the path India should be taking. A change sooner than later will add to the benefits of a Green Economy. Plus, the growing concern about the environment in the media has made consumers more aware about corporates and their purchases reflect their choices. Similarly, investors and venture capitals are also becoming conscious of their future and are avoiding financial and business risks associated with carbon and environmentally unfriendly practices.

Along with the rapidly growing economy, Indian business owners are also getting involved with Multinational Corporation and business beyond borders. In a very short span of time the involvement of business owners in the International market is rapidly increasing, making it absolutely essential for them to abide by the global climate agreement that will put a price on carbon that will effect business worldwide, including India. With international agencies involved such as the World Bank and United Nations, it posses both as a threat and opportunity for the Indian Economy. For business that start accounting for their activities will have a competitive edge and positive recognition in the international market, while businesses that carry forward as usual will eventually loose the battle to the more innovative with their reputation as a price to pay.

On the other hand, to achieve this idea of green economy, India first needs to tackle many issues coming its way. First of which are deprivation levels, that are constantly increasing, raising many questions over the kind of paradigm being followed by the government. UNEP believes the biggest concern amongst that includes food, energy, water and other essential goods and services to its growing population. Besides, the number of people who lacked access to electricity and clean cooking technologies in

India was 404 million and 855 million respectively in 2009 (IEA, 2010). Moreover, India still lags behind many other countries in terms of other measures of development. According to UNDP's Multidimensional Poverty Index (MPI), 53.7% of India's population is poor (UNDP, 2011) making it very difficult for India to invest in green technology when the basic needs for human survival is not met.

Furthermore, with the growing manufacturing sector, increasing mining, expanding infrastructure and increasing power production, along with increasing responsibility to be "greener", India is in a very tough spot "where its emissions could explode upwards or it could move heavily down the 'green' route". Sadly, to add to the problem is the fact that this challenges seem to be getting worse everyday as the efforts to "achieve green growth is translating into a green versus growth issue".

McKinsey & Company published a report in 2012 where they suggested India will grow at a very fast pace for the 20 next years, where it could build 80% of its infrastructure and industrial capacity that will establish the India of 2030. The problem that lies here is the magnitude of development that will lead result in a tremendous increase of carbon emissions. India cannot afford to do that, specially now where there is an enormous amount of pressure for world communities to reduce carbon emissions. Therefore, the question that lies here is; should India give up developing its infrastructure and services for a better tomorrow of the public and compromise the environment or should it concentrate on the environment now and hope to develop the country in the process.

Elaborating on the growth v/s green debate, at the end of last year there was a disagreement between the Ministry of Environment and Forest and several representative form India Inc. as well as many union ministers on the green issues discouraging development in the country. Union ministers have constantly complaining that environmental laws and clearances are becoming an "weakness" and hampering the countries development, whereas, Ministry of Environment & Forest claims that they are just discharging the duty diligently of protecting the environment. Hence, at this crucial time when various ministers need to work together to achieve the bigger goal of nation's development while keeping the environmental concerns in mind, they seem to be going through the debate of growth v/s green which in turn is leading to indecisions and delays in projects. This is gone so far that a popular Indian Magazine even went to the extent of calling Ms. Jayanthi Natarajan (Environmental Minister of India) a "Green Terrorist", "claiming that the outdated environmental laws and inflexible minister is turning out to be detrimental to the economic growth". On the other hand, Natarajan apparently also gave clearance to few projects, highly opposed by many environmental groups. For instance, the Lower Demwe hydro project in Arunachal Pradesh. That got clearance from the Environmental Minister, even though the construction of dam will involve deforestation of over 50,000 trees along with serious threat to the habitat of wild animals like the dolphin, the wild buffalo and the Bengal Florican.

Thus the pressure on the government to "do the right thing" is constantly building. They not only have the challenge of ensuring that the growing demands of people for commodities and energy are met without compromising the environment but the production to satisfy those demands also cannot be at the cost of the environment, making it a very difficult task.

In conclusion, one step closer to solving the problem will be the joint effort of the ministry with the environmental groups, with either one or both groups compromising to a certain extent to get the work done. Specially, with over one billion people, four world religions and over 1500 languages across the country, it is a challenge to come to with a decision that satisfies everyone. During the recent turmoil over Uttarakhand disaster, where the death toll is likely to rise over 5000 due to floods and landslide on the River Ganges and her tributaries, "Environmentalists say the disaster in Uttarakhand was inevitable due to rampant construction, felling of trees and building of dams in the name of development". This river holds more than 505 dams that are a part of 244 hydroelectric projects, constant construction on mountain tops, mining and sewage disposal directly in the river has made it a man made disaster. With several lives still at stake and millions of rupees worth infrastructure already destroyed, maybe this will serve as a wake up call for the people and government of India to take actions promoting a greener economy. In the end, Green Economics has also been called "The Economics of Sharing" emphasizing the need of change in behaviour which will help sustain everything and everybody on a long term basis.

References:

Aggarwal.M. (2013). *Uttarakhand floods: Deconstructing a disaster.*Available: http://www.dnaindia.com/india/1852688/report-uttarakhand-floods-deconstructing-a-disaster. Last accessed 25th June, 2013.

BBC. (2012). *India's boom in green technology business.* Available: http://www.bbc.co.uk/news/world-asia-india-18391116. Last accessed 25th June, 2013.

Chabba.A. (2012). *"Green Economy" with respect to India.* Available: http://in.reset.org/blog/green-economy-respect-india. Last accessed 25th June, 2013.

Green Economy India. (2007). *why a Green Economy.* Available: http://www.greeneconomyindia.com/why_green_economy.htm. Last accessed 25th June, 2013.

Green Economics Institute... Available: http://www.greeneconomics.org.uk/page0.html. Last accessed 27th June 2013.

Gupta. A. (2012). *Why India's green growth dream is turning into a nightmare.* Available: http://www.greeneconomycoalition.org/know-how/why-india%E2%80%99s-green-growth-dream-turning-nightmare. Last accessed 25th June, 2013.

Kennet, M. and Heinemann, V. (2006) 'Green Economics: setting the scene. Aims, context, and philosophical underpinning of the distinctive new solutions offered by Green Economics', Int. J. Green Economics, Vol. 1, Nos. 1/2, pp.68–102.

Staff.N. (2013).*Uttarakhand tragedy: Death toll likely to cross 5000, heavy rain hampers rescue ops.*Available: https://www.niticentral.com/2013/06/24/uttarakhand-death-toll-may-cross-5000-heavy-rain-expected-to-hamper-rescue-ops-94248.html. Last accessed 25th June, 2013.

Teri. (2012). *India's Green Economy: Road map to an inclusive and equitable growth*. Available: http://www.teriin.org/upfiles/projects/ES/ES2011EM08.pdf. Last accessed 25th June, 2013.

Varma.S. (2013).*Recipe for disaster in Uttarakhand: 1 crore population, 2.5 crore tourists*. Available: http://articles.timesofindia.indiatimes.com/2013-06-23/india/40146281_1_forest-land-land-revenue-land-use. Last accessed 25th June, 2013.

UNEP. Available: http://www.unep.org/greeneconomy/AboutGEI/WhatisGEI/tabid/29784/language/en-US/Default.aspx. Last accessed 25th June, 2013.

UNEP. (2012). *Green Economy, a mantra for the modern world Read more at: http://indiatoday.intoday.in/story/green-economy-a-mantra-for-the-modern-world/1/199136.html*. Available: http://indiatoday.intoday.in/story/green-economy-a-mantra-for-the-modern-world/1/199136.html. Last accessed 25th June, 2013.

Weaver.S, Weaver.A. (2011). *Greening the Economy - A Discussion Paper*. Available: http://www.globe-net.com/articles/2011/january/11/greening-the-economy-a-discussion-paper/. Last accessed 25th June, 2013

Photo Miriam Kennet. The Jurassic Coast 50 million years of history reminds us of how recent our species is and how survivability is by no means assured.

Part 4: Food and Health
4.1 Global Health and Food Security - Analysis and Solutions

By Bianca Madison-Vuleta

Addressing the challenge of global food security through the twenty first century is linked with other global issues, most notably climate change, population growth and the need to sustainably manage the world's rapidly growing demand for energy and water. Our progress in ensuring a sustainable and equitable food supply chain will be determined by how coherently these long term challenges are tackled.

This will also determine our progress in reducing global poverty and achieving the *Millennium Development Goals*. The challenge is to deliver nutritious, safe and affordable food to a global population of over 9 million in coming decades, using less land, fewer inputs, with less waste and a lower environmental impact. All this has to be done in ways that are socially and economically sustainable. It is clear that research is vital to meeting this challenge.

Global food security is fast becoming one of the most pressing challenges facing states today. The scope and the breadth of the issue encompass all the peoples and the governments of the world and demography is the driving factor pushing it to the top of the agenda. The human population is set to surpass the 9 billion mark midway through the century, with the attendant cost of ever greater pressure applied to the Earth's finite resources.

The World Bank has predicted that wheat production will have to increase by 50% and meat production by 85% over the next 20 years if we are to meet the demand.

The challenge facing us is to be able to feed the great mass of humanity in a sustainable manner and one that does not threaten the precarious balance of our ecosystems. Climate change is the other defining source of stress with its manifold repercussions upon water access and supply, the spread of pests and disease and the potential for ever more extreme and unpredictable weather patterns.

The UN estimated that almost one billion people are chronically hungry and malnourished in the world and over 6 million children die each year due to starvation. Judging by current trends this number is set to rise in the near future. Recent climactic developments have also given both humanitarians and policy-makers alike more serious cause for concern. At a time when the recession is biting in many parts of the world, and where booming populations have already made food scarce and prices high, this crisis could have extremely severe humanitarian, and indeed strategic, implications.

Global food security is, obviously, one of the key issues for the future of humanity, along with water, climate, and peace and security. The UN has a commitment to supporting governments as they work towards the millennium development goals (MDG) that were agreed in 2000 and that require us all to achieve some significant outcomes by 2015.

The first of these goals is to halve the number of people living in hunger from 860 million to 500 million, but it looks as though by 2015 we will be looking at well over 1 billion living in hunger. If we look at the bigger picture, the situation of poverty and hunger seems to be similar around the globe.

We have resistant poverty in sub-Saharan Africa, similar figures to 1990. In South Asia we have achieved reductions in the percentage of the poor; but given that there are so many people living in South Asia, the ratios are still too high.

Poverty in Sub-Saharan Africa has proved itself to be very resilient and hunger has remained disturbingly high, with more than 25% of the population hungry at any one time. There are still 29 countries across the globe where levels of malnutrition are life threatening.

There is a pressing need to ensure adequate nutrition, including not only calories but all necessary macro and micro nutrients for healthy and balanced diets and for deprived populations throughout the world.

At the same time as increasing numbers of people globally are inadequately fed, the over- consumption of high calorie diets adds to the rising demand for food; with all the associated economic, social and environmental impacts.

The most important challenges arising are:

The world will need to produce more food in the future using less water, land, fertiliser, energy and other key resources, and distribute that food more efficiently and equitably. There is a need to reduce losses and waste, greenhouse gas emissions and other adverse environmental impacts throughout the entire food supply chain; from production to consumption and waste management.

Food must be safe, nutritious and affordable, yet be supplied and distributed in ways that meet the needs and aspirations of consumers in different economic, social and cultural contexts around the world. People need to be well informed and guided to make healthy choices.

There is a need to balance different uses of land and seas, often with competing priorities, such as sustainably increasing food production while maintaining ecosystem services on which food production critically depends.

There is a need to balance increased productivity from food producing animals with their welfare, recognising that absence of disease and high productivity do not always equate with high welfare standards and outcomes.

The complex and inter-related problems outlined above can only be tackled through coordinated and integrated interdisciplinary research, coupled with its effective translation into practice and policy.

Our aim is to help improve the sustainability and security of UK and global food supplies.

The challenges range from those with a local or UK national focus to more wide-ranging European and global issues. Food security for the UK is inextricably linked to global production, demand and supply and must be considered in this broader context.

There is clearly a key role for UK led research in helping to address the global challenges, especially those in developing countries.

IS THE GLOBAL MARKET THE SOLUTION TO THE CURRENT FOOD CRISIS?

Some economists argue that the food crisis is an aberration of capitalism and that the markets will right themselves in time. In particular, some predict that price rises will lead to increased investment in agriculture, leading to increased food stocks and therefore lower prices again.

We have been told for generations that the market responds to demand. People of the Global South have been told by economists, academics, world institutions and the governments of the West that the free market is the way to enrich their countries and lift their people out of poverty. This has, sadly, been proven to be wrong.

Despite embracing of the market-mentality, poverty and hunger remain virulent. Small farmers are killing themselves in huge numbers across the Global South. In India around 250.000 farmers have been driven to suicide in the last few decades. Jeffrey Sachs, an advisor to the UN general secretary, has warned against relying on the market to help when the people in need have no money to pay!

It is likely that food prices will begin to stabilise to a degree. However, most economists - including those who think the market can solve the crisis, predict that prices will remain at high levels for the next decade. THE ECONOMIST warned last year that we face an *"end to the era of cheap food"*.

One thing is for certain: the demand for the market to 'solve' he problem is a demand for more of the policies that have led to the current crisis.

WILL PRICE RISES BENEFIT THE RURAL POOR?

Photo Miriam Kennet

Some commentators have suggested that price rises might hit the urban poor but at least they will help subsistence farmers by pushing up the value of their crops. Unfortunately, it is not as simple as that. Poor farmers, often already severely in debt, are being squeezed badly by rising input costs such as fertilisers, seeds, pesticides and transport costs.

These prices are forcing thousands off the land as they simply can't afford to work it any longer. Heart-breaking after generations have worked and prospered.

Another problem facing small farmers and agricultural labourers is their position at the bottom of a global agricultural chain. Whereas, the real power is fully concentrated in the food processing corporations, grain traders and supermarket suppliers. Rising food prices exacerbate this problem by pushing up the value of farm land. This means many small farmers and landholders who are already deep in debt or on the poverty line can't afford to expand production.

The only people who can afford to expand in these circumstances are those with access to major capital or large amounts of credit - the big farm corporations and agribusinesses.

The Food and Agriculture Organisation (FAO) has shown that in most countries the majority of rural households are net buyers of food, not sellers. On average across the countries surveyed they found that only 31 percent of rural households are not sellers of food. Unsurprisingly, the FAO's research concluded that the poorest households and the landless are always the most badly hit.

ARE SMALL FARMS THE ANSWER?

It is becoming increasingly obvious that the industrialisation of food production and the centralisation and concentration of agriculture have failed to give food security to millions around the globe. Some postulate that a return to small farms is the answer. Writer and campaigner George Monbiot argued this in the GUARDIAN in June 2008, pointing out that small farms are actually more productive than large ones. There is much research to back this up.

Large farms are invariably run by multinational agribusinesses seeking to maximise their profits fast. This leads to a short-term view of farming; where soil, water and chemicals are overused without regard for the erosion of the soil or damage to the environment.

Larger farms are more likely to grow a single crop rather than a mix of crops, depending on what is profitable. This depletes the nutrients in the soil and erodes the fertility of the land over time.

Large farms are often owned by companies with many other investments and sources of income. They do not have the same incentive to maintain sustainable farming methods as small farmers do. If larger farms over-exploit their land they have the resources to move on to new land. Smaller farmers don't.

It is widely believed that the effects of climate change - floods, droughts, extremes of temperature and other events are directly responsible for the food crisis.

Blaming climate change for the current food crisis is politically convenient. It implies that we are powerless to act in the face of extreme weather conditions and disasters. In reality, there is much that could be done to both deal with climate change and minimise its effects.

Sadly, many poor countries do not have the resources to deal with the impact of climate change. Every year ten million deprived people face flooding because the necessary investments have not been made.

Other countries have the resources but lack the political will to prepare for the effects of climate change - shown to devastating effect by Hurricane Katrina in New Orleans in 2005.

None of this is to say that climate change is not important or that it does not have an impact on food production or prices. But there is no reason for it to result in famine and hunger.

To simply blame climate change for these things hides the political, economic and social policies and structures that determine the impact the climate change has.

FOOD AND THE GLOBAL MARKET

The recent sharp rises in food prices can only be explained by referring to specific short term factors - such as the price of oil, increased speculation on food commodities, on global markets and the weakened dollar. But there are also long term factors shaping food production. They act to make the sudden crisis much worse.

Photo Miriam Kennet. Plum pie in season in Italy

A major factor is the changing nature of global food production. Poorer countries, in particular, have seen huge changes in land use, resulting in less food being produced for domestic consumption. As capitalism expanded its reach across the world, it pulled more countries into the world market and transformed them.

The power is concentrated in the hands of fewer and fewer people, as small units are eaten by the bigger ones. The concentration and centralisation of capital have naturally increased over time. This can be seen today in US agriculture. Since the Second World War the average farm size in the US has more than doubled, while the number of farms has fallen by two thirds.

The concentration of agriculture means that production can be undertaken on larger farms by fewer people. Sophisticated machinery has developed with the aim of cutting the number of workers needed. Impoverished small farmers are pushed from rural areas towards cities in search of work.

A similar dynamic is taking place in many parts of the Global South where many people are being driven off their land and forced to look for work in the cities.

The "liberalisation" of trade (removing restrictions on trade between countries) is a key part of the neo-liberal agenda of the world's most powerful governments today. In India, as well as many other developing countries, the impact of "trade liberalisation" has been to reduce food production, productivity and efficiency, undermine food security and sustainability, and increase the power of multinational food corporations.

Poorer countries are also often hampered by debt. Debt acts to make poorer countries beholden on richer ones. It forces them to produce cash crops for export rather than food for domestic consumption, as this is more profitable.
Bodies like International Monetary Fund (IMF) have been fundamental in shaping the agriculture of developing countries through Structural Adjustment Programmes (SAPs).

SAPs were agreements that poorer countries signed up to in order to receive aid or loans, or to "restructure" existing debts. Key elements of the agreements included cutting government spending, increasing privatisation, and opening up the economy to global markets. They have devastated agriculture in poorer countries.

The policies included in the SAPs lead to a decrease in food production in the countries that signed up to them. They increased the dependence of millions of people on the world food market - which, in the long term, pushes up global prices and makes poor people especially susceptible to fluctuations in global prices. SAPs have now been cynically renamed "Poverty Reduction Strategies" but the policies remain essentially the same.

The development of the food industry has been marked by the concentration of profits and power in the hands of multinational agribusiness. Neo-liberal policies have eroded support for small farmers, making it virtually impossible for them to survive.

A food industry based on 'competition and profit' has failed to meet people's most basic needs, despite the advances in production that have taken place.

GENETICALLY MODIFIED CROPS

The current food crisis has sparked a demand for Genetically Modified (GM) crops to 'stop people starving'. These are crops which are modified in ways which make them resistant to diseases, pests and the effects of climate change. As such, it is said, they have the potential to produce higher yields.

But there are several question marks over GM crops. They pose a threat to wildlife by killing certain insects and so destabilising ecosystems. Crops which have been modified to contain insecticide, threaten to lead to resistant strains of insects developing. The long term effects of GM foods are completely unknown.

If GM crops pose such a potential threat to our health and the environment, why are they touted as the solution to global food insecurity? Major chemical and pharmaceutical multinational companies have patented them and have a vested interest in promoting them to make profits.

One should not, of course, be opposed to using science to improve food production, nor oppose GM crops on the grounds that they are not "natural". The problem with GM crops is that they have increased the power of multinational biotechnology companies over the global food industry and increased the dependence of poor countries on richer ones.

Also, there is growing evidence that GM crops do not actually increase yields. What GM has done is to radically increase inequality but has not solved world hunger. Those who present GM crops as the solution to the food crisis start from the wrong explanation for hunger.

People do not go hungry because not enough food is produced - they go hungry because they don't have the means (i.e. money) to access it.

SPECULATION, OIL AND BIOFUELS

The increased incorporation of agriculture and food production into the world market over recent decades has laid the basis for the current price rises, but it doesn't explain the dramatic increases of the past few years.

The single starkest factor is the growth of speculation on food and agricultural products on the world market. This explains how "spring wheat prices", as measured on the US markets, could jump by 25 percent in just one day at the beginning of 2008. Commodity speculation is based on gambling on the future prices of food, agricultural goods, metals or oil.

The credit crunch and accompanying panic in the financial and property markets have driven investors to look for safer investments in commodities. With food prices rising, this is seen as a sure way of making money quickly.

This link to the market means that domestic policies have a big impact on food prices. As a crisis in rice prices hit the world stage a few years ago, most rice exporting countries rushed to impose export bans. These temporarily protected domestic supplies but caused sudden extreme shortages on the international markets and led to panic buying and hoarding. This pushed the prices up even further.

The rising price of oil has also helped to drive up food prices. As farming becomes increasingly intensive in much of the world, it requires larger amounts of oil and other fuels to produce fertilisers, to power farm machinery and to transport and process crops.

According to FAO, the cost of many fertilisers nearly doubled in one year.

Many of the poorest countries are net importers, not only of food but also of oil, and are thus hit doubly by the rising prices imposed on them.

The rise in oil prices has been one of the factors causing a rush to invest in biofuels over the past decade or so. Biofuels were hailed as the new "green solution" to the financial and environmental costs of fossil fuels - but their green credentials have turned out to be a gross misconception.

In the rush to cash in on the profits to be made from biofuels, a great deal of land and grain has been diverted away from making food to producing fuel. In the US, the government funds the biofuel industry heavily, with federal subsidies, alone amounting to more than $7 billion per year (on average).

The IMF has estimated that 20 to 30 percent of the food price increases in the last few years is accounted for by biofuels. The central dynamic causing soaring food prices is the way the market transforms food from a basic human need to a tradable source of profit. This creates the situation in which it is possible to have an abundance of food, but hundreds of millions of people who cannot afford to buy it. This is the root of the current food crisis!

"This is the new face of hunger... There is food on the shelves but people are priced out of the market. There is vulnerability in urban areas we have not seen before."
- Josette Sheeran, head of the UN World Food Programme, quoted in the Guardian

"When circumstances refer, it impossible to feed their hungry children, normally passive citizens can quickly become militants with nothing to lose. "
- Tony Karon: "How hunger can topple regimes"

Food price rises have plunged millions into hunger and created food insecurity in a very short space of time. The "new hungry" have been fighting back through protests and strikes that have shaken governments and world institutions.

Since the first wave of major protests in Mexico in January 2007, there have been angry protests, riots and strikes in many countries, including Bangladesh, Cameroon, Egypt, Haiti, Ivory Coast, Yemen, Indonesia, Morocco, Senegal, Mauritania, Jordan, Uzbekistan, Honduras, Mozambique and India.

In some countries, resistance has meant the hungry pouring onto the streets in an upsurge of anger and desperation. In others the issue of food has fuelled wider workers' struggles.

Some protesters have demanded an end to "free trade" policies that have impoverished much of the Global South.

Others have demanded subsidies on food and fuel, or distribution of food aid to the hungry. Many have fought for higher wages to match the rising food costs. Rising food prices have created a crisis across the globe and brought the issue of food production onto the centre stage of food politics. In the poorest countries of the world the price rises have been catastrophic- plunging millions into a state of hunger and malnutrition. In richer countries, such as Great Britain and the United States, the situation is not so acute but many millions of people are finding it an increasing struggle just to feed their families.

The price rises have also focused the minds of governments and global trade and finance bodies around the world, which fear the growing resistance and instability caused by millions of newly hungry people fighting back. Yet the international organisations and governments have no lasting solutions to the crisis. They all see the world market as part of the way to solve the crisis. Both the IMF and the UN Food and Agricultural Organisation have emphasised the role that business and the market should play in addressing the problem.

Sadly, more of the market-trading will not solve these enormous problems, as it was the global market that brought us to this crisis in the first place. As we have seen, over the last fifty years, world food production has been rapidly, and often violently, transformed as it has been incorporated into the global market. This process has turned agriculture into a massive global business and dramatically altered how food is produced, processed and sold. Food has become a valuable commodity to be speculated on in the futures markets.

The drive to produce more food for less money has also created massive health problems worldwide and dependency on monocultures and chemical fertilisers and pesticides that harm the environment and threaten the basis of future agriculture.

Even what we eat has changed - with world markets creating a dependence on a smaller number of key crops to feed the majority of the world. However, as mentioned before, there has been massive resistance every step of the way. People have fought back against the impact of IMF and World Bank policies, and free trade agreements have been implemented across the Global South.

This new Anti-Globalization Movement has taken up these protests to the global summits of the rich and powerful; from the World Trade Organisation to the G8 group of the leading nations. We must continue to fight to drive back the market's control of food production around the globe. We should build solidarity with the others who are fighting back and make connections amongst the different struggles. But it is clear that much more fundamental change is needed to secure access to food for those who need it.

Capitalism is the most dynamic economic system the world has ever seen, yet even at "normal" times of supposed relative stability, hundreds of millions of people around the world starve because they cannot afford food.

Resistance towards gross injustice around the world shows that those hit by the price rises are not just victims: they have the power to force change. And this is true not just of those who eat the food but of those who work to produce, process and distribute it.

Food production is the single largest industry in the world. It involves huge numbers of people, including 2.5 billion *directly* involved in food production in the Global South. Changes in how food is produced have created hundreds of thousands who are employed to work on the land or in the processing and transporting food and who have the collective interest and power to change the way things are organised.

Food is fundamental to all human life! Surely there can be no bigger indictment of a system run for profit than the fact people are starving in a world of such abundance of resources.

References:

1. Food and Agriculture Organization of the UN (FAO): "The state of food insecurity in the world", 2012.
2. FAO, "The state of Food and Agriculture 2012- investing in agriculture for a better future", fao.org/doc rep./017/13028e/13028e.pdf
3. Intergovernmental Panel on Climate Change
"Prioritising climate change adaption needs for food security in 2030", "Programme on Food Security and the Environment Policy Brief", 2008.
4. World Food Programme, www.wfp.org
5. Parrott N. &T. Marsden: "The Real Green Revolution", Greenpeace Environmental Trust, London 2012.
6. G. Fisher at al: "Socio- economic and climate change impacts on agriculture: an integrated assessment, 1990-2080, Philosophical Transactions of the Royal Society, Biological Sciences, 2005.

4.2 The Food Crisis in Latin America

By Carlos Francisco Restituyo Vassallo

The idea for this discussion chapter emerged after reading the article by Peter Rosset, titled "Food Sovereignty in Latin America: Confronting the 'new' Crisis". That article served as springboard for the chapter and deals with many topics, from the immense, unregulated power of Multinational Corporations, to the plight of the poor that find themselves starving at the expense of these corporations that profit on their misery. Rosset's article also talks about Biofuel production and its effects on food prices. In the end, it was Peter Rosset's article that provided the inspiration and the focus needed to identify the debate in this problem: Was Biofuel production the main cause of the rise of food prices in Latin America in 2008? This chapter will take into account arguments both for and against the given premise. The chapter argues that the main cause of the rise of food prices in Latin America in 2008 was Biofuel production, because it withdraws food products from the food market. While the topic is not as current as it could be, looking back at this event and its causes can give insight to what circumstances are ideal for catastrophes such as the one examined in this chapter. This can ultimately lead to better preparation for such crises or learning to avoid them altogether.

There are many causes for the rise of food prices all over the world seen in the years 2007 to 2008 (Daniel, 2008) (Senauer, 2008). One can choose to focus on just one of them, but in reality many factors came together to cause this collapse in the world food markets. To find a proper reason for why this crisis came to be, one must ask not just what triggered it, but rather look for the underlying causes that set the stage and helped elicit what occurred in the years of 2007 and 2008. There are some who would argue that there were more factors to play a role in this incident. Causes such as more people having access to a more varied diet, the poor economic policies employed by Latin American countries, Multinational Corporations keeping food off the market deliberately to cause shortages, and policies taken during the onset of the crisis such as the ban of exports of certain foodstuffs (Daniel, 2008) (Flammini, 2008) (Senauer, 2008) will serve to explain that the current thesis is false. While biofuel production may have had some role in the surge of the prices of food commodities, a myriad of other forces were of more relevance to determine what started the food crisis that affected Latin America, and the World, in 2008.

Many problems, not just biofuel production, triggered the food crisis of 2008 in Latin America; changes in diets are one of them. Increased access to a better balanced diet, as more people are improving their living conditions, is creating a surge in demand for more varied foodstuffs, as was argued by then-President of Brazil, Lula Da Silva, and Chancellor of Germany, Angela Merkel (Heller, 2008) (Pedro, 2008) (Senauer, 2008).

The same is true of policies adopted by Latin American countries in the years before the crisis. These policies made Latin American markets more susceptible to discrepancies in their economies (Daniel, 2008). Many of the Latin American countries are part of Trade Agreements with the United States such as the North American Free Trade Agreement (NAFTA) or the Central American Free Trade Agreement (CAFTA) that puts their economies, including their agricultural sectors at the mercy of US Multinational Corporations. This domination of the market causes Latin American economies to be heavily dependent on US imports (Daniel, 2008). Further, "hoarding and price speculation by grain-trading corporations" can be blamed for surges in prices during this time. For example, there is Mexico with Cargill and corn prices. , or Venezuela with Nestle and Parmalat, and the rise of milk prices (Rosset, 2009).

 The essential difference is that even as big corporations made excessive profits off the surge of prices (Rosset, 2009), suppliers of these corporations, the local farmers in Latin America, found themselves at the mercy of these businesses, who would buy from them far too cheaply, to then sell far too expensively (Daniel, 2008). This drastically reduced not only the profits of local farmers, but also their purchasing power, which then hindered them from buying their necessities.

To add to the crisis, countries around the world were banning exports inside their borders so as to control the rise in prices of foods. Countries as varied as Vietnam, Russia, Argentina, Bolivia, Mexico, and others stopped exporting certain foodstuffs in order to counter the increase in prices of those same goods within their borders, creating shortages all over the world, including Latin America (Senauer, 2008) (Rosset, 2009) (Daniel, 2008).

Finally, being the number one producer of corn (Food and Agriculture Organization data), the United States expanded corn production some years before the crisis. This led to decreased production on other foods, such as wheat and rise. There was an increasing demand in world markets for these commodities (Senauer, 2008), and thus, increased corn production led to their prices going up.

The food crisis in 2008 is essentially a supply and demand problem. Bad economic policies, higher incomes per households, and price speculation and control all came together to produce the problems experienced by the people of Latin America, and the world. While biofuel production may have had something to do with the price increase, to claim that it was the main cause for the crisis may seem a stretch. The real causes behind the crisis in Latin America are the one's stated above.

Just as there are some that argue against biofuel production and its role in the food crisis of 2008, there are others as well who will argue the opposite. These sources would claim that while there were many causes that played a role in this debacle, there is one factor that stands out of the rest, and that would be Biofuel production (Flammini, 2008). As was noted already in the counter-argument, the United States is currently the number one producer of corn in the world. Through trade agreements, many countries in Central and South America are heavily dependent on the US corn supply for food, as is the case of Mexico (Daniel, 2008). Because of the US doubling its Biofuel production from 2004 to 2007, "taking 2.3 billion corn bushels from the food supply chain" (Senauer, 2008), and increasing maize crop for ethanol production (36% per year) compared to food use of ethanol (1.5% per year) (Mitchell, 2008), created a shortage in supply of corn for international markets, which led to an increase in prices of that commodity, such as was the case in Mexico, where prices of corn doubled (Rosset, 2009).

The question still remains about the rest of the foods' prices, and how these went up as well. It is argued that since corn is so important to the food system, fluctuation in its price means that other foods' prices will also go up, such as beef, eggs, even soft drinks (Senauer, 2008). Food processors, livestock and poultry producers, exporters, and ethanol producers all bid for the same grain (Senauer, 2008), so when the supply shortens for exports, there are such price spikes as seen in Mexico in 2008. Another main importer of corn in Latin America is Colombia, where according to the Food and Agriculture Organization, prices for maize went from two hundred dollars per ton in 2004, to three hundred fifty one in 2008. In Chile, the same commodity went from one hundred fifty one to two hundred sixty one dollars in the same timeframe (FAO data). In Argentina, there was a less dramatic rise from eighty one dollars per ton in 2004, to one hundred and thirty seven dollars per ton in 2008.

There are also indirect effects to the increased corn production in the United States. The rising demand for corn-based ethanol has led many farmers to shift from rice and wheat production to corn for biofuel production purposes, raising prices for these commodities as well (Rosegrant, 2008).

To verify the effect of Biofuel production, the International Food Policy Research Institute (IPFRI) conducted an experiment in which they found out that biofuel production could have accounted for thirty percent of food price increases worldwide, and determined that biofuel demand accounted for 39 percent of maize price surge (Rosegrant, 2008). Furthermore, IPFRI argued that if prices of 2007 food commodities were frozen, there would be price decreases into 2010, and further declines by 2015. (Rosegrant, 2008)

There are many approaches used to calculate the influence of biofuel production on the rise of food prices in 2008, but even that being so, most studies agree on it being the main contributor to the crisis (Mitchell, 2008). The International Monetary Fund, for example, estimated that biofuel production was responsible for up to seventy percent of maize price surge, and forty percent of soybean oils' price increase. (Mitchell, 2008)
The United Nations knew this would be a problem as well, and so in 2007 Jean Ziegler, the Expert on Food Security asked for a five-year ban on biofuels, hoping that by the time the ban would end third generation biofuels would have been created (Lederer, 2007), which would alleviate the ever increasing demand of grains and oils for biofuel production. This action illustrates the concern of the United Nations of biofuel prices and their effects on the food prices.

Another factor of biofuel production that needs to be addressed is government support in the United States, The European Union, and Brazil, which are the leading exporters of biofuels in the world (Senauer, 2008) (Daniel, 2008) (Rosegrant, 2008). In the US, blenders get tax credits for $1.00 dollars per gallon, as well as an import tariff of $0.54 per gallon (Rosegrant, 2008). The US mandated in its 2005 legislation 7.5 billion gallons of biofuel by 2012, and 15 million by 2022 which would mean they would have to double their production to meet these goals (Rosegrant, 2008). In Europe, member states can exempt and reduce excise taxes on biofuel (Rosegrant, 2008), and some countries within the EU enforce mandatory blending requirement, as well as tax credits. These serve to make biofuel production an attractive business, therefore encouraging its expansion (Rosegrant, 2008).

Addressing the points made in the counter-argument, both sides can concur in that there were many causes for the food crisis in 2008 in Latin America, however the difference between the argument and counter-argument lies in the conflicting priority of factors, that is to say, which one was most important in contributing to this event, and to that respect, there are things to discuss regarding the argument against the thesis.

The fact that the President of the United States, the President of Brazil, and the Chancellor of Germany spoke in favor of biofuel production during the food crisis is irrelevant, because the arguments made by these individuals against biofuel production being the cause of the crisis in Latin America ignores the fact that these three countries are the major producers of biofuel in the world (Senauer, 2008). A bad reputation of such a rapid-growing sector such as biofuel production would no doubt have catastrophic effects in their economies, and so it is in their duty to defend production of biofuels in that time. That, however, does not signify that their judgments are balanced, or even trustworthy. The presence of conflicts of interests in these countries make them unreliable sources to use against the thesis.

While slowly, the rise in levels of income in countries in Latin America have indeed contributed to a steady rise in food prices, however this increase was not pivotal to the price increase in 2008. (Senauer, 2008) There were other factors that had a bigger relevance to sparking the situation.

While policies taken by Latin American countries in past year did have something to do with the price hike in 2008, this evidence does not go against the thesis; rather it serves to strengthen it. Trade agreements with the United States indeed made Latin American markets more susceptible to price fluctuations and variations in imports (Daniel, 2008), which is why the lack of supply of corn due to its increased allocation from food to ethanol production would have dire consequences to whoever depended on US food imports to feed its population. This information serves to exemplify the adverse effects of food shortage due to increased biofuel production on Latin American economies.

The same could be said by the claim that increased corn production by the US. This was done for the sole purpose of expanding Biofuel production, which is why there was a decrease in other foods such as rice and wheat in subsequent years (Mitchell, 2008).

Indeed, it might be argued that while the purchasing power of small farmers in Latin America was greatly diminished due to low prices by big MNCs (Daniel, 2008), but one must take into account that their income from their sales was further reduced by the purchase of fertilizers, cattle feed, and other necessary products needed to harvest, due to their prices going up as well, as a consequence of the reduced supply of corn and other ingredients key to the farming process (Diouf, 2008).

While both arguments clearly have some common ground in agreeing that there were many factors in producing the food price crisis during 2007-2008 in Latin America, the main difference lies in which one of them all is the most important in having caused the actual debacle, in which case it seems hard to refute the conclusion that it was biofuel production that served as the main trigger for the food crisis during the year 2008 in Latin America (Mitchell, 2008), because there were other factors which arguably counted for more support towards this premise. The crisis was a supply-demand problem, in which there was not enough food supply to fill the demand (Senauer, 2008).

Looking at the issue from this point of view, it is quite easy to see that biofuel production served as catalyst for the disaster that ensued in 2007 through 2008, while having the other factors playing other, lesser roles in this economic catastrophe. To claim that the other factors alone would have been able to precipitate a food shortage of such magnitude to increase prices of food double or triple fold in some instances would be to assess the problem in this situation very superficially. In the end, these other factors were a minor piece that needed to be in place for this crisis to unfold, however a regrettable incident could have feasibly been avoided had it not been by the increasing world demand of biofuels, and the willingness of the main producers to satisfy this demand, at the expense of food security in the Developing World.

References:

Bush, G. W., 2008. *Transcript of Press Conference by the President,* Washington, D.C.: Office of the Press Secretary.

Daniel, S., 2008. *THE FOOD CRISIS AND LATIN AMERICA: Framing a New Policy Approach,* s.l.: The Oakland Institute.

Diouf, J., 2008. An Era of Unprecedented Opportunity?. *UN Chronicle,* 45(2/3), pp. 31-42.

FAO, 2008. *FAO Commodity Price calculator.* s.l.:Food and Agriculture Organization.Availiable at: http://faostat.fao.org/site/703/DesktopDefault.aspx?PageID=703#ancor [Accessed 25 February 2012]

FAO, 2008. *FAOSTAT.* [Online]
Available at: http://faostat.fao.org/site/339/default.aspx
[Accessed 25 February 2012].

Flammini, A., 2008. *Biofuels and the Underlying Causes of High Food Prices,* s.l.: Global Bioenergy Partnership.

Group, W. B., 2007. *Biofuels and the Risks,* s.l.: World Bank.

Heller, G., 2008. *Bad policy, not biofuel, drive food prices: Merkel,* Berlin: Reuters.

Lederer, E., 2007. *Production of Biofuels 'is a crime',* s.l.: The Independent.

Mitchell, D., 2008. *A Note on Rising Food Prices,* s.l.: World Bank Development Prospects Group.

Pedro, E. S., 2008. *Brazil President Defends Biofuels,* s.l.: BBC News.

Rosegrant, M., 2008. *Biofuels and Grain Prices: Impacts and Policy Responses,* Washington DC: International Food Policy Research Institute.

Rosset, P., 2009. *Food Sovereignty in Latin America: Confronting the "New" Crisis,* s.l.: NACLA.

Senauer, B., 2008. Food Market Effects of a Global Resource Shift Towards Bioenergy. *American Journal of Agricultural Economics,* 90(5), pp. 1226-1232.

4.3 Green Economics: The Greening of Food, Farming and Agriculture. Wasting Food – Where Chefs and Greens Agree

By Rose Blackett-Ord

Photo: Rose Blackett-Ord. Winter in the North of England.

Wasting Food – where chefs and greens agree

As a chef and food writer, my take on the greening of food is often a little different. I love to work with the occasional exotic product, and I haven't always thought about the air miles involved in getting it to my kitchen. After a long day at work cooking for other people, I've been known to duck out of cooking for myself and indulge in some lazy fast food. I continue to be a omnivore, albeit one with pretty stringent opinions on the standard of living I expect for the animals I eat. But where I do coincide with the green movement is in the knowledge that over the next few decades, my way of thinking, and that of the rest of humanity, is going to have to change.

For a good few days a year, I'm a chef. And if there's one thing a decent chef hates, it's wastage – the food we buy in but don't end up using. It shows disrespect for the quality of your produce and, of course, it's bad for profit margins. We avoid it in all sorts of creative ways, honing knife skills to trim the least amount possible from meat and vegetables, putting trimmings into stocks, sauces and soups and leftovers towards staff meals or 'specials'.

Of course, it's not just chefs who think like this – many of the general public take a similar attitude to buying and using food. We try to buy the best we can afford within our budget, and we try not to waste too much of it because to waste the food we've bought is to waste our hard-earned cash. Sadly, this well-meaning attitude is not enough – there's still a staggering amount of wasted food throughout the supply chain.

There's the food we throw away which could be eaten (or at the very least composted and used to grow more food). There's the food which never makes it to us because it doesn't meet the supermarkets' aesthetic standards or because it's fed to animals mass-produced on factory farms. And then there's the food which never gets grown in the first place, because the land needed to grow it is used for biofuel crops or monoculture.

Chefs and green thinkers have something in common – we both hate wastage. But for greens, the world is the kitchen, the wastage is global, and what's at risk is not profit but our own survival.

As we stand – the situation so far

The scene as it looks now is, in some ways, very frightening. On a planet with resources which sometimes seem unlimited to us, we are already struggling to feed our population – and it's an unnecessary struggle. According to the FAO, in 2011, 900 million people in the world were undernourished, even though enough food is produced globally for the Earth's population (fao.org (2011)). We simply fail, as a global species, to share with each other. It is horrifying to think how often starvation and obesity sit side by side – even in the UK, where problems with obesity are much discussed in the media, the number of food banks is on the rise as organisations and even individuals take on the responsibility of feeding those who, for whatever reason, can no longer always afford to feed themselves.

Elsewhere in the world, of course, the shortage is sometimes much worse, and this is helped along by the fact that a surprising amount of land, often in third world countries, is used to farm acres of monoculture crops to feed western appetites rather than a sustainable mixture to feed local communities (see http://www.carbontradewatch.org/issues/monoculture.html for more information). It is entirely reasonable to argue that 'buying local' in wealthier countries risks depriving growers abroad, some of whom are already living in poverty, of an essential source of income.

However, this perhaps misses the wider point. If big businesses did not farm this land in order to move one crop thousands of miles to feed someone else (using valuable energy and polluting the air in order to do so), the land would be available for at least some local people to grow a selection of crops to feed themselves and their immediate community. They would have a better chance of being smallholders in the true sense, rather than dependant on international trade for their livelihood. They, as well as we, would have the chance to eat more locally grown food.

The "flip-side"of starvation, obesity and its associated problems, also has some of its roots in unsustainable food practices. All the way from field to mouth, most of us don't know what goes into our food anymore, from the pesticides which permeate some supermarket fruit (foe.co.uk) to horse DNA and drugs in burgers. Mass-produced chicken and pork is fed on fish from already endangered stocks and dependant on antibiotics because they do not have the diet or the exercise necessary to develop a healthy immune system. Colourants and chemicals are in our food, and their names on the label mean nothing to most of us. E-numbers, which were introduced as a way of reassuring us that chemicals had been certified by the EU as safe for human consumption, have come to mean almost the opposite, vaguely linked in our minds to cancer and ADHD.

If people don't know what goes into their food, they can't make an informed decision about the best diet. The amount of food high in sugar, fat and carbohydrates available in supermarkets fools us into thinking that this represents a normal diet for a human being. It doesn't – and obesity, among other evils, is the result.

We need to re-connect with food, so that we understand what real, organically grown, home-cooked food tastes like, and how much of each food group we can reasonably expect to eat. Sadly, when our food comes in plastic packets, that's hard to do.

Some children (quite understandably in my opinion) have come to imagine that meat grows in little cellophane packets and vegetables 'come from the shops'. Well, what did we expect them to think, if they've never seen anything grow?

Too much, too fast
In addition to this, we are using up the planet's resources at a terrifying rate. This is a fact that's often brought out in relation to the energy crisis ('the oil will all run out by

2050', for example). I hear it mentioned less in relation to food, but it is equally true: according to the UN, as the matter stands global food production would need to increase by between 70 and 100 per cent from present levels by 2050 in order to feed the world's growing population (un.org). This is not because enough food isn't being produced – it is – but because of the huge amount of waste involved in current farming methods.

For example, Compassion in World Farming estimates that 1/3 of the world's cereal crop every year is fed to farm animals reared for meat, eggs and dairy – the majority of them on factory farms – rather than going directly into human stomachs (ciwf.org). These animals are often mistreated or unethically reared, and they also contribute 18% of the greenhouse gases casing climate change (ciwf.org) This demand for animal feed, as well as the demand for biofuel crops, encourages monoculture of one or two commercially viable crops, rather than healthy crop rotation (the 'three field' system of medieval England, for example).

This lack of a natural balance severely damages the soil's nutrient levels. It's one of things which led to the North American 'dust bowls' and financial depression during the 1930s. As with crude oil, metals and minerals, when big business farms, it is not putting back into the earth what it takes away.

Compounding the problem
Instead of rotating crops to preserve the nutrient balance in the soil and prevent disease, we try the quick fix of artificial fertilizers to replace what was lost unnaturally quickly, and pesticides to deal with the creatures drawn to such a large concentration of food. Both can be harmful to animals, not to mention that the monoculture they support causes huge disruption to local ecosystems and food chains, unbalancing the delicate equilibrium and rich biodiversity which is the life support system upon which humanity relies. The very fact that we are having to help the soil out (it did perfectly well for millions of years before we came along!) should warn us that something is wrong. As I write, we are still witnessing the terrible aftermath of the fertilizer explosion in Texas, yet another reason to be wary of artificial fertilizing. Our thoughts go out to those involved and affected.

Diversification

According to the FAO, 75% of the world's food is generated from only 12 plants and 5 animal species, which, aside from the problems discussed above, makes the global food system highly vulnerable to shocks. (fao.org (2012)) The key to our survival is to diversify, so that when it comes to food sources we don't have all our eggs in one basket, and to farm food in a sustainable way so that the planet continues to provide for us and all our descendants. This means varying our diet and farming organically so as to preserve the soil's natural balance, encourage biodiversity, and preserve the planet's natural equilibrium. It is likely to mean giving up or significantly reducing our meat intake, as producing meat requires feeding animals crops which could otherwise be eaten directly by humans and housing them on land which could otherwise be used to grow other sources of food. The only really sustainable animal farming is smallholding, when animals can either graze only where no alternative food source will grow, or can have their grazing grounds rotated with crop fields, so that the waste they produce is recycled to enrich the soil for food crops to grow.

But we already know all this – don't we?

The problem with labels

These days, many of the general public and even parts of the food industry at least claim that they give some thought to 'the environment' and sustainability. Head chefs, for example, are constantly evaluating who's the best supplier: who can give them the best produce at the lowest price? Nowadays we know, too, that 'best produce' doesn't just mean quality: it means eating local, eating seasonal, eating ethical. Thanks to the glimmerings of change in consumers' habits, there does seem to me to be more of a demand for traceable, local food than there used to be. Working freelance in private houses and events catering, I often see clients asking for 'local' meat, 'organic' vegetables, 'homemade' this and 'fair trade' that. The right kind of demand is starting to emerge.

The problem for me is that this demand is sometimes misdirected. At the end of the day, chefs, farmers and other food industry professionals make their living from selling their food to the consumer. If the demand is for 'fair-trade' or 'locally sourced', the industry tries to make sure people get just that. But the length of the supply chain and the prioritising of profit means that the vocabulary used to sell food doesn't always accurately represent its overall sustainability. For example, 'organic' is not always 'local' – a percentage (between 30% and 70%, depending on your source) of the food sold as organic in the UK is in fact imported, so the food miles often outweigh any benefits from organic production methods; and at least some of it is likely to be mechanically farmed, albeit to organic standards. Is the labelling on this food accurate? Strictly speaking, yes. Is the food totally sustainable? Strictly speaking, no.

What's the answer?

It's natural to feel confused or downright let down by misleading labelling, but more accurate labels – while desirable in the short term – are not the ultimate answer. The answer, in the long term, is to drastically cut the length of the supply chain. If what we are eating is grown, raised or foraged either in our own garden or by local friends and neighbours, we don't need labels to tell us it's local – we know. We don't need labels to tell us it's organic – we grew it ourselves, or we know the person who did. We don't need to be told it's seasonal, because if it were out of season we wouldn't have been able to get it. The only way to do away with inaccurate or misleading labelling is to do away with the need for labels. The only way to do that is to take responsibility for our own food.

It's vital that we stop leaving the negotiating to suppliers and supermarket buyers, because of course they're going to tell us what we want to hear. We wanted burgers at 4 for £1.00 - and we got them. We just failed to ask what they were made of. The horsemeat scandal was, amongst other things, a result of consumers who didn't understand (or care) enough about the effort and expense which goes into producing ethical, good-quality food to realise that if meat was priced that low, something somewhere was very wrong. We must learn what it is reasonable to expect from the planet, from our food sources and suppliers. We must educate ourselves, to re-connect with our food from field to table, so that we can learn how to ask the right questions.

Land use, urbanisation, and the permaculture solution

Yet another problem with land use is that all of us need a place to live and a roof over our heads. This inevitably takes up a certain amount of space. As humans we naturally gather together in groups of varying sizes, and the industrial age has led some those groups to expand exponentially, as cities became practical. But land covered in concrete can't currently provide for us, and city dwellers find it hardest of all of us to buy local or grow for themselves, with many feeling totally disconnected from the origins of the food they eat. Growing food in an allotment or garden can help, as can visiting farm open days or just moving out of the city altogether! But ultimately we've got to live somewhere, and there are too many of us nowadays for everyone to have the meadows and wide open spaces they crave.

Perhaps the answer is in the way we design our dwellings and communities, as well as in our lifestyle. Movements like permaculture combine guidelines for living and design with a recognition of human needs and the needs of the rest of the planet to come up with solutions for problems like these and suggestions for a lifestyle which is all about stability and sustainability. Its principles provide a set of universally applicable guidelines that can be used in designing sustainable systems (permaculture.org, *Principles*). In the words of the Permaculture Association, '*The word 'permaculture' comes from 'permanent agriculture' and 'permanent culture' - it is about living lightly on the planet, and making sure that we can sustain human activities for many generations to come, in harmony with nature. Permanence is not about everything staying the same. Its about stability, about deepening soils and cleaner water, thriving communities in self-reliant regions, biodiverse agriculture and social justice, peace and abundance.*' (permaculture.org, *Basics*)

This certainly seems to me to go a long way towards the solution we are aiming for.

There is hope yet - eating local, eating wild, and respecting your food

The process of each individual taking responsibility for the food they eat could take generations. The ideal – that we each produce enough to feed ourselves and any young or elderly dependant on us, while leaving the land and environment we use to do so unharmed – can seem a long way away off, especially to those living in cities. But it is possible. I've lived in shared houses for the last 6 years, and quite a few of them have had a garden, back yard or outdoor space of some sort. Failing that, at least a windowsill. But none of the gardens was ever cultivated. That kind of land and space is full of the potential for self-sufficiency and your own sustainable food, and with access to the internet it's now even easier to take advantage of that potential. Smallholdings are a statistically viable alternative to big business farming - when sustainable agriculture is adopted, average crop yields have been show to increase by 79% (fao.org (2011)). You *can* grow your own, whether it's in a field, a garden or a window box. The slow food movement, which advocates small-scale, local, sustainable sourcing of the best-quality food possible, and taking the time to prepare it in a way which makes the most of its value, is very relevant here and is well-worth researching and following – if you haven't already!

Wild Food

Looking around as I walk through town, I'm often also surprised by some of the wild food opportunities that exist in unlikely places – wild garlic, elderflower bushes, young dandelion leaves, they are there if you look for them. The world is full of wild food if you know what to look for – it's worth reading up on what's around in your local area and taking advantage. As long as you forage sustainably, leaving enough behind to keep the population growing, there's a wealth of wild food to enjoy. Not only is it free, but when treated properly it's green too. In this book's recipe section, there are a few pieces of advice on beginning to eat wild food, including some of my favourite wild food options and what you might consider doing with them. Please note, however, that this is only a tiny starting point – any foraging book or website will give you much more information. In fact, **we thoroughly recommend that you develop a good working knowledge of your local area and strong food identification skills before you begin to forage, ideally by learning from an experienced professional forager in your area**. Failing this, please **consult an experienced forager or industry professional before eating anything you are not 110% sure about. Misidentified wild food can be fatal. If in doubt, don't eat it. We cannot accept liability for personal injury or even death that resulting from foraging or consuming wild food.** Take responsibility for your food by triple-checking that you have identified it correctly, and by handling and preparing it appropriately. If, after this dire warning (sorry – necessary for complicated legal reasons!), you prefer not to forage yourself, you can buy your wild food from a local foraging expert or a reputable local supplier with traceable, sustainable methods.

Local Food

Even those of us who don't want to eat wild food and can't grow their own can eat locally sourced produce. Because demand for cheap food is so high and many customers aren't too concerned about quality, sustainability and animal welfare, small-scale farmers are at a disadvantage: if they stick to ethical and organic standards, they can't produce enough to meet demand or charge enough to meet their costs. Many small-scale farmers in Britain are undercut by big producers and foreign importers. For this and other reasons (trade protectionism among them), the EU subsidises large portions of the UK and other EU farming industries. According to Civitas, Nearly three-quarters of EU farmers have an income under £5,000 per year (although some only farm on a part-time basis) and incomes in the agricultural sector are just 50% of the average in other sectors (civitas.org.uk). This is not the fault of farmers, but of consumer demands and national and international policies and regulations. Also according to Civitas, farming sector employment in the EU fell by 25% during 2000-10 (civitas.org.uk). If we're not careful, we'll have no local farms left! By buying from local farmers, farmers' markets, box schemes and other sources with short supply chains, you can support local farmers and your local economy, as well as help to create closer-knit communities in which people can begin once more to trust each other and the food they are eating.

It would also drastically reduce the waste, pollution, greenhouse gases, and wasted energy which result from food transport and excessive packaging. Best of all, it means you can keep the closest possible eye on what goes into your food and how it is produced. Being closer to the beginning of the supply chain also means we have the chance to teach our children where their food comes from, promoting a respect for sustainable methods which will last a lifetime and be passed on to their children in turn.

Fish, meat and game – have some respect

Meat and game
With regard to eating the flesh of animals and fish, as well as other products associated with them, there's a fair bit of controversy out there. What's certain (see above) is that over the next few decades we are going to need to make a very significant reduction in the amount of meat and meat products we eat, as well as adopting much more sustainable fishing habits. This much is clear, as discussed above and elsewhere in the book. But should we all become totally vegetarian? People's opinions differ widelyindeed. Here's my take.

We developed partly as hunters and, later, herders (it has even been said that the calories derived from eating cooked protein helped our brains to evolve into their current state (livescience.com)). That isn't to say that we should remain hunters or herders, and indeed the opposite seems increasingly true. But whether or not we are all vegetarian in the future, if we're going to eat meat now, it's a question of sustainability and, above all else, respect.

If a living thing is going to give up its life to feed you, have the decency to respect its sacrifice. Ensure that the life it lived was a full and healthy one, spent in its natural habitat, able to express natural behaviours, reproduce, eat its natural diet, see the sun. Try mutton instead of lamb: the sheep has had a longer –hopefully a fuller – life. Don't eat factory farmed pork or battery hens. When death comes, ensure (by buying local and traceable, by asking the right questions) that it was as quick, painless and dignified as possible, with the absolute minimum of cruelty and distress. Ideally abattoirs should be local (although these are increasingly rare due to factory-scale farming and some EU regulations), so that animals are not distressed by being stuck in a truck for hours or frightened by unfamiliar places and smells.

After its death, don't make light of an animal's sacrifice by wasting the resource it has provided for you. Use all parts of the animal that you possibly can. Cows are not made of steak alone! Eat less popular cuts. Learn to love offal. Make proper stock from bones instead of using odd-tasting, freeze dried, chemical-filled cubes. If you have a local butcher, ask them what to do with an unfamiliar cut, where it came from, whether it's high-welfare (if not, ask WHY NOT!) – that's what they are there for. You may be surprised by how happy they are to discuss these things with you. If you eat meat and you don't have a local butcher, get one.

Lastly, and most controversially: if you want truly sustainable meat and to show some deference towards the life you've taken, eat meat you have either raised or hunted in the wild and killed yourself (as long as you are skilled enough to ensure a fast, dignified death). Yes, it is controversial. No, it is not the ultimate solution. But in the short term, it creates a lot more of a connection and respect for the animal that is shown by the average meat-eater these days. You shouldn't eat meat if you are not prepared to connect with the process which leads to it – ie, to take a life. Anything less shows, to my mind, a sickening want of respect.

At the end of the day, it's undeniable that meat as we use it now is a completely unsustainable food source. In the future, to ensure our survival, it should be phased out completely or reserved for the elderly, the young, the weak or unwell. But in the meantime, if you do eat meat, sustainability, limitation and – above all – respect for life should be your bywords.

Fish
As far as fish are concerned, for me, the rules are similar if not the same. The only difference is that we eat a much wider range of fish species than we do species of domesticated animal (chicken, beef, pork and lamb for the majority of our meat choices). If we catch these species from the sea using sustainable methods such as line-catching, dive-catching or harpooning rather than farming or trawling for them, there is a possibility that we could reasonably include a limited amount of fish or seafood in our future diet. Fish-farming and most kinds of trawl fishing and dredging are not sustainable, as the former spreads disease and removes wild fish from the natural food chain in order to feed the farmed ones, and the latter two cause harm to the seabed and species other than that being fished for. There is a longer discussion of sustainable fishing in the recipe section of the book, with the fish recipes, as well as some tips on how to tell farmed and wild salmon and trout apart.

Sustainable and permanent – getting the ball rolling
The message in this book is that the green economics approach most certainly applies

to food. Live lightly on the planet. Let plants and animals exist with the minimum of interference from us – nature has managed by itself for millennia. Eat from diverse sources to celebrate and preserve the beauty of our planet's infinite variety, and because removing one link in the chain could have far-reaching and unforeseen consequences.

Take time to think about what you eat. Take responsibility for it. Take an interest in where it comes from. Try to involve yourself in its processes and production. Find out about and support movements like slow food and permaculture – they advocate the kind of connection with and respect for environment that we are going to need as a species to survive even the next hundred years. Respect all food sources, plant and animal – they make your existence possible. Show your respect by caring about where you buy them and how you prepare them, and by providing for yourself as much as you can.

Yes, it's not always feasible to produce 100% of what we eat ourselves, or even have it come from within a 2 or 3 mile radius. But we can make a start. So to get the ball rolling towards fully sustainable food habits, each one of us needs to change our attitude. Where possible, we need to take full responsibility for feeding ourselves by growing or raising our own produce with whatever space and skills we have. Where that's not possible, we need to keep pushing at the food trade. We need to buy from suppliers with the shortest food supply chains – if possible, directly from the grower or farmer – and keep on creating a demand for local and traceable products with clearly sustainable methods behind them.

We need to demand organic AND local AND small-scale AND seasonal AND ethical food. Some people have already moved a step in the right direction, others more than one. Some refuse to move at all. But in the end, if we want it done properly, then we all need work together and do it for ourselves. In the pages which follow, you should find information which will help you work out what and how to change and inspire you to begin.

References:

Christopher Wanjek, *Meat, Cooked Foods Needed for Early Human Brain*, _Livescience Journal_, eaccessed 19/04/13: http://www.livescience.com/24875-meat-human-brain.html

Civitas, *EU Facts: Common Agricultural Policy (2013)*, accessed 19/04/13: http://www.civitas.org.uk/eufacts/FSPOL/AG3.htm

Compassion in World Farming, *Sustainable Food*, accessed 19/04/13: http://www.ciwf.org.uk/your_food/sustainable_food/default.aspx

Food and Agriculture Association, *Greening the Economy with Agriculture*, (2011),

accessed   19/04/13:
http://www.fao.org/fileadmin/templates/nr/sustainability_pathways/docs/Fact
sheet_GEA.pdf

Food and Agriculture Organisation, *Smallholders and Family Farmers* (2012) accessed
16/04/13:
http://www.fao.org/fileadmin/templates/nr/sustainability_pathways/docs/Fact
sheet_SMALLHOLDERS.pdf

Friends of the Earth (2004), *Pesticides in Supermarket Food*, accessed 20/04/2013:
http://www.foe.co.uk/resource/briefings/pesticide_supermarket_food.pdf

The   Permaculture   Association,   *Basics*,   accessed   20/04/13:
http://www.permaculture.org.uk/knowledge-base/basics)

The   Permaculture   Association,   *Principles*,   accessed   20/04/13:
http://www.permaculture.org.uk/knowledge-base/principles

UN (2011), *The Great Green Technological Transformation*, accessed 19/04/13:
http://www.un.org/en/development/desa/policy/wess/wess_current/2011wess.
pdf

Photo Miriam Kennet. Young Professional women's binge drinking is starting to impact their health. This is very much an economics issue as liberalisation of, making money for and promotion of longer drinking times and more available drinks, to help the large drinks companies, has led to a focus on young professional women as an untapped market. Now younger women and indeed older professional women are starting to experience all kinds of health effects from having grown up in a drinking culture. Our member Liz Vine seen above has done extensive and interesting research into this issue. Women are experiencing high levels of alcohol dependency and other associated health problems with all the costs to society that this brings to the economy.

4.4 A Survival Mechanism for the Poor and Equity in a Mutual Symbiosis: A Case Study of Street Food Vendors in Urban Indonesia

By Tutik Rachmawati - (Indonesia)

In Indonesia, as in any other less developed country, the informal sector has become the backbone of economic development particularly in the aftermath of the Asian financial crisis in 1996. It has become the alternative to the formal sector, which is now unable to accommodate the workforce. It also offesr an option to non-farm labour which is especially true in the case of urbanisation. The informal sector is most visibly appears in the form of street vendors, mostly selling food as a means of earning a living, which requires minor financial capital and low skills.

Many supermarket, malls and mega malls are built as part of cities. In the back of these malls, mega malls and supermarket, or on the narrow pathway alongside these mega buildings, there are to be found hundreds of street vendors offering various types of foods. Readers might question why is this happening? Why are street vendors allowed to sell food competing with food courts inside the mall buildings? Why are they allowed to expose people to a risk of a dilapidated and unhygienic conditions as a result of the activities of the food street vendors? It seems to be paradoxical to allow the formal economic sector represented by the malls buildings to operate side by side with the informal, or moreover the illegal economic sector, depicted by food street vendors. There is only one answer to it: the food being sold inside the malls are so expensive that only the rich can afford to eat there. Everyone else has to shop outside!

But there is much more important underlying answer to that question. The main customers of these street vendors are indeed, the lower level staffs and workers of those malls. They need a survival mechanism against the unaffordable living costs of the city. Therefore, there is a mutual relationship between these two parties; a mutual symbiosis. Most malls obviously acknowledge this mutual symbiosis so that they allowed these street vendors to establish their business right next to their premises

This is termed as a mutual symbiosis for an important reason. For the poor and the most deprived part of community in urban area, this is their survival mechanism. Both who are involved in this symbiosis and both need this relationship in order to survive the expensive urban life. For workers in the urban area whose wages are barely enough to meet their food needs, being able to pay an affordable price means reducing their overall expenses. The proximity to the ready meals also means less time spent on breaks from work, therefore reducing the chance of obtaining a lower performance work evaluation. Eventually, the can secure their job by keeping their good work performance. Keeping their job means securing their livelihood.

On the contrary, for the street vendors selling the food, this is their main livelihood, the sole income source. Therefore, being able to carry on their business securely and closer to the customer is very important. As the adage of *'location defines the market'*, direct access to the customer is the key to business survival for the food street vendors. To put it extremely, if it is required, food street vendors will bring their mobile kiosks into the middle of jammed up roads for customers who are inside busses, cars, or any kind of motor vehicle who want to buy food from them whilst perhaps stopping at the traffic lights. This creates the competitive ability of food street vendors that no other informal economy actors have. Even though their competitive advantage is something that is violating public space rights, urban planning and urban management.

Local government may have thought that food street vendors with their survival characteristics are a bad feature of the city that contribute to the slowness of investment rate coming into the city. Most of programs intended for food street vendors are programs that discourage them to grow because these programmes are fixed upon a logic of mainstream entrepreneurship not on survival entrepreneurship. Programs such as upgrading skills and knowledge, re-location to a 'better' building which keeps them away from the customer or giving risk analysis workshops are examples of local government programs that are meant to help food street vendors to graduate from being a survival business to becoming a small scale business. But on the contrary, these programs do not actually in reality, work in accordance with the survival of food street vendors. They have to invest capital, tool or material not to upgrade but in order to diversify or to add other similar business so as *'not to put all their eggs in one basket'*. The relocation of the business to another area as an act of risk taking is a big NO on the part of survival entrepreneurs. In fact, in orderfor them to secure their business, they need to stay in the commercial areas.

Whilst the malls willingly provide space for food street vendors as the acknowledgement of the mutual symbiosis, local government should be more supportive to food street vendors. Local government should also acknowledge that there is an opportunity for a win-win relationship amongst the stakeholders, that is around the malls – the street vendors and the local producers, whose products are the main raw materials for the food street vendors products.

Being street vendors selling food also provides greater access for local producers. Most raw materials to make the food can come from the local producers and local farmers. By doing this it also helps to sustain the employment in the urban agriculture sector, especially the subsistence farmers who struggle to market their products.

Taxing as Social Corporate Responsibility

Equity is an important aspect to ensure the mutual symbiosis to continue. Without it, the mutual relation will be jeopardized. When permission is given to the food street vendors to operate behind or alongside the outer side of the malls building, this must be questioned by food stall owners inside the malls building. The question of inequity is rooted in the difference of financial charges between the food stall owner, whilst the food stall owner have to pay a large amount of money for the renting space and services within the malls building, the food street vendors, if are asked to pay a small amount of money as a tax for running the business at the same premises. The food street vendors mostly will object to a tax collection. They will claim that running their trade outside malls buildings means that they often receive no services provision from the malls. The malls management should be able to provide an answer that satisfies both parties.

Tax exemption for food street vendors will only lead to an unfair condition between the street vendors and the food stall owners inside the building, but enforcing heavy tax to later will create a bad image for the malls' management. Therefore charging tax differently can be justified under the Corporate Social Responsibility Programs. Even though it is complicated to construct a tax collection that reflect the equity, the CSR program for the informal economy particularly the food street vendors will also enable to determine a fair tax collection for the food street vendors.

The tax collection under the CSR program should also answer the question about who should collect the tax. There will be no more debate as to whether the local government or the malls management that should collect the tax. The argument that the food street vendors operate within the malls premises, therefore it is the malls that should collect the tax, will be supported by the decision to create a CSR program for food street vendors.

Another important aspect is how best to collect the tax, and how it will be used to manage the street vendors. Money collected from tax can be matched with the funds provided by the malls under CSR programs and can be used to maintain sanitary and health services for the street vendors.

In the long term, the tax collection by the malls will alter the food street vendors from informal small scale business into a formal one. Even though it can be predicted that it will create more inequity problems, this will start the process of creating a future for f the food street vendors.

Social capital and Corporate Social Responsibility

Blair and Carrol (2012) argue that the informal economy such as street vendors relies on social capital. This type of business is mostly based on the trust. Trust is reflected on the capital used to finance the business and it is normally a pool fund by the family and friends without any legal binding such as loan from formal institution (bank). The traders and the consumers normally share similar value as they have both experienced hardships in their life The relationship between traders and customers is often also based on trust, taking food and paying for it later when their wage is paid is normal practice. Therefore, trust has to be regarded as an important feature of food street vendors in any CSR programs.

Using the logic of formal economy, a small scale business only obtains a financial support, when it meets the criteria of the logic of business projection; when it has survived for a certain length of time and when it has gained a certain amount of profit. When this criteria is applied to food street vendors it will be irrelevant because for them gaining profit will be the very last thing of the business purpose. Survival of the business will be more likely their main concern, and for this survival the food street vendors put their trust in the malls' management to allow them to do their trading in the malls' premises. Therefore, a CSR program must provide a guarantee that they will be allowed to sustain their business.

The entry requirements to this type of business are different from the formal economy. Because of their informality, food street vendors have no access to any financial support from any formal financial institution such as banks for their business development. When they are given a financial support, often they will use this not to enlarge their business but to open another similar business involving another member of the family or close friends. Therefore, the opening of another business will not be based on the logic business projection but relies on trust among family or close friends. The decision about the business location will also normally be based on word of mouth.

The CSR program targeted for food street vendors should be aiming at the creation of self compliance and the maintenance of trust.

Empowering the Female Food Street Vendors and Local Government Role

Various Studies by the World Bank shows that the size, the composition and the contribution of the informal sector such as food street vendors are even larger than what is shown by statistics (Chen, M.A., 2001).. Considering the fact that most women's work is unpaid work and is uncounted towards the formal statistics of economic development. This is true for female food street vendors, they work for their husband or their family running the business while also nursing their children and providing family well being. On the other hand, food street vendors are characterised as having a low levels of literacy, particularly female literacy. A CSR program should be designed to enable female food street vendors to realise their independence of owning their own small scale business, and should provide child care to ease the duty of nursing the children while they work, and should include running evening class to improve the female street vendors literacy. These can be done with local government. The local government is often frustrated by the informal sector as they are unable to exercise their constitutional rights and duties because of their low level of literary. Working 'together with malls; management in this CSR program will ease the burden of the local government.

Local governments can learn from Rotterdam city's experience in putting unemployed people back into work by cleaning up the street. As an addition to the services provided by the malls' management such as hygiene, sanitation and safe access to water, local governments may regulate food street vendors in such a way that they do not create bad image for the city's physical appearance by requiring them to do the clean up. In exchange for this cleaning up, food street vendors will be exempted from paying tax. In this way, the street vendors are empowered to ensure the cleanliness of their business premise. They also need to be regulated in such away so as not to congest the streets nor to cause traffic jams, so that it can help them to ensure the air quality. In conclusion, food street vendors can run their survival businesses whilst making excellent contributions to a good urban environment which includes urban cleanliness. This eventually will affect the ability of the city to attract investment for the development of formal economic sector.

4.5 Genetically Modified Food

By Bianca Madison-Vuleta

We all have the right to eat and plant GM-free food. We are fighting to protect your choices from corporate interests to secure safe, sustainable agriculture for all. We are also calling for a moratorium on GM food and crops until it is clearly and independently proven safe. We are looking for public involvement in decisions about GM, laws to make GM companies liable for harm their products cause and independent safety research on GM and its impacts.

TEN MYTHS ABOUT GM FOOD AND CROPS

1. WE NEED GM TO FEED A GROWING WORLD POPULATION The vast majority of the world's crops are not GM - GM is only planted on about 2.75% of global agricultural land. Most of this goes to animal feed, fibre and industrial scale agrifuels.

What's left is in processed food (primarily unlabelled in North America). The current push for GM is about a falling industry trying to save itself. The world's underlying approach to food should not be about market control, patents and profit. Feeding the world means tackling poverty, improving access to the food we already produce, ending the waste of 30-40% of the world's food, reducing losses in storage, making trade fairer, curbing overconsumption and investing in effective research. We don't need GM to do any of this.

2. GM HELPS FARMERS GROW MORE IN DROUGHTS AND FIGHT CLIMATE CHANGE

All crops need the right mix of sun, water and healthy soil to produce a good yield - GM cannot change this. Despite many promises and billions of pounds spent over decades on research, not a single GM drought tolerant crop has been developed that farmers can grow. Traditional plant breeding, using modern techniques, has produced successful drought tolerant crops in fields where farmers need them now.

3. GM DELIVERS MORE FOOD ON LESS LAND

No current GM crops have <u>been</u> shown to boost yields, independent US studies show up to 10% les yield in GM soya - manipulating a few genes gives unpredictable results. Increased yields in the past decade are due to developments in traditional plant breeding, not GM.

4. GM HELPS FARMERS USE LESS CHEMICALS

Herbicide tolerant crops: initially GM did reduce the use of weed killers, but weeds quickly developed resistance to the chemicals used on GM crops. The resulting "super-weeds" are forcing farmers to use more chemicals, including older, more dangerous ones, at considerable expense. Some US GM cotton farmers have to hand weed whole fields when chemicals stop working.

Insecticide crops: GM maize and cotton are engineered to produce toxins in every part of the plant - including the parts we eat. This is a change in the way pesticides are used, not a reduction. The toxins kill some insects and pests, but not all. Monsanto now admits that pink bull worm in parts of India is resistant to GM cotton. Yet emerging evidence shows toxins may harm non-target insects (like butterflies), and there are serious concerns about the safety of the toxins for human health.

5. EU OPPOSITION TO GM IS HOLDING BACK DEVELOPING COUNTRIES (or, it is only well-fed activists who oppose GM)

The Indian Government put an indefinite moratorium on GM brinjal (aubergine) - a flagship project for the GM industry - until safety questions are answered. There are GM bans, active protests and legal opposition in Thailand, Indonesia, Ethiopia, Pakistan, Mexico, South Africa, Kenya, Argentina and elsewhere. EU opposition to GM leads the way, showing that GM agriculture is not inevitable because citizens have the right to make our own decisions about what we grow and eat.

6. THE EU IS GOING TO BE LEFT BEHIND IN SCIENCE IF WE DON'T DO GM (or, we need GM for our economy)

GM hasn't delivered. Farmer training needs to be improved around the world, including in the UK. Rather than throw good money after bad, the UK should establish centres of excellence in areas like soil husbandry and advanced traditional plant breeding to lead the world in a more sustainable and equitable approach to managing farmland and forests.

7. GM IS SAFE - THEY HAVE BEEN EATING GM IN THE US FOR YEARS AND NO ONE HAS EVER BEEN HURT

GM is unlabelled and untraced in the US food supply, so there is no way to determine where GM is going or what health impacts it might be having, or even how much GM is actually been eaten. It is impossible to study, so this claim has no scientific basis.

8. PEOPLE ARE CHANGING THEIR MINDS ABOUT GM

When US dairies started labelling their milk as free from GM hormones; they were so popular Monsanto went to court to get them banned. They failed. A 2010 NOP poll showed 89% support for labels on animal products in the UK showing where GM feed is used, like they have in Austria and Germany. If the GM industry believes people are changing their minds, they have nothing to fear from using such labels and letting the market decide.

9. WE NEED GM TO KEEP FOOD PRICES DOWN AND THE MEAT INDUSTRY GOING UP.

It was not a lack of GM that caused food prices to go up - GM was produced throughout the 2007/8 price rises. Regional droughts, diverting food crops into industrial scale biofuels, financial speculation in food markets and the rising costs of fertilisers and fuel were key contributors, but GM cannot fix these. The EU has become far too dependent on imported animal feed, much of it GM.

Policies favour a highly concentrated industrial farm model that has resulted in poor animal welfare and forces smaller farmers out of business. We need a more accountable and responsible food production system. Research across EU is helping us find the kind of crops and breeds we need to be less dependent on importing GM animal feed and exporting the damage it does to communities and the environment in faraway countries.

10. OPPOSITION TO GM IS BASED ON EMOTION (OR POLITICS), AND NOT SCIENCE!

The US and Indian courts are showing that the science behind GM is far from sound, particularly when approvals have been based in safety dossiers provided by the industry itself. In any case citizens are not obliged to accept whatever is scientifically possible. Non-GM alternatives do the scientific job better, with less risk and no public rejection, keeping farmers and consumers on the same side so everyone benefits.

WHY SHOULD WE SUPPORT THE GM FREEZE?

Despite growing scientific uncertainty about the safety and performance of GM and overwhelming public rejection, the UK Government still backed GM potato trials in England every year between 2007-2010. At the same time supported every new GM application in the EU. They still say GM will help tackle global hunger but: 400 global scientists in the biggest independent global scientific investigation on the subject (the International Assessment of Agricultural Science and Technology for Development) disagreed, saying: "Assessment of GM technology lags behind its development, information is anecdotal and contradictory, and uncertainty about possible benefits and damage is unavoidable".

In 2010 the Chief Administrator for the UN Development Programme said: "I don't think GM is the solution to the food security problem."

We think it is time for modern solutions to modern problems. When GM food reached supermarket shelves people rejected it. Today it is hard to find food without GM ingredients but shops can't sell what people won't buy. There is a hidden exception: milk, cheese, meat and eggs from animals raised on GM feed do not legally need a GM label. So there is no way to tell if your pint of milk is supporting the GM industry.

Since people rejected GM as food, the vast majority of GM crops (around 80%) have no place to go except into animal feed. Yet we simply don't know the extent of the many problems with GM crops, including:

GM has not been proven safe for consumption.

Industry safety claims are based on their own, not independent, data. National authorities are not testing food either to find GM or to confirm independent studies showing GM damage to animals' guts, lower nutritional value and allergic reactions or reactions in immune systems.

GM DNA from feed can pass into animals' blood. Pesticides in GM animal feed are not routinely monitored, so we don't know what our livestock are eating.

We do know the maximum legal residue limit for weed-killers glyphosate in food was raised 200% when GM soya came on the market.

Environmental damage

GM herbicide tolerant crops have accelerated the development of weed-killer resistance.

There are now 140 types of herbicide tolerant "super-weeds" in 40 US states, with 13 species resistant to glyphosate, and even the industry admits it takes older, more dangerous chemicals to control them.

Corporate control

Patented GM crops give companies like Monsanto and Bayer unprecedented control over the supply of seeds and food. They say we need GM animal feed to keep the costs down, but GM prices spiked just as steeply as non-GM in 2007/2008 - and we pay them even more to avoid it. OUR RIGHT TO CHOOSE ANOTHER WAY

Without clear labels; we don't know where the GM feed is used.

While we look for better ways to feed our animals (like feeding cows grass and clover), Brazil alone grows enough non-GM soya for at least 80% of the EU needs without further damaging the Amazon - we don't need GM!

Austrian and German shoppers have labels on non-GM feed foods, and France and Ireland are introducing them soon. Supermarkets say it is too confusing to give consumers the information about what they want. Our supermarkets can and should insist that the diary, meat, fish and eggs they sell are produced without GM crops and back this up with clear GM-free labels.

OUTDATED GM OR MODERN SCIENCE?

Modern science shows genes have far more complicated interactions with one another and the environment than was first imagined. Therefore many of the promises of the GM industry based on moving a few genes between species may simply prove possible.

Marker Assisted Selection (MAS) is an advanced genetic technique used to identify valuable traits in parent plants before fertilisation to ensure those genes are passed to offspring plants.

This cutting edge development of traditional plant breeding has already produced breakthroughs where GM has failed (including deep water rice, drought resistant rice, high protein corn, pest resistant potatoes, disease resistant barley, millet and watermelon).

STILL NO RESPONSIBILITY FOR GM MULTINATIONALS

Like the cigarette industry, GM companies resist taking legal responsibility for their products. In order to protect us and make them more responsible, it is time that the GM industry was made fully and strictly liable for all environmental, economic and health damage that may arise from GM food and crops, especially before we accept "coexistence" of GM crops with conventional agriculture. If they believe their products are safe, the companies have nothing to lose.

Over 97% of the world's farmland grows non-GM crops. Despite spending billions on research over decades, GM crops have not improved yields or solved drought tolerance, so they can't help feed the world any better than conventional crops.

The tide is turning against GM multinationals: in recent times US courts had ordered Bayer to pay farmers over US$53 million in costs and damages for the contamination of rice farms in 2006, with thousands more claims in the pipeline.

Governments and industry say we need GM crops to ease rising food prices, but in 2008 10% of GM crops went into biofuels, not to feed people.

Claims that GM is safe are based on the industry's own studies, and they rely on "commercial confidentiality" to prevent key raw data on safety being used by independent researchers.

GM research promising "GM jam tomorrow" continues to soak up public funding that should be spent finding sustainable solutions that work.

Part 5: Our Health and Food
5.1 The True Cost of Factory Pig Farming

By Tracy, Marchioness of Worchester

Introduction

As we wander through the English countryside pigs grazing happily beside their small arcs, might give one the impression that we, in the UK, have escaped the intensive factory pig farming model that exists in the USA and Europe. However, that nightmare has taken a step closer with the revival of a planning application for a 25,000 pig factory farm in Foston, Derbyshire. The applicants, Midland Pig Producers, have 'tweaked' their original application but have still not come up with any ideas about how they propose to stop toxic bioaerosols and antibiotic resistant bacteria from drifting 150 metres downwind and sickening, among other residents, the inmates and staff of Foston Hall Prison.

The National Pig Association (NPA) and National Farmers Union (NFU) have come out solidly in favour of industrial agriculture and support the Foston plans, reflecting the free trade neo-liberal views of the Cameron government, apparently forgetting that they are supposed to represent farmers not just corporate agribusinesses. Instead of promoting intensive indoor factory farms like the one proposed at Foston, why does the NPA not support an increase in outdoor pig farming, or indoors with plenty of straw, daylight and fresh air, where the sows and fattening pigs have space to move around at will, do not require antibiotics and where there is no risk to the health of local residents?

It's remarkable that the NPA still pushes for this defective system at a time when authorities in other European countries, notably Germany and the Netherlands, are refusing applications for the building of new factory farms, and ordering some existing facilities to be scaled down in size. A recent report by the Netherland's equivalent of the UK Health Protection Agency has said that intensive livestock units should not be built closer than 250 metres from where people are living.

My 2009 film Pig Business describes the animal cruelty, health hazards and destruction of rural communities that giant US factory pork producer Smithfield Foods has wrought in the USA and Poland. Featuring Robert Kennedy Jr and a confrontational interview with the Smithfield Vice President, the film was screened at the UK and EU Parliaments and on Capitol Hill, Washington, and has now been translated into 21 languages.

Under the banner 'Farms Not Factories' our small team are campaigning against the building of new factory pig farms worldwide, including the current Foston project. Celebrities including actors Dominic West, Lesley Ash and Sir Roger Moore have supported the Farms Not Factories campaign against Foston, believing that if it were allowed to be built it would open the floodgates for many more factory pig farm developments in the UK and undermine the few pig farmers we have left.

FNF has started answering requests by local residents campaigning against factory pig farms to make country- specific versions of Pig Business. Finished versions are now being used in the US, Canada, Germany, Romania, Hungary and Ecuador. Films in Chile, Latvia and Ukraine are in progress.

People who have watched Pig Business know that if we in the UK want to avoid the factory pig farm system we must only buy pork, bacon, ham or sausages with a welfare label saying either Freedom Food, Outdoor Reared, Free Range or Organic. Factory farms all over the EU (and Chile) supply the UK market with cheap pork, and the Smithfield Foods website announces proudly that it intends to become one of the five main suppliers to the UK food service industry, ie to prisons, schools, hospitals and the army.

Much of the UK's imported pork is raised in conditions which are illegal in the UK; sows are kept up to four months a year in steel stalls in which they cannot turn around. EU laws forbidding routine tail docking and requiring bedding material are widely ignored according to a recent survey by Compassion in World Farming. Our farmers cannot compete in this unfair market and consequently we have lost half our pig herd in the last twelve years.

Trade agreements, special-interest lobbying and cross party 'neo liberal' policies over the past twenty years have consolidated the stranglehold of industrial agribusiness over every sector of the global food market. The competition to produce the cheapest food has resulted in an epidemic of obesity, heart disease and cancers caused by excessive consumption of meat and dairy and the deliberate elimination of family farms whose mixed farming systems nurture soils and conserve biodiversity. Food quality, security and sovereignty has been swept aside in favour of industrial monoculture crops that depend on high inputs of chemicals and fossil fuels to feed not only humans but also animals in intensive indoor meat factories that confine the animals in miserable conditions and contaminate the surrounding air and water with toxic waste.

The routine use of antibiotics on factory farms has led to the appearance of a new strain of MRSA, ST398, which affects pigs and passes to humans. In the Netherlands 50% of pig farm workers are carriers and 29% of MRSA hospital cases are the new pig strain. The National Pig Association in the UK recently announced that there is no MRSA in UK pigs, but how they know this is a mystery as the government has not tested for it. It is very unlikely that there is no MRSA in British pigs; at present 27% of all antibiotics used in the UK, by people and animals, are given to pigs, primarily in intensive indoor factory farms to keep them alive in the overcrowded, stressful and contagious conditions.

Most of the pig feed used by factory farms in Europe is supplied by Cargill, one of the giant corporations that dominates the global market in animal feed. Having grabbed huge tracts of land in South America and evicted the indigenous smallholders, often with violence, it supplies genetically modified soya to factory pig farms in Europe which supply pork to every supermarket and corner shop in the UK. Many thousands of hectares of soya are grown on cleared rainforest and cerrado habitats and on land that was formerly divided into small scale holdings, poisoning the land and people with herbicides and pesticides and depriving locals of a means to grow food to feed their families.

If food was exempted from the trade agreements we would be free to protect our remaining farmers, not least those pig farmers that have miraculously survived the Blair government's dysfunctional policy of raising UK welfare standards while at the same time allowing cheap imports from factory farming methods that are illegal in the UK. If we all make consumer choices that support the UK's healthy and humane small scale farming, we can keep our farmers on the land where they have been producing healthy and wholesome food for generations.

5.2 Compassion in World Farming: Food Sense

By Philip Lymbery

One of the most important challenges of our time is how to feed a growing world population at a time of shrinking resources. And what role should be played by industrialised animal rearing, or 'factory farming'?

A common sense approach to feeding the world

Planet Earth recently heralded its 7 billionth baby. Nearly one billion people are currently hungry[1]. By the middle of the century, there will be 9 billion people or more to feed. We need an important reality check – factory farming is not feeding the world; in fact, the grain-feeding of confined animals uses more food than it produces[2]. It is part of a highly resource-intensive and wasteful food system. The present failure to feed people is scandalous and requires nothing less than urgent action. Industrialised animal rearing is a major factor holding back our ability to feed all of the world's people.

The United Nations estimates that food supply needs to increase by 70-100% by 2050[3, 4]. The current food system, increasingly based on the industrial model, is hugely wasteful. More than half the food value of the world's crop harvest is lost; through losses after harvest, food waste and feeding vast quantities of grain to factory farmed animals[5].

Compassion in World Farming is arguing for '**Food Sense**'; a common-sense approach to feeding the world that puts people first, reduces food waste and is based on farming like tomorrow matters.

Put people first

A third of the world's cereal harvest is fed to farm animals[6, 7, 8]; if it were used directly for human consumption it would feed about 3 billion people[9]. In addition, 97% of the world's soyameal is destined for farmed animals[10].

Industrial livestock production involves feeding vast quantities of human-edible food to confined animals. If given the chance under more natural conditions, those animals would convert things that people don't or won't eat into edible food for humans. For example, ruminants, like cows and sheep, will turn grass into meat and milk. Chickens will search pasture, woodlands and orchards for food; producing meat and laying eggs. Along with pigs, they will recycle food waste with great enthusiasm.

The rise in industrial animal rearing in recent decades has put farm animals directly in competition with people for food. And people are losing out. For every 6kg of plant protein such as cereals fed to livestock, only 1kg of protein on average is given back in the form of meat or other livestock products[11]. In terms of food value, for every 100 food calories of edible crops fed to livestock, we get back just 30 calories in the form of meat and milk[12]; a 70% loss.

Factory farms are food factories in reverse; they waste it, not make it; and they waste valuable cropland in the process.

As a recent UN food security report put it:

"When livestock are raised in intensive systems, they convert carbohydrates and protein that might otherwise be eaten directly by humans and use them to produce a smaller quantity of energy and protein. In these situations, livestock can be said to reduce the food balance[13]."

The story is repeated when we consider our dwindling fisheries. Up to a third of the world's fish catch never reaches a human mouth; much of it is diverted to feed farmed fish, pigs or poultry. Producing one tonne of farmed fish like salmon and trout takes between two[14] and five tonnes[15] of wild fish.

People don't have to choose between eating cereals or meat. Both can be produced far more effectively if farm animals are kept in ways that add to the world's food supply, rather than detract, as they do on factory farms. The industrial approach forces animals and people to compete for food in a way that ill-serves them both.

Stop wasting food

North America and Europe waste up to half of their food. That's enough to satisfy the hunger of the world's billion undernourished people between three and seven times over[16].

Globally, about a third of food produced for human consumption is lost or wasted[17].

That excludes the vast quantities of food fed to livestock. Developing countries can experience losses of 30-50% of staple crops simply for want of decent storage facilities, refrigeration and transport[18, 19].

Much greater effort is needed to reduce food waste. Householders in the UK alone, for example, throw away a quarter of the food they buy. Reducing food waste in storing, manufacturing, distributing and consuming food would free up much of what is needed for a growing population. It would also make better use of the resources that went into making it; land, oil, water and the inevitable greenhouse gas emissions. For example, the irrigation water used to grow the world's wasted food would satisfy the domestic needs of 9 billion people[20].

Reducing food waste is key to an effective food system. It will require changes in practices and investment, but they could be transformative. Humanely kept pigs and poultry potentially have a big role as nature's recyclers through turning unavoidable food waste into food products.

Farm like tomorrow matters

The world's farmland could decline in productivity by a quarter by the end of the century according to the United Nations[22]. Soil erosion is already affecting over 30% of the world's cropland[23]. Europe and North America have been losing soil at 17 times the rate at which new soil is formed[24]. Cropland cannot simply be expanded; it is being lost to urbanisation, salinisation and desertification at the same rate or faster than we are adding to it[25]. It is under pressure from the rise in land use for biofuels and the continued growth of industrialised livestock farming.

Degraded land becomes less productive or useless for crop production. Monocultures with their reliance on chemical pesticides and artificial fertilisers can be punishing to the soil and the environment. Much greater emphasis is needed on soil-healthy rotational farming with a mix of crops and farm animals. Nitrogen-fixing rotational crops integrated with livestock can reduce reliance on artificial fertilisers, as well as providing for better animal welfare.

Food Sense

What is needed is 'Food Sense' – a common-sense approach to producing food. A more effective food system geared toward putting food into people's mouths. Keeping animals humanely is fundamental – on farms, not in factories. 'Food Sense' can be seen through five guiding principles for animal production and consumption:

1. Pasture-reared ruminants

Food from ruminant animals, such as beef, mutton, lamb and milk, should be produced by grazing on mixed, rotational farms, permanent pastures or marginal lands. This converts plant-life that humans can't eat into edible food. The wasteful practice of feeding grain to confined cattle for intensively produced beef or milk should be ended.

2. Pigs and poultry on food waste and foraging

Pigs and poultry are nature's great foragers and recyclers – the perfect recipients of food waste. They should no longer be factory farmed; instead, being integral to mixed farms where they can forage and turn food waste into eggs and meat. The current practice of feeding them cereals and soya squanders vast amounts of food.

3. Food from mixed farms of crops and animals

Mixed farms where animals are rotated with soil-enhancing crop rotations should be encouraged. Most pigs and poultry in Europe and the USA are currently confined on factory farms. Restoring the natural link between farm animals and the land needn't require huge amounts of extra space. The UK, for example, rears over 800 million meat chickens a year. Keeping them free range would need an area around a third of the size of the Isle of Wight; less than one thousandth of the nation's total farmland[26]. Integrating them within mixed farming systems would benefit animal welfare and sustainability.

4. Fish for people, not livestock

Up to a third of the fish landed in the world is not consumed directly by people. It is used mostly as feed for farmed fish and other livestock. Overfishing and the practice of throwing back dead or dying fish are now well documented. The plundering of our seas to feed confined farmed animals is less well-known. Ending the practice would take pressure off our often overexploited seas.

5. Avoiding over-eating meat

Most people in the west eat more animal fat and protein than they need. The saturated fat in many meat and dairy products can be harmful to health and may contribute to obesity, type-2 diabetes and heart disease[27]. Reducing consumption of saturated animal fats by 30% would lead to about a 15% reduction in heart disease in the UK and Brazil[28]. Ensuring a balanced approach to eating resource-intensive meat, dairy and eggs would help reduce the high environmental impact of animal farming and improve human health.

Conclusions

In industrialised nations in particular, the last half century has seen many farm animals disappear from the land to be caged, crammed or confined on factory farms. Our global society currently wastes more than half its food in two ways.

We waste it by feeding farm animals with enough food to satisfy billions of people. An even greater amount is binned, sent to landfill or rots for want of basic technologies. Land is often being driven so hard that we are playing off tomorrow's sustainable harvests against today's short term gains.

With the prospect of 2 billion more people to feed by 2050, our food system needs to be 70-100% more *productive*, more *effective*. That cannot mean simply doubling farm outputs in a business-as-usual fashion.

Just doubling output from our current food system would be like a water company with badly leaking pipes, losing half their water, simply laying down a second set of equally leaky pipes. Yes, it would double the water to peoples' homes. It would also double the waste. Far better to have more effective pipes, free from leaks, than more of the same.

'Food Sense' is a call for a common sense approach to feeding the world. One that ends the competition for food between people and farm animals; reduces and recycles food waste; supports the keeping of animals on farms, not in factories; and delivers more effective food systems geared toward feeding all people, now and in the future.

Philip Lymbery, Chief Executive, Compassion in World Farming

References

[1] FAO (2010) The state of food insecurity in the world

[2] FAO (2011) Livestock in food security

[3] Bruinsma, J. (2009) How to feed the world in 2050

[4] UN (2011) The great green technological transformation

[5] Lundqvist, J., *et al.* (2008) SIWI Policy Brief

[6] Government Office for Science (2011) Trends in food demand and production

[7] Msangi, S. and Rosegrant, M. (2009) FAO: How to feed the World in 2050.

[8] Steinfeld, H., *et al.* (2006) FAO: Livestock's Long Shadow

[9] Calculated from FAOSTAT (2009)

[10] Steinfeld, H., *et al.* (2006) op. cit.

[11] Pimentel, D., *et al.* (2008) Human Ecology

[12] Lundqvist, J., *et al.* (2008) op. cit.

[13] FAO (2011) World livestock 2011

[14] Costa-Pierce, B.A. (2010) Marine Tech. Soc. J.

[15] Tacon, A.G.J. and Metian, M. (2008) Aquaculture

[16] Stuart, T. (2009) Waste

[17] Gustavsson,J. *et al.* (2011): FAO

[18] Parfitt, J., *et al.*(2010) Phil. Trans. R. Soc

[19] IMechE (2011) Population: One planet, too many people?

[20] Stuart, T. (2009) op cit.

[21] Lundqvist, J., *et al.* (2008) op. cit.

[22] Stuart, T. (2009) op cit.

[23] Brown, L. (2009) Plan B 4.0 Earth Policy Institute

[24] Pimentel, D., *et al.* (1995) Science

[25] Fedoroff, N., *et al.* (2009) Science

[26] Own calculation

[27] Lock, K., *et al.* (2010) The Lancet

[28] Friel, S., *et al.* (2009) The Lancet

This document is available online with full references, ciwf.org/foodsense

About Compassion in World farming

Compassion was founded in 1967 by a British dairy farmer who became horrified by the development of factory farming. We believe that factory farming is the biggest cause of animal cruelty on the planet. Today we campaign peacefully to end all cruel factory farming practices. Our passion is supported by hard evidence and fact. This underpins all our campaigns and makes us the leading experts in our field.

Raw is an initiative of Compassion in World Farming, developed in order to help achieve our mission of ending factory farming and advancing the wellbeing of farm animals worldwide.

5.3 Learning to Re-Value Nature

By Kristof Nordin and Stacia Nordin

In 1997, my wife and I were asked by the government of Malawi, Africa to move to this sub-Saharan nation to work on issues of HIV and nutrition. We quickly came to the realization that our initial efforts of attempting to integrate HIV with nutrition were incomplete without an additional emphasis on agriculture, economics, overall health, and sustainable living. When we began to explore the issues pertaining to Malawi's agriculture, we found that the great majority of the country had become dependent upon the production of a single staple crop—maize (corn)—to meet the demands of 'food security'. We also found that it was this limited agricultural focus which was leading, both directly and indirectly, to many of the other problems that the country faced in terms of malnutrition, poverty, disease, and environmental degradation. This compelled us to begin looking for local solutions to these local challenges. What we found not only amazed us, but transformed our entire perception of terms such as 'agriculture', 'food security', 'economics', and 'development'. We'd like to take a moment to share a few of these findings:

A Tradition Shift

Throughout the world, a growing number of farmers are finding themselves locked into ever-deepening cycles of economic despair and dependency. In order to find our way out of this oppressive maze, we need to take a look at how we arrived here. Prior to the tapping of the first successful commercial oil well, known as the Drake well, in the American state of Pennsylvania in 1859, traditional agriculture throughout the world was predominantly based upon systems of 'current sunlight'. The annual rays of the sun's energy were converted into plant growth that, in turn, was converted into animal growth (including humans), allowing all living organisms to form complex networks of mutually-dependent existence. All needs were met through these natural systems: food, fuels, building supplies, medicines, oils, fibers, and more. All of these things were, and still are, needed for the economical management of a healthy and sustainable household, which is where the very origin of the word 'economics' stems from; being the derivative of the Greek 'oikos' meaning 'house' and 'nemein' meaning 'to manage'. Due to the great importance that humanity once placed upon these natural resources, it was customary to find early communities fostering and cultivating a wide diversity of crops. It was not uncommon to find traditional agricultural systems harvesting as much—if not more—from forested areas as they did from their cleared field-crop systems. These 'natural' areas were a boon for ensuring habitat for wild game animals, for the provision of seasonal fruits, for firewood and timber crops, as well as for non-timber forest products such as mushrooms, root crops, honey, dyes, herbal medicines, and much more. Initially, it was in the midst of these wooded areas that smaller clearings were carved out to allow for the production of grain crops such as millets, sorghums, or maize.

Just over 150 years ago, however, a great deal of that changed when the world's energy source moved away from 'current sunlight' to the use of 'ancient sunlight' that had been trapped in the earth's crust in the form of fossil fuels. This extremely energy-dense source of fuel became the basis for revolutionizing the way that the world operated. Energy, by definition, is the capacity of a physical system to do work, so the extra energy that was provided through advancements in petroleum-based technologies allowed many countries to greatly intensify their workload outputs, resulting in what has been termed the 'industrial revolution'. This push towards ever-increasing output was quickly applied to the agricultural sector. By the early 1900's the first gasoline-powered tractors were making their appearance, eventually allowing farmers the ability to clear and cultivate ever larger tracts of land. The manually-cultivated fields and modest homestead gardens quickly grew into vast expanses of mechanically-plowed tracts of land. As urban areas expanded due to the migration of the rural workers to the factories jobs of the cities, these cities also began to demand specialized raw materials for production purposes as well as for convenient ways to feed the burgeoning masses.

Monocropping, the practice of growing a single crop or plant species over a large area, was quickly adopted to meet the growing demands of these industrialized populations, as well as to conform to the specialized innovations that were being made to a variety of farming implements and equipment, making the processes of planting and harvesting more suitable to the use of machines. This shift towards monocropping did several things. First and foremost, it served to reduce the diversity of plant and animal species upon which societies had become accustomed to using. This not only contributed to the deficiency of natural resources that many communities currently find themselves facing, but it also began to drastically alter people's eating habits, lifestyles, and their resulting health. Diets that had once been rich in diverse and seasonal nutrition—often utilizing up to hundreds of different food options—have now become limited to a handful a high-carbohydrate crops that are grown and harvested in a limited growing season.

This one-time harvest of all the year's food has also led to the problem of how to store all this food. Despite the efforts of agricultural organizations to improve storage techniques, there is still a great deal of post-harvest losses that occur due to spoilage, insects, and rodents. It has been estimated in some countries, such as Malawi, that there can be post-harvest losses averaging up to 25%. (Malawi Ministry of Agriculture and Food Security, 2011) It has also been reported that aflatoxins, a toxic derivative of a fungus called Aspergillus, can develop on just about any major staple food crop which is improperly stored in high-moisture conditions, and is believed to contribute to the growing number of esophageal cancer cases that countries such as Malawi are encountering. (Mlombwe, et al., 2009)

In terms of natural systems, one would be hard-pressed to find a more 'un-natural' approach to food production than that of monocropping. Consider for a moment a typical agricultural field anywhere in the world. These fields are generally areas that have been cleared of all trees, stones, or other 'obstructions' that are thought to interfere with the desired crop's growth. Often times even the groundcover is removed, or turned into the soil, through a process of plowing. These fields are then generally devoted to the planting of one variety of one species of one crop—most often a staple food crop. At the end of this process, that single crop is harvested and the remaining crop residue is very often removed from the field, or, as seen in many parts of the world, it is burned. This results in the soil being left bare, unprotected, and exposed until the following planting season when the entire process starts again.

Now, imagine for a moment what that very same field would look like if it were allowed to remain untouched by human intervention for a period of ten years. If you envisaged a young forest system then you would be correct. Nature is continually trying to move in the direction of diversified ecosystems, but we, as humans, have gotten into the habit of impeding or prohibiting this natural progression. Nature always plants in succession, meaning that it will start with short grasses and fast growing pioneer species to secure the soil in place and begin to rebuild the nutrient base and structure that is necessary to support ever-larger species of plants. Soon, one sees small shrubs and tree emerging, eventually evolving into systems that can support large trees, animal life, climbing plants, and millions of intricate and interconnected ecosystems. These ecosystems work in cooperation with each other, not in competition as is often thought when we witness the sometimes unsettling scene of a predator taking another creature's life for the purpose of nourishment.

Contrary to often excessive and wasteful behavior of humans, however, the behavior of the vast majority of the world's other predators serves to create a system of 'checks and balances' which work to ensure a natural harmony within natural systems. Take, for instance, the example of the tiny agricultural 'pest' known as the aphid. These small sap-sucking insects have the ability to reproduce asexually, eliminating the need—as well as the time that it takes—for the mating process. They are able to give birth to live young that get on very quickly with the process of reproducing the next generation. The adult female aphid can give birth to up to 12 offspring a day, and these progeny are often ready to carry on the reproductive process within another 7-8 days. It has been estimated that if all conditions were favorable, without any limiting factors of natural predators, disease, or other life-threatening factors, a single aphid could potentially reproduce a population of up to 600 billion aphids in a single season! Fortunately, this rapid overpopulation is constrained in natural systems due to the balance that is created by predators such as ladybugs, lacewings, hoverfly larvae, and parasitic wasps, as well as a variety of natural bacteria, viruses, and fungi. If we remove the habitat that supports the existence of these natural control measures, then we have immediately created an 'imbalance'. Lacewings, for example, are generally found on trees, shrubs, and grasses. When all the trees, shrubs, and grasses are removed from our agricultural systems we have, in essence, also removed the beneficial lacewings.

This leaves us with the problem of what to do with the now uncontrolled and growing population of aphids. Conventional wisdom of industrialized agricultural has repeatedly encouraged farmers to fill this gap through the use of chemical pesticides, and when pioneer plant species arrive on the scene to perform their natural function of protecting the soil that has been disturbed by tilling they are labeled as 'weeds' and eliminated through the use of herbicides, and when the soil fertility becomes depleted because there is no longer any natural return of nutrients we are persuaded to compensate with the purchase and application of chemically-synthesized fertilizers. All of these chemical-based approaches have, rather insipidly, come to be regarded as 'agricultural inputs'.

Towards the end of World War II, agricultural researchers also began to have quite impressive and rapid successes with the cross-pollination of certain varieties of crops. This process, known as 'hybridization' built upon the work of the Austrian scientist, Gregory Mendel, who in the mid-1800s made great strides in the understanding and application of hereditary traits that are expressed through the offspring of plants and animals. In the late 1940's this technology was adapted to target specific staple crops, such as maize, wheat, and rice. These crops were specifically hybridized to become higher-yielding and to carry with them intentionally desired traits such as drought or pest-resistance. This enhancement in the qualities of a plant or animal that has been crossbred is generally referred to as 'hybrid vigor', but a major drawback to this technology is that a significant percentage of the subsequent generation is rendered sterile. Early animal breeders recognized this phenomenon when they would cross a female horse with a male donkey. The result was a 'mule' having the combined strength of a horse with the endurance of a donkey—extremely useful attributes in societies that depended heavily upon animals for assisting with manual labor—but the majority of these crossbreeds were also rendered barren, possessing 'hybrid sterility'. For farmers, this 'hybrid sterility' within crossbred varieties of crops also meant that they could no longer save seeds from year to year for replanting—a time honored tradition in many agrarian societies. Another drawback to the hybridization of crops—and a factor which is seldom added to the equation—is that for each generation of new hybridized seed-stock that is produced, land that could have been used for food production is displaced solely for the cross-pollination purposes of seed production, meaning that it actually takes two seasons on the same amount of land to produce one season's worth of food.

With new innovations in plant breeding, these modified varieties of crops came to be viewed as the solution to many of the world's food security problems. It was similarly found that these hybrid crops tended to maximize their production through the use of monocropping technologies. So, in an initiative that came to be known as the 'Green Revolution', hybrid seeds, synthetic fertilizers, and pesticides were swiftly introduced to countries around the world.

There was one other event that contributed to the rapid expansion in the production and spread of synthesized fertilizers, and that was the declaration in 1945 that World War II had officially ended. During wartime, countries such as the United States had been using large amounts of nitrates in the production of gunpowder, munitions, and larger explosive devises such as bombs. Nitrates, in certain states, tend to be highly explosive, but scientists also found that they can offer agriculture a very soluble and bioavailable form of nitrogen—a nutrient that is essential to plant growth, as well as being a fundamental component of all proteins which are essential to animal growth. When World War II ended, many of these nitrate-producing munitions factories were simply converted to the manufacturing of nitrate-based fertilizers. This is one of the reasons that, even to this day, persons or organizations that make large purchases of chemical fertilizer are closely watched by both domestic and international regulatory authorities.

An Economic Shift

Prior to the onset of the Green Revolution, traditional agricultural practices were predominantly considered to be—at least from an economic standpoint—'low-to-no-input'. Farmers were able to cultivate their crops without the need for the purchase of seeds, fertilizers, pesticides, or other any other expensive chemical inputs. The only real 'input' in terms of early farming systems was not economic at all; it was physical— and often based upon generations of cultural observations—consisting primarily of the labor, knowledge and skills that were required. And, in forest-based agriculture, even the labor was drastically minimized, comprised mainly of the traditional knowledge required for seasonal foraging and harvesting.

After more than 60 years since the onset of a 'Green Revolution' type of agriculture, which was intended to solve many of the world's food security problems, we are finding instead that many of these practices have actually led to the creation of even worse problems. Take, for example the traditional farmer who has chosen to sacrifice seasonal diversity in favor of the planting of only one crop that is harvested at one time of the year. The success of this hybridized crop now depends upon purchasing seeds, fertilizer, and very often chemical insecticides or herbicides. Now, this farmer finds that even in a bumper-crop year, he or she may be faced with the necessity to sell off much of the harvest simply to recover the expenses that have gone into the crop's production. Then, the farmer still needs to consider the financial capital that will be required for the following year. Many farmers will also attest to the fact that these annual operating costs tend to be continually on the rise. This is due to several factors. Firstly, these 'inputs' are extremely susceptible to fluctuations in the price of oil which is used in the manufacturing and transport of many of these 'inputs', and secondly, without any efforts being made to restore the soil's fertility, structure, or the balance of natural ecosystems, the farmer generally needs to compensate for these shortfalls with ever-increasing amounts of synthetic fertilizers and other chemical inputs.

In terms of traditional seed procurement, generations of observation taught humans that plants reproduce themselves through various methods of seed-dispersion. Farmers discovered how to mimic these natural methods as well as how to furnish creative means for the collection and storage of these seeds. Entire communities became accustomed to setting aside the hardiest seeds, sorting them in terms of their potential viability, and storing them until the following planting season. Today, these re-plantable seeds have come to be known as 'open-pollinated' or 'heirloom'— a wonderful term as 'heirloom' depicts something of value that is passed along from generation to generation.

A great example of this ingenuity, which is still in practice in several parts of the world today, is evidenced in the planting practices of the seed from the Winter Thorn Acacia tree (Faidherbia Albidia). This tree is often promoted as an agro-forestry species, especially throughout the Southern African region, due to the fact that one of the tree's useful characteristics is that it drops its leaves at the onset of the rainy season (unlike many other species that produce their leaves at this time). The tree's leaves are high in nitrogen, so the dropping of these leaves serves to fertilize the soil; while at the same time allowing sunlight to pass through the canopy layer permitting rain-fed crops to thrive. The seeds of this tree, however, are enclosed in an extremely hard-shelled casing. When establishing these seeds in a nursery, it often involves a rather painstaking process of physically cutting or notching each individual seed and then soaking the seeds in warm water for several hours before planting. Traditional farmers learned to sidestep this process by observing that cattle enjoy browsing on the fallen seed pods, which provide an excellent fodder. The digestive process of the cattle turned out to be sufficiently corrosive enough to break down the seed's hard covering. So, astute farmers learned to feed their cattle these pods and then send their cattle out to graze in the post-harvest fields. The seeds would pass through the animals and be deposited throughout the field in ready-to-grow mounds of nutritious dung, awaiting the onset of the next-season's rains.

This simple traditional planting technique is actually an ecologically complex and beneficially interconnected system that serves to pair animal management with improved plant growth through the use of locally available resources. It is a system that is designed for long-term gains as the increased maturity of the Acacia trees leads to the production of more seeds, more fodder for the animals, more nutrients for the soil, and higher yields of food for people. In addition, the tree's flower's serve to attract bees for the production of honey, the bark contains medicinal properties, and the trunks and branches are commonly used for firewood as well as in the manufacturing of beneficial products such as tools, canoes, pestles and mortars.

These long-term, low-input, and integrated approaches have typically become overshadowed by industrialized agriculture's push to 'clear the fields'. When monocropped techniques began to take hold, farmers were encouraged to remove many of the trees from their field as they were viewed as 'competition'. This push was further strengthened when countries began to displace manual labor through the use of tractors and other machinery as the existence of trees in fields made it difficult for the use of this mechanized equipment. As a result of this 'clear cutting' mentality, many people have now become convinced that we must choose between forests or food. By adopting agricultural systems that promote the extremes, we seem to have lost sight of any middle ground.

Even within 'reforestation' efforts, we often see these projects being approached with a singular 'monocropped' mentality. It is not uncommon to find communities being encouraged to plant hundreds or even thousands of a single tree species in one area, often in methodically spaced straight lines. To make things even worse, many of these projects often use introduced species of trees that are not edible for humans, not well-suited to the growing conditions, or worse, that even become detrimental to the area. A well-documented example that can be found throughout the Southern African region, and one which forestry 'experts' still routinely encourage, is the planting of large woodlots with the tree known as Eucalyptus or Bluegum (Eucalyptus camaldulensis). This tree is notorious for its ability to deplete groundwater levels. Early colonialists were well aware of this property as they frequently used Eucalyptus trees to dry up the wetland areas around marshes in an effort to minimize the spread of malaria. Eucalyptus is also said to give off a chemical 'growth inhibitor' from its leaf litter and root system, a process known as 'allelopathy', making the growing of other crops near these trees extremely difficult. These trees may serve a very important function in the Australian areas from which they originate, but when introduced to Southern Africa for their fast-growing properties they have ended up creating more problems than solutions for many of these communities. In some countries such as Brazil, Uruguay, Thailand, India, and South Africa where large monocropped plantations of eucalyptus trees have been established for the paper pulping industry, many local residents have complained of lowered water tables, droughts, deterioration of water quality, and a loss of fishing and other water resources, earning these plantations the label of 'green deserts'. (Environmental Paper Network, 2007)

Another shift that has taken place is that even when reforestation projects are being undertaken, they tend to have shifted from the 'free-of-charge' traditional systems that mimicked nature, to become economically high-input. A simple glance at a typical list of materials that are now frequently recommended for the 'construction and management' of a tree nursery will include: hoes, watering cans, polyethylene tubes, machete knives, fence posts, reeds or grass for fencing, topsoil, sand, manure, and labor costs. Communities very often come to associate these financial 'inputs' with financial 'limitations', and end up convincing themselves that any improvement to individual or environmental health depends upon outside funding or outside assistance. This serves to foster a self-depleting cycle of dependency where we find communities turning towards the solicitation of handouts to solve their problems rather than to the utilization of locally available solutions.

A personal example of this shift away from simplified solutions may help to illustrate this point. When we first moved to Malawi the soil around the house that we moved into had been swept bare in accordance with a cultural belief that bare ground equates to 'good hygiene'. In an effort to begin the natural process of rebuilding the soil's structure and fertility, we went out in search of organic matter to use for mulching. We were living within the campus of Malawi's largest Agricultural Research Station and were fortunate to find a large pile of leaves that had been raked up under a large tree, but which had not yet been burned as is also the customary treatment of most organic matter. We convinced a rather dubious-looking gardener to allow us to take these leaves off of his hands, of which we brought back to our house and spread on the soil. About a month later the rainy season began and we noticed a peculiar thing happening in the areas where we had mulched. Hundreds of seedlings were sprouting! This prompted us to go back and identify the tree that the leaves had initially come from, and to our surprise we found out that it was Red Mahogany (Khaya Nyasica), a tree that, due to its high economic value as a timber tree, has been rapidly disappearing throughout the country and has now become subject to government regulation. One day the Farm Manager from the Research Station paid a visit to our house. Upon seeing the hundreds of Mahogany seedlings sprouting up out of the ground he declared, "How did you get those to grow? They are very difficult to propagate in the nursery." He seemed a bit surprised when we explained that we really hadn't done anything except for following the natural processes of what one might find occurring in a forest system; allowing seeds to fall from a tree, covering them with fallen leaves, and then allowing the rains to do the rest of the work. That year, as others struggled to find the funding to obtain polyethylene tubes, watering cans, build fences and get their seeds to germinate, we ended up having more than enough surplus seedlings to share with just about anyone who was interested...for free.

A Value Shift

In many countries, local resources are not just being overlooked or forgotten about, they have actually become stigmatized. For many people, as the emphasis has shifted away from traditional food crops towards the cultivation of a handful of hybridized crops, the perceived value of these traditional crops has significantly decreased. A decrease in value quickly equates to a decrease in the cultivation, utilization, and even in the knowledge of the use of these resources. Traditional knowledge that used to be passed down from generation to generation is now often viewed as 'backwards,' and crops that once sustained generations of humans have come to be viewed as 'famine food.' As the perceived value of these resources continues to decline, the use of local resources is now often labeled as the last resort of 'poor people'. In fact, many of these resources are no longer even viewed as 'resources' any more, which according to the dictionary are things 'that can be turned to for support or help', but they have instead come to be viewed as 'trash'—'worthless or discarded material'.

This depreciation in value of low-input resources also means that there has been a great shift in the perceived value that is placed on high-input resources. This tends to manifest itself in ways that are contrary even to common sense. For example, I remember working in a Malawian village during the rainy season of 2002, a year which experienced a terrible 'hungry season'. There were several reasons for this so-called famine, ranging from political corruption to poor farming practices, but the major reason that was publicized throughout the media was that there had been a drought. The hungry season, however is triggered by the maize reserves from the previous year running short, so a 'drought' would have had to occurred during the 2001 rainy season for it to have an impact on food security during 2002. However, according to a World Bank report on Disaster Risk Management it reported that: "Forecasts for the 2001/02 wet season in Malawi were for near normal conditions. The total rainfall for the season was near normal, but despite this many observers have indicated that the weather conditions over the wet season may have been one of the triggers the 2002 food security crisis. This was due to the intra-seasonal variability of the rains. Such variability is characteristic of the rains in Malawi...Both prolonged dry spells and locally heavy rains were experienced, which adversely affected overall crop production." (Clay, et al., 2003) We find, when examining the evidence, that the main problem was not a 'drought' but rather about a two-week gap in the rains at a particularly vulnerable time during the maturation process of the country's predominant agricultural crop—maize. Ironically, about this same time it was reported by the World Health Organization that: "In 2000-2001 the worst floods in the past ten years were registered in Malawi, whereby 14 out of 28 districts and around about 120,000 families (660,000 people) were affected by floods." (World Health Organization, 2009) This highlights a problem which is becoming more common throughout many countries with climate change experts forecasting ever-more erratic rainfall patterns, it is not uncommon for monocropped fields, devoid of organic matter, to be plagued by heavy rains and dry-spells within the same year. These erratic weather conditions, however, should not come as any surprise as they have been consistently predicted for several years, and as we see in the World Bank statement 'such variability is characteristic of the rains in Malawi.'

For whatever the reasons that year, the maize crop didn't mature properly leaving many subsistence farmers extremely vulnerable. It was estimated that "from January to April 2002, between 500 and 1,000 people died of hunger or hunger-related diseases in the southern and central regions of the country." (UNDP, 2008) At this time, people became so desperate to acquire maize that many were resorting to selling personal property. I personally observed local villagers selling their goats, which at that time had a market price of about $30-40 US dollars, for the equivalent of about $1-2 US dollars. When I enquired I was informed by most people that they wanted to use the money to buy maize flour for food. At that time, the quantity of maize flour that the sale of a goat for two dollars would be able to buy would just barely amount to one day's worth of meals (primarily consisting of carbohydrate) for a small family. If, on the other hand, the maize dependency was removed from the equation and the owners of the goat actually viewed the goat as 'food,' the same family could have eaten for several days while gaining a great deal more in terms nutritional benefits. The following table highlights the nutritional differences from the described scenario between the consumption of a single goat (approximately 20 kgs) and the compared value of the two dollars worth of maize flour (approximately 4 kgs) that people were converting the goat into during that particular 'hungry season'. It is based on nutrients for an adult's needs with the bolded areas showing the superiority of individual nutrients:

Selected Nutrients		Approximate needs for Female 31-50y per day:*		20 kg Meat Goat 100 gm x 200 fresh, w/o bone		4 kg Maize Maize 100 gm x 40 whole kernel, dried	
		Units	amount	amount	adult days	amount	adult days
Macro-nutrients (provides energy)	Energy	Kcal	2,000	37,600	19	14,480	7
	Protein	g	46	3,480	76	324	7
	Fat	g	25	2,520	101	144	6
	Carbohydrate	g	130	0	0	3,076	24
Vitamins	V-B1 Thiamine	mg	1.1	12	11	15.6	14
	V-B2 Riboflavin	mg	1.1	22	20	8	7
	V-B Niacin	mg	14	440	31	144	10
	V-B6	mg	1.3	46	35	12	9
	V-B Folate	ug	400	800	2	1000	3
	V-B Panothenic Acid	mg	5	56	11	17.2	3
	V-B12	ug	2.4	262	109	0	0
Minerals	Iron	mg	18	240	13	140	8
	Phosphate	mg	700	27,200	39	9,640	14
	Potassium	mg	4,700	47,600	10	11,480	2
	Zinc	mg	8	580	73	72	9

Calculated by S. Nordin using local food composition tables

*(National Academy of Sciences, 2004)

Just by looking at energy alone, we see a drastic difference in being able to feed up to 7 people for a day with a bit of maize flour as compared to feeding 19 people for that same amount of time with an entire goat (or a family of 6 for one day compared to the same family of 6 eating for up to three days). No matter how you break it down, many of these current maize-based 'economic' choices that people are making concerning food security, whether it be in terms of its more modern financial use of the word or in the ancient Greek sense of 'household management', they just simply don't make good economic sense.

Throughout the Southern African region one of the cherished vegetable crops that is now frequently cultivated is that of cabbage (Brassica oleracea). This crop, native to the Mediterranean region, tends to be susceptible to insects and diseases when planted outside of its native areas. A common list of diseases that may affect cabbage include: black stem, black ring spot, black rot, cabbage wilt, club root, wire stem, and more. The list of insects that pose a threat to this crop is even longer: cabbage worm, cabbage aphid, cabbage fly, cabbage leaf miner, striped flea beetle, zebra caterpillar, cabbage looper, cutworm, etc. To ensure a successful cabbage crop, farmers must often purchase hybrid seed as well as various insecticides, fungicides, and chemical fertilizers. After all of these inputs, many farmers opt to sell their cabbage crops in local markets as a cash crop, indicating that consumers have placed a high enough value upon this crop to make it economically viable to compensate for the farmer's expenses. On the other hand, let's take the example of a vegetable that is commonly found growing wild throughout the Southern African region such as Bidens pilosa, (Blackjack or Spanish Needles in English). This vegetable is generally classified by agronomists as a 'weed' and farmers are encouraged to remove it from agricultural fields. It is an extremely hardy plant, tolerating wide fluctuations in rainfall, temperature, and soil conditions. It grows without the need for purchasing seeds, and is not susceptible to damage from insects or diseases. In fact, the plant contains pest-repellent properties that may be used to protect other crops. But, when we take a comparative look at the nutritional and medicinal properties between Blackjack and Cabbage it is where we really start to get a sense of the significant differences in 'value' between these two crops. The following chart looks at these contrasts with the bolded values—primarily in the Blackjack column—indicating the favorite:

Food Name / Type	units	Needs	Cabbage	Blackjack
Energy	kcal	2000	22	**39**
PRO	g	46	1	**3.8**
FAT	g	25	0.4	**4**
Fib	g	26	2.8	**2.92**
V-A	ug	700	13	**1800**
V-C	mg	75	20	**63**
CA	mg	1000	31	**1354**
copp	mg	2	0.01	**10**
Iron	mg	18	0.2	**15**
Phos	mg	700	15	**504**
Potas	mg	4700	97	**267**
zinc	mg	8	0.1	**19**
Antidiabetic			-	**Yes**
Antihypertensive			-	**Yes**
Antimicrobial			-	**Yes**
Antimalarial			-	**Yes**
Antioxidant			-	**Yes**
Anticancer			Yes	Yes
Anti-inflammatory			Yes	Yes
Antiulcer			Yes	Yes

Calculated by S. Nordin using local food consumption tables

When one considers the fact that so many countries in the world today are attempting to address problems of malnutrition, including micronutrient deficiencies such as Iron and Vitamin A, it begins to call into question the conventional wisdom of spending our money on low-nutrient, high-input, difficult-to-grow foods while quite literally throwing away the high-nutrient, low-input, easy-to-grow ones. This is only one example out of numerous similar comparisons that could be made. When seen in this light, many of the world's food security problems—especially in terms of adequate nutrition—should no longer be viewed as 'poverty-based' problems because the solutions do not necessarily require any financial inputs. If anything, many of these solutions help to break the financial dependency that farmer's have found themselves locked into through the expensive requirements of a 'Green Revolution' type of agriculture.

Another great example of an undervalued resource may be found in that of the Baobab tree (Adansonia species), which is native to the African continent. These trees have the unique ability to grow outward rather than upward, creating an unusually bulbous and stout trunk. They produce hard-shelled oblong fruits, which are extremely high in vitamin C (210 mg / 100 g of babobab fruit). The powder of the fruit can be used in many ways such as to make juice, jams, added to porridge, or in baked goods such as sour dough breads. The seeds of the fruit yield oil that is edible in small quantities, but more often used for commercial purposes such as cosmetics. The seeds may also be roasted and ground into a coffee substitute. The leaves are edible, tasting similar to spinach, and are a high source of iron (78g per 100g of dried baobab leaf powder). The bark yields a fiber that may be sustainably harvested without killing the tree and woven into fabric and rope. The multi-functional economic value of this tree has been tremendously overlooked by most of Africa and the world. According to National Geographic Magazine, the potential value of the international market for baobab products stands at a billion US dollars per year. (National Geographic staff, 2012) Unfortunately, despite the growing economic interest, we have yet to see many individuals or projects devoted to the replanting or replenishing of these trees. One of the reasons for this may be due to the fact that they don't need to be replanted very often as the baobab tree has been estimated to live for upwards of 2-4,000 years! That's an amazing return on your energy since it only takes 5 minutes to put a seed in the ground which has the potential to give food to a nation for the next several thousand years. If protected from human destruction, they often sprout on their own and grow where people have eaten them and simply thrown the seeds on the ground. This marvelous tree should be celebrated as an African 'miracle' for all of its uses, but instead (as with many other local resources) it is all to often viewed as a 'bush food' and, at times, even cut down to allow for the further planting of maize crops.

When one begins to break the cycle of monocropped-thinking, it opens up a virtual plethora of opportunities for diversified income-generating activities. Taking a lesson from nature, we find that it is through diversity that the effects of extremes are balanced. This lesson may also be applied to the economics of income generation and livelihoods; the more diversified the income-base becomes the more likely it will be able to respond to fluctuations in market prices, variations in supply and demand, and even disasters (natural or otherwise).

Consider the typical maize, rice, or wheat farmer anywhere in the world that has planted the vast majority of his or her land to the production of a single crop. By choosing to disregard the diversity of natural systems the farmer has immediately created an extremely precarious situation which becomes highly susceptible to the effects of floods, drought, pestilence, crop diseases, and even malnutrition and human diseases. In addition, any reduction in the yield of this singular crop will also carry with it significant implications for the economic value of that crop. Whether or not the crop succeeds, the farmer is still faced with the economic inputs that went into the effort of production. If the crop succeeds the farmer must sell off a certain percentage to recover his or her costs, but if the crop fails then the farmer must consider selling other things. In many countries, crop failure has resulted in selling off land, livestock, and even attributed to situations of bonded labor, child labor, or prostitution. On the other hand, let's assume that it is a successful growing season and everybody reaps a bumper harvest. In terms of economics, this too has adverse effects, especially if everybody is producing the same product. This surplus tends to flood local markets, driving down the market price, and leaving the farmer in a situation where they have to sell off even larger amounts of their harvest to recover the costs that went into production. Amidst all these market fluctuations, people tend to overlook the fact that these staple crops are not 'commercial products' that are being traded, as limited as they may be in nutrients, they are still people's food—the sustenance essential for an organism to maintain life, health, and growth.

Now let's look at the same system from a 'diversified' point of view. For whatever the reason, many so-called 'developing' countries which face seemingly disproportionate challenges of food insecurity, malnutrition, and poverty tend to lie within the 'tropical' or 'semi-arid tropical' zone. This means that one of their greatest assets is a relatively warm climate that generally tolerates plant growth throughout the entirety of the year. This is in sharp contrast to many temperate climate zones where the cold winters prohibit plant growth for sometimes up to two-thirds of the year. For this reason, let us look at a diversified cropping system within one of these tropical zones. Maize originated in Mexico and rapidly moved northwards into North America. If one looks at the line which indicates the start of the tropical region, referred to as the 'Tropic of Cancer', we see that it runs through the southern part of Mexico and downwards until it reaches the 'Tropic of Capricorn' in the Southern hemisphere. Anything between these two lines is considered 'tropical', but the area outside of these lines is generally considered to be temperate or, as one approaches the poles, frigid. This means that as maize originated above the Tropic of Cancer and comfortably made its way even further northward into the northern temperate regions, this can very easily be considered to be a 'temperate crop'. In fact, of the top ten countries which routinely produce the most maize in the world, 8 of them lie either completely or significantly within the temperate regions: United States, China, Mexico, India, France, Argentina, and South Africa. The two exceptions to this are Brazil and Indonesia. With this in mind, we see that in many of the tropical countries of sub-Saharan Africa, it is not necessarily a tropical crop which has come to dominate the agricultural landscape. Along with trying to get a temperate crop to adapt to tropical growing conditions, farmers in these tropical regions, despite having 12-moth growing seasons, have also adopted a temperate-climate system of agriculture which attempts to grow all the food for the entire year in a short 3-4 month period. This is what one might expect to see in the Midwest of the United States where the growing season is naturally abbreviated by a short summer and prolonged winter, but it does not necessarily make sense to adopt this system for countries that can be harnessing the potential of year-round seasonal production.

Diversification removes these limitations very quickly. For instance, in a country such as Malawi the rainy season typically begins around December and runs until March. Currently most farmers plant their maize in the beginning of the rains in December and wait until March or April to reap the benefits of that crop. Ironically, it right in the midst of this rainy season that many family's maize reserves from the previous year run short and they are left without food until the March/April harvest. This means that in the middle of the country's most productive agricultural period—the rainy season—is when the country now often faces chronic 'hungry seasons' leading on numerous occasions to situations of famine and even starvation. If a Malawian farmer chooses to plant more than one staple crop, however, many of these problems are quickly eradicated. For instance, maize can be harvested in March/April, but traditional staple crops such as millets and sorghums often mature around May/June. With the addition of a couple root crops like sweet potatoes and cassava the farmer now has access to staple foods in July-September, and crops such as local yams can be harvest right throughout the year. Numerous fruit and legume crops can be staggered throughout this mixed-cropping system contributing additional crops in every season of the year. And, vegetable crops, rich with essential vitamins and minerals, often reach the pinnacle of their abundance during the time that is currently viewed as the 'hungry season'. When these diverse cropping systems are combined with the sustainable management of other natural resources such as woodlots for fuel and building supplies, animal management systems that provide sources of protein and well as income generation and soil fertility, and water harvesting systems that save energy and create opportunities for dry-season irrigation, one begins to see a picture emerging of a well-balanced, economically secure, food secure, and sustainable way of living.

Now we can start to calculate some of the extra economic value that can be derived from a natural, organic, and integrated system. If a local farmer can move away from the high costs of synthetic fertilizers through the use of composting, mulching, crop rotation, intercropping with leguminous plants, worm farming, agro-forestry, making 'compost tea' or liquid manure, the use of composting toilet systems or any other of the number of natural soil-fertility building measures, he or she can literally save the equivalent of hundreds, even thousands, of dollars in production costs. Next, through diversified cropping systems that use companion planting principles, fragrant pest-repelling herbs, the utilization of beneficial predators, and the utilization of other integrated pest management (IPM) techniques, the farmer can eliminate the need for expensive (and toxic) chemicals. Through proper seed saving techniques and the use of open-pollinated varieties there is no longer a need to buy expensive hybrid seeds. Eventually, all of these savings begin to add up to huge economic benefits. If a farmer doesn't have to put money into a production system then any sale of produce or products from that system transforms itself into immediate profit. If families find that they are not spending a small fortune on agricultural inputs, these savings can be turned back into investments in the family member's futures, such as the cost of education, healthcare, or even future savings. Diversified living systems also have the added advantage of providing expanded business opportunities. For example, the addition of integrated animal systems offers the potential for the additional sale of eggs, milk, manure, meat, leather, and the animal's offspring. Diversified woodlots may provide economic opportunities for the sale of timber, firewood, honey, mushrooms, medicines, fruits and tubers. Simplified food processing can open up possibilities for the sale of dried goods, herbal teas, spices, jams, jellies, dairy products, pickles, oils, syrups and more. With a bit of creative thinking many other on-site natural resources may also be turned into an economic advantage. For example, various grasses may be used for thatching, weaving, wicker or cane products; bamboos may we turned into fencing and building materials as well as a wide variety of products from drinking cups to rain gutters; educational opportunities may even arise to serve as a facilitator for community trainings, to offer informational tours, or to conduct demonstrations of various techniques, all of which have the potential to generate additional income.

In a bit of an over-simplified metaphor, diversification is the polar opposite of 'putting all our eggs in one basket'. By putting a variety of eggs (along with a whole host of other provisions) into an assortment of baskets, we increase the ensured success of a system while decreasing its vulnerability. In a diversified system, if one egg should happen to crack, there is no need to trouble ourselves with thoughts of famine; we simply feed the damaged egg to the cat to maintain its strength for helping to balance out the rodent population. Ideally, the aim of any sustainable system is to get to a point where the inputs going into the system are less than the total sum of the outputs from that system. These 'closed-loop' systems are made possible through the creative integration of the system's components, through the re-cycling of resources within that system, through designs that mimic the well-established sustainability of nature, and through the harnessing of the direct, or consequential, energy of current sunlight.

A Paradigm Shift

If diversification through the use of natural resources holds so much potential for the sustainable development of the human race, and for the resolving of so many of today's challenges, then why has it not gained greater acceptance? There are several answers to this question. First of all, the social paradigm that has swept across 'industrialized' countries in the wake of the fossil fuel (ancient sunlight) revolution has convinced many people, including those in non-industrialized countries, that all systems previously based upon systems of current sunlight are now obsolete or even 'primitive'. This is in line with the 'stigmatization' of resources that we have already discussed. Instead of using the vast stores of the world's traditional knowledge as a foundation upon which to build our future, we have discarded the great majority of it as being 'archaic'. This has resulted in a situation where we find ourselves believing that the challenges we currently face in terms of food security, energy, economics, nutrition, education, population growth, health care, etc are all unique to our specific generation and there are no precedents or guidelines for us to follow. We end up blindly trying to weave our way through a future in which we have unknowingly become the source of our own blindness.

As industrialized countries have capitalized upon the unrestricted use of resources and the use of unsustainable sources of energy, they have also grown to dominate the global discussion concerning the definition of 'development'. This model has come to exemplify the ideal to which many in the world now believe the whole world should now be aspiring. There is often an unspoken sentiment which underlies many discussions concerning the adoption of sustainable systems that goes something like this: 'All of the richest countries in the world have gained their wealth through industrialization. Why must we experiment with "sustainable development" on the world's poorest countries when it is all based on an unproven idea?' The very premise of this argument is inherently wrong. Sustainable systems are actually those that have been tested and proven to be effective in the sustaining of thousands upon thousands of generations of people. The current model, however, when placed against the backdrop of human history, amounts to no more than a blink of the eye. Yet in that short period of time the dizzying pace at which the planet's resources have been consumed has managed to produce a whole host of new hurdles which will need to be surmounted, primarily by subsequent generations.

The true economic impact of the industrialized approach has yet to be realized in its entirety. Take for instance the global crisis of malnutrition. Due to the nutritional limitations arising from the current monocropped approach to 'food security,' we see many nations now adopting expensive supplementation and fortification programs to compensate for the nutritional shortfalls. To illustrate the economic costs associated with these programs, take an example from Malawi that was highlighted in a USAID document stating: "Current public health responses to vitamin A and other micronutrient deficiencies include mass food fortification and the dissemination of nutrition supplements. In Malawi, for example, the government distributes vitamin A capsules through health centers and works with local food processors to fortify cooking oil. Because deficiencies continue to be a problem, the government recently initiated a program to fortify the country's sugar supply with vitamin A. Irish Aid, the Irish government aid agency, has since committed 4 million euro to assist with roll-out and implementation." (AIDSTAR-One, 2012)

The other factor to keep in mind is that these programs are not generally designed for long-term sustainability. They are, instead, a therapeutic approach to an ailment that has arisen out of human shortsightedness. Many of these programs are founded upon foreign assistance and the importation of resources rather than upon the local use of natural resources. This puts additional economic strain on the governments of these countries to fund these projects, often achieved through the use of loans that accumulate interest and end up being even more expensive than the initial start-up costs. Due to the fact that supplementation and fortification programs are based upon the immediate assistance to affected individuals, frequently without a concerted emphasis being placed upon behavior change, when these programs are phased out many countries quickly revert back to the deficiencies that they were facing at the time of the programs' commencement.

If, on the other hand, people are educated about locally available high-value sources of nutrition, it offers them an opportunity to attain the knowledge that is needed for assuring the health and wellbeing of a population. This education does not need to create an extra financial burden if integrated into the already-established institutions of a country's health, education, agriculture, or extension sectors. This education can, and should, also be integrated with knowledge of natural medicines, biofuels, building supplies, timber crops, fodder for animals, dyes, oils, etc—this, in turn, serves to reinforce practical application of this type of education, consequently influencing the diversification of all public and private sectors in the direction of the sustainable provision for the diverse nutritional needs of any society. When communities are encouraged to save seeds, propagate, share and utilize their natural resources, we end up with a system that become self-replicating and sustained by low-input community efforts rather than on the need for outside financial assistance. Again, we find the diverse sustainability of low-input high-output systems becoming a logical replacement for the current high-input low-output systems that so many societies have come to rely upon.

The majority world's current challenges will not be solved through economic means, but rather through a change in people's thoughts, attitudes, perceptions, and behavior. It is common to hear the argument being made that as a result of growing population pressure, the amount of available land throughout the world that is available to support the world's food requirements may be inadequate. A publication for the United Nations Food and Agriculture Association (FAO) states: "In the developed countries, the area of arable land in crop production peaked in the late 1960s, then remained stagnant for some time and has been declining since the mid-1980s. Hence growth in crop yields accounted for all of their growth in crop production and in addition compensated for declines in their arable land area." (Bruinsma, 2009) This underscores a typical error in reasoning which theorizes that since agricultural land in diminishing the only way to intensify production is to make the limited crops that we've come to rely upon ever-more efficient and higher yielding. Just as hybridization was offered as the solution to the world's food production problems in the 1940's, genetic engineering is being promoted under the same guise today. Proponents of this new technology claim that genetically altered plants will have the ability to help end hunger and malnutrition in the world, while critics of genetic engineering often focus on the unforeseen dangers to people who eat these new foods. There are many people who are concerned that there has not been enough research on the long-term effects that these plants may have on consumers. The validity of these concerns may certainly deserve further investigation, but at the same time they seem to be taking emphasis away from the bigger picture—the fact that the need for this approach is completely eliminated through the resilience of diversification.

This new science has many implications for humans and animals, but currently much of the research is being focused on the creation of new varieties of plants, which will have certain desirable characteristics. These characteristics can generally be grouped into three main categories: higher yields, pest or disease resistance, and nutritional modification. When viewed in this light, we need to ask ourselves why we would be so quick to jump to a hi-tech, expensive, and potentially risk-carrying technology when we have time-tested, natural, low-cost and risk-free solutions that are being ignored. For instance:

- Higher overall yields can easily be achieved when one compares the production of year-round mixed crop systems to the single-season monocropped methods that are currently being used. We may see a smaller yield of one particular plant within the system when compared to the monocropping of a single food and its one-time harvest at the end of a single season, but this is quickly offset and drastically surpassed by the production of diverse and continual harvests throughout the year in an integrated mixed-crop system. By using seasonal and diverse cropping systems, there is no need to genetically modify single plant species for higher yields; we simply need to use the ones that we've always had available to us more wisely and abundantly.

- Insects and diseases become naturally managed as the balance returns to the land and we begin to take advantage of local plant and animal resources that have adapted over many years to their various conditions. Diversified ecosystems improve the health of the soil, the health of the plants, and encourage the proliferation of beneficial predators. This eliminates the need for genetically modified 'resistant' plants.

- Growing and eating a wide variety of healthy plant foods on a year-round basis eliminates nutritional deficiencies. This takes away the need to genetically alter single food crops to include all of the nutrients that a person should be receiving. Trying to meet all of our nutritional needs through the use of a limited handful of plants is not only unhealthy for us as humans, but also unhealthy for the environment from which we receive our food.

The idea that the world has run out of room to meet its needs is, plain and simply, a myth; a fallacy of reasoning, which has caused us to believe that there is only one accepted way in which the world's needs can and should be met. When one looks at concepts such as vertical food stacking, urban gardening, functional landscaping, forest farming, permaculture, or any other of the myriad of integrated sustainable production systems that currently exist, but which have so often been overshadowed by the industrial approach, we quickly get a sense that we have yet to even come close to tapping into the world's, or human's, ability to provide for our needs. In one of the first books on the techniques of 'forest farming' systems, the authors, J. Sholto Douglas and Robert A de J Hart, state that, "Of the world's surface, only 8-10% is at present being used for food production...With the aid of trees, at least three quarters of the earth could supply human needs, not only of food but of clothing, fuel, shelter, and other basic products." (Douglas & Hart, 1978)

Most critics of genetic engineering are neither anti-science nor anti-research. In fact, many have been advocating for more research, but in a sustainable and integrated direction. My wife and I live at Malawi's largest institution dedicated to the research of agriculture, but when one really digs into the truth we find that for the past 60 years or so the great majority of time, energy, and money has gone into the researching of only one plant from the Americas...maize. And now when maize has reached its physical limits we want to change its genetic make-up to push it to even further extremes, and when a solely maize-based diet has resulted in 48% of Malawi's children presenting as nutritionally 'stunted' we want to genetically change maize to change the nation's nutrition or artificially fortify commercial food products. Malawi is rich with natural resources. There are literally hundreds of traditional food crops that could incorporated into the research paradigm, doubling or even tripling the size of many research stations, creating value-added products, opening up export markets, providing employment opportunities for the nation's youth who are graduating from colleges, and more. These resources could also be used to end the chronic 'hungry season', reverse the country's dismal record of malnutrition, eliminate micronutrient deficiencies, and alleviate poverty (both by saving money and by creating new opportunities to make money). We don't have to study our natural resources with a mindset of 'how do we change them' or 'how do we design a chemical to get rid of them', we need instead to establish the mindset of 'what do these resources have to offer us and how can they be naturally utilized to their fullest potential'. This eliminates the need for genetic engineering and quickly places us into agricultural systems that are diverse, nutritious, organic, natural and sustainable.

The integration of natural systems should not be seen as an economic 'hindrance'; it is, in fact, quite the opposite. What we have found in Africa is that when traditional foods, which have become stigmatized over time as being 'poor people's food,' are finally learned to be re-valued in terms of: their nutritional value, their value for improving food security, their value for reducing agricultural inputs, and their value as a 'resource' rather than as a 'waste', it is then that markets begin to emerge. A great example of can be found in the Blackjack plant that we highlighted earlier in this chapter. In Malawi it is all too often seen as a 'poverty food' and shunned as a weed, but just across the boarder in Zambia, where the exact same plant is valued for its taste and nutritional value, it has become a market commodity that is dried, professionally packaged, and sold in country's grocery stores. The only difference between the discarded Blackjack plant in Malawi and the economically viable Blackjack plant in Zambia is a mental perception of the plant's value. When we learn to re-value every aspect of our natural resources, we will finally be able to 'capitalize' upon these resources in an economically and environmentally sustainable way that will ensure that the needs of the planet's population will be continued to be met long into the future. We simply need to keep in mind the fact that solutions for humanity's ensured existence already exist. We also need to keep an optimistic outlook on how we meet these challenges. We can choose to view the plant's 7 billion people as 7 billion problems, or, we can choose to transform those 7 billion people into 14 billion hands that are working towards sustainable solutions. These solutions are readily available and can be implemented throughout the world without the need for expensive financial inputs, but in order to make this a reality we need to come to the realization that our ensured existence depends upon nature's ability to provide for all of our needs. We would do well to remember that it is not nature that we need to change to suit the needs of humanity; but rather it is humanity that needs to change to suit the needs of nature.

References

AIDSTAR-One, 2012. Technical Brief Permaculture Design for Orphans and Vulnerable Children Programming. s.l.:USAID.

Bruinsma, J., 2009. Expert Meeting on How to Feed the World in 2050, s.l.: Food and Agriculture Organization of the United Nations. Economic and Social Development Department.

Clay, et al., 2003. Disaster Risk Management Working Paper Series, No. 7, Malawi and Southern Africa Climatic Variability and Economic Performance. s.l.:World Bank.

Douglas, J. S. & Hart, R. A. d. J., 1978. Forest Farming. s.l.:Rodale Press.

Environmental Paper Network, 2007. Social Impacts of the Paper Industry. s.l.:s.n. Malawi Ministry of Agriculture and Food Security, 2011.

Malawi Agricultural Sector Wide Approach: A prioritise and harmonised Agricultural Development Agenda: 2011-2015. Lilongwe: Malawi Government.

Mlombwe, Y., Dzamalala, C., Chisi, J. & Othieno-Abiny, N., 2009. Oesophageal cancer and Kaposi's Sarcoma in Malawi: a comparative analysis. Malawi Medical Journal, 21(2), pp. 66-68.

National Academy of Sciences, 2004. Dietary Reference Intakes (DRIs): Recommended Intakes for Individuals, Vitamins, s.l.: s.n.

National Geographic staff, 2012. Africa's Iconic Baobab—the vitamin tree. [Online] Available at: http://blogs.ngm.com/blog_central/food/[Accessed 7 July 2012].

UNDP, 2008. Development Report 2007/2008: Fighting Climate Change: Human solidarity in a divided world, s.l.: s.n.

World Health Organization, 2009. Humanitarian Appeal Country Profile: Malawi. s.l.:s.n.

Part 6: Green Economics: The Economics of Environmental Justice and Survivability
6.1 Avoiding Extinction: The Economics of Survival and Resilience

By Graciela Chichilnisky

What Next?

For the first time ever, humans dominate planet Earth. We are changing the basic metabolism of the planet: the composition of gases in the atmosphere, its bodies of water, and the complex web of species that makes life on Earth. What comes next?

The changes we are precipitating in the atmosphere are fundamental and can lead to disruptions in climate and global warming. Signals abound: in the Southern hemisphere melting glaciers are observed and ice sheets are melting in Antarctica; in the Northern hemisphere Alaska's permafrost is melting, sinking entire towns whose inhabitants are being relocated at a cost of $140,000 per person. Greenland's ice sheet is gone, creating hostile climate conditions for a number of species such as the polar bear that are now close to extinction. In Patagonia and the Alps we observe mountains without ice or glaciers, reducing the ability of these regions to store water needed for human consumption. In the Caribbean seas 50% of corals are already extinct. Desertification has overtaken 25% of China's land mass. Climate's instability has led to Australia's longest draught on record, followed by the worst floods in that continent's history. We observe disappearing summer ice in the Arctic Seas and soil erosion and storm surges in Alaska. Where is all this coming from? The rapid industrialization of wealthy nations during the last century is responsible for most of the changes and for the risks they entail. Historically OECD nations originated 70% and now still 60% of all global emissions of carbon, emissions that most scientists in the world, including those in the United Nations Intergovernmental Panel on Climate Change, believe to cause climate change. China's inexorable industrial growth of the last two decades is a sign of things to come: it accelerates the risk of climate change and underscores that in 20 or 30 years into the future most emissions could come from today's poor nations as they assume their turn to industrialize.

Water expands when it warms. Since the seas are warming they are rising all over the world. This irrevocable upward trend is well documented: slowly but surely the rising waters will sink the Maldives and most other island states – there are 43 island states in the United Nations representing about 23% of the global vote and most or all could disappear soon under the warming seas.

The current shift in climate patterns has led to habitat changes for many insect species and therefore vector illnesses, for example new outbreaks of malaria in Africa. 25 million people are reportedly migrating due to drought and other climate change conditions, and the numbers are increasing rapidly.

In the US the consequences are less extreme but they stack up: the mighty Colorado River is drying up, its basin under stress prompts orders to turn-off farm water. Lake Mead's waters in Nevada exhibit record lows threatening the main supply of water to Las Vegas, and arid areas spread quickly as Vegas new sites double water use. Wild fires from drought conditions multiply and spread rapidly around the region and in California since 2006.

The world is aware of the connection that scientists postulate between climate change and the use of fossil energy. The largest segment of carbon emissions, 45% of the global emissions of CO2, originate in the world's power plant infrastructure 87% of which are fossil fuel plants that produce the overwhelming majority of the world's electricity.

This power plant infrastructure represents $55 trillion according to the International Energy Agency, about the size of the world's economic output. New forms of clean energy are emerging such as wind farms in Scotland and solar farms in Spain in an attempt to forestall carbon emissions. But the process is necessarily slow since the world's fossil power plant infrastructure is comparable to the world's entire GDP, and therefore changing this infrastructure can take decades. This timeframe - several decades - is too slow to avert potential catastrophes that are anticipated in the next 10 - 20 years.

What is the solution?

Below we propose a realistic plan that involves market solutions in industrial and developing nations, simultaneously resolving the problems of economic development and climate change and the global climate negotiations. But the climate change issue is just one of several global environmental areas that are in crisis today. Biodiversity is another: industrialization and climate warming threaten ecosystems. Endangered species include sea-mammals, birds such as cockatoos, polar bears, and marine life such as coral, sawfish, whales, sharks, dogfish, sea-turtles, skates, grouper, seals, seals, rays, bass and even primates survival is at risk, our cousins in evolution.

Scientists know that we are in the midst of the 6th largest extinction of biodiversity in the history of Planet Earth, and that the scope of extinction is so large that 75% of all known species are at risk today. The UN Millennium Report documents rates of extinction 1,000 higher than fossil records.

The current 6th largest extinction event in planet Earth follows the dinosaurs' extinction that took place 65 million years ago. But today's extinction event is unique in that it is caused, created, by human activity. And it puts our own species at risk. There is a warning signal worth bringing up: all major recorded planetary extinctions were related to changes in climate conditions. Through industrialization we have created environmental conditions that could risk our own species' survival.

99.9% of all species that ever existed are now extinct

Are we the next?

Will humans survive?

The issue now is how to avoid extinction.

Women and Survival

To avoid extinction we have to develop social survival skills. This seems reasonable and natural – yet the social skills that are needed are not here and are not obvious either. These skills could be quite different from what human societies' have achieved such as the individual survival skills that we are familiar with. A simple but somewhat unexpected experimental finding involves colonies of bacteria, which are one of the world's oldest living species. They have been around for billions of years and have shaped the planet's geology and atmosphere to suit their needs (Lynn Margulis). Bacteria are champions of survival. They seem to understand that they need appropriate survival skills, and have developed some unexpected skills based on 'altruism'. Yet since bacteria are some of the longest lived species in the planet, many times longer lived than relatively recent humanoids, we need to take their skills seriously as a model of survival. Bacterial colonies know how to avoid extinction. Here is new data: new findings indicate that *Escherichia Coli* ---- and indeed most known bacteria colonies -- when exposed to a pathogen or stressor such as antibiotics – not only evolve to develop resistance but the evolved members produce specific resistance tools that they do not need in order to share with the rest of the (non-evolved) members of the colony (cf. Hyun Youk & Alexander van Oudenaarden, <u>Nature</u>, 2010). In other words - when exposed to stress, mutant bacteria use some of their own energy - altruistically - to create a chemical called "*indole*" that protects non – mutants from the pathogen. This way the entire group survives. A way to summarize this finding is to say that *altruism* is an effective survival tool and bacteria -- those champions of survival – have developed and mastered altruism for this task.

This finding is quite different from what we believe to be effective survival skills in human colonies or societies. Until now human survival skills have focused on avoiding natural risks and confronting successfully the threats posed by other species that preyed on us, species that are dangerous to us. Altruism is often considered a weakness in human societies; it is considered to be a desirable trait rather than a survival skill. Yet, it is a survival skill. Aggressive and individualistic behavior may have been a useful survival tool until now. The war society that humans have created has become an efficient killing machine. But when things change, as they are changing right now, then what used to be strength can become a weakness. And things have fundamentally changed and they continue to evolve quickly. Indeed physical strength and aggression matter much less today for human survival than intelligence. Some of the worst risks we face today are caused not by other species that prey on us, but by traits that evolved to succeed against our predators – for example extracting energy and burning fossil fuel to dominate nature and other species. in other words, we are now at risk due to the impact of human dominance on the planet. Our success as a species has become the source of our main social risks. Humans are causing some of the worst risks humans face. The situation is somewhat unusual and is new for our species, and it is also new for the planet itself. As the situation changes, the rules we used to follow for survival must change too.

Let's start from basic principles. Survival is about protecting life not just about inducing death. Life is difficult to define, but we all agree that it is a phenomenon characterized by reproduction. Only those systems that incorporate reproduction are said to be alive. Life forms are able to reproduce. To be alive means to be part of a time series of reproductive activities. Reproduction characterizes life. Destruction does not. Asteroids destroy very effectively, and so do volcanoes. But they are not alive, because they do not reproduce. We humans are alive because we do.

But reproduction requires fundamentally altruism rather than dominance and aggression. How so? This is simple. We must donate our energy and even our bodily resources and substance to be able to reproduce, sometimes at the cost of our own.

Yet in our male dominated society the essence of life is viewed differently. It is viewed as the ability to conquer, dominate and kill. Men think of life skills as those skills that allow them to win the battle for survival. War is an example. Ask any man what characterizes life. He will very likely say "the survival of the fittest" and "dog eats dog". This is a man's view of life. This may be because of the evolutionary role that males had originally in human's societies, a role that is somewhat outdated. The reality is that humans could not be live and indeed we could not be part of the chain of life, unless we reproduced. Women understand that reproduction means life, and requires altruism. Women donate their physical substance such as eggs, blood and milk – and they do so voluntarily – for the sake of reproduction. This is what reproduction is all about: voluntary donation of one's substance. All living beings - animals and plants - do the same. They donate their substance voluntarily to the next generation, sometimes at the cost of their own welfare and their own lives. Observe that donating voluntarily one's own substance, one's flesh and body fluids, is the very essence of altruism. And that this altruistic donation is the key to the survival of the species. The great British author and social commentator Jonathan Swift - once suggested, as a 'humble proposal' to the problem of poverty in Ireland, that humans should eat their own children (Swift, 1729). This is not as outlandish a proposal as it may sound at first sight. It helps to illustrate the point I want to make clearly. If the essence of life was the survival of the fittest, then humans would eat their children who are totally powerless at birth –nothing is less fit than new born infants. Their bodies could certainly provide a lot of protein and nutrition to fit adults. No species who ate its children would survive – it may not even get started as a species.

Survival depends crucially on reproduction and this means protecting the weak – the weakest of all – the small children. This is quite different from the blanket policy of survival of the fittest, which re the adult members of the species. Indeed, I venture to say that survival is more than anything about altruism and cooperation, and about the protection of the weakest. It is not about 'dog eat dog' -- it is not about dominance and survival of the fittest. It is about the nurturing and protection of new generations; it is about voluntary donations, about protection and nurturing of the weakest, sometimes at the expense of our own survival. These are facts of life, facts that women understand well. We could say that men got it all wrong.

Women understand because their evolutionary role is to protect the weakest of all – namely the children at birth. Women are critical to human survival – they are the key to reproduction and they provide voluntarily their substance and energy to give birth and protect the weakest as needed for the survival of the human species. Men miss this important aspect of survival because of their evolutionary role appear to values physical strength more than anything else. This is a role that seems increasingly out of date.

It is fitting to raise the issue of 'avoiding extinction' in this lecture, during the month of March, Women History Month, when this lecture is delivered. Women History Month takes place in the midst of a male dominated world and a male dominated culture that is focused on violence, economic competition, and wars of choice. It is particular fitting as to understand how, among the changes we need to avoid extinction, we need to assure a changing role for women so the entire ethos of destruction and dominance that permeates our male dominated society is balanced out by a modicum of altruism and the critical and necessary nurturing and protection of the weakest that is required to avoid extinction.

It is true that there have been changes in the role of women, most of all their rapid entrance in the market for labor in industrial societies. But this change has not been fast enough. Modern societies such as the US have enormous statistics of abuse of women at home and elsewhere, both physical and economic abuse. For example the US has a 30% gender difference in salaries, which does not budge. These are the salaries that are paid to men and women even when comparing men and women with equal training, same age and experience, with everything other than gender being equal. The gender inequality is prevailing, persistent and systematic. In any given society, there is a deep connection statistically between the amount of housework a woman does at home and the difference between male and female salaries in the economy as a whole. These are two different statistics that are apparently unrelated -- two indices of abuse – but they are indeed related, because when women are overworked and underpaid at home this leads them to be overworked and underpaid in the marketplace (Chichilnisky: "The Gender Gap") . Gender inequality in salaries is in reality legally sanctioned – for example the US still does not have an Equal Pay Act. Unequal pay is legal in the USA.

Why? Is there a reason to pay women less than men? If so, what is it?

The deepest suspicion created by sexism to explain the persistent unequal situation is based on a rationale of "genetic inferiority" of women. Even a former president of the oldest University in the US, Harvard University, Larry Summers, presented this suspicion in public as a plausible hypothesis to explain the 30% difference in salaries between women and men in our economy. Furthermore, when he was subsequently fired by the Harvard University faculty he served he went on to become an economic advisor of President Barack Obama. One wonders whether Mr. Summers would have been selected as an economic advisor of the President of the US – the first black US president - if he had presented in public his suspicions about the genetic inferiority of blacks, rather than the genetic inferiority of women. I venture to say he would not have been selected by President Barack Obama if he had said in public that blacks are genetically inferior. But saying this about women is acceptable, and went through and indeed was rewarded by President Obama with the economic advisory role. This was an amazing and very discouraging event for some of us, but not for the many US men who secretly or openly believe that women are indeed genetically inferior to men. One cannot but reflect the connection of the situation with the excuses that the Nazis presented to themselves to explain the most savage Holocaust in memory – namely, they explained Nazism as based on the genetic inferiority of the Jews. This is how serious is the issue of claiming genetic inferiority of some groups in our society.

Raising in public the hypothesis of genetic inferiority of women to explain their economic exploitation is not an innocent remark.

It is a way to justify a systematic way in which male dominated societies perpetrate economic and cultural abuse, violence and brutality against women, pornography, torture of women and rape that represent a form of social control and intimidation, and ultimately a deep social instinct against the altruism, protection of the weak and reproductive health that women bring to society and that is a necessary precondition for the survival of the human species. Our society's manifested hate and violence against women is critically connected with the self-destructive aspects of our society – and the problem of avoiding extinction that we face now.

Until we change the current male dominated culture of abuse and its barbaric treatment of women – until we revolt against the seeming acceptance of electronic games that the US Supreme Court found acceptable for children in their recent 2011 decision, games involving the systematic torture and killing of women as entertainment, and until we develop altruism as an efficient survival skill, our society will not be well prepared to avoid extinction.

Avoiding Extinction: Summary of what is to come

The future of humankind may be played out in the rest of this 21st Century. Here is a summary of the situation and what to do about it – which I will develop further in the rest of this piece.

First let's take stock of the world today: in a nutshell we see energy limits confronting enormous future global needs for energy today and in the future. The problem of overuse of natural resources, more generally, continues to be a clash of civilizations: it is a North – South impasse in using the world's resources. The North are the rich nations that inhabit mostly the Northern hemisphere of planet Earth, the South the poor. The former have about 20% of the world population, and the latter, about 80%. We examine the market's role in getting us here and in finding a solution, and define three building blocks that are needed for any solution going forward. We discuss the next generation of green markets; how to bridge the global wealth gap and to transform capitalism as needed for this purpose – and whether is this possible? We examine the role of the United Nations Kyoto Protocol and its Carbon Market in this global transformation process – by itself and in conjunction with other global markets for environmental resources – for water and biodiversity – that are still to emerge. We examine the critical role of women, how the global financial crisis fits into all this, what is the light it throws onto our future, and the lessons we have learned.

Avoiding extinction is the ultimate goal of Sustainable Development.

Financial and Global Environmental Crisis

While we try to climb up from the depths of a global financial crisis that started its deadliest stages in 2008, the world knows that the game is not over yet. Judging by the threats from the Eurozone, it could all re-start next year. The recent downgrading of the US as a debtor nation – for the first time in history – and its financial markets shocks underscore these points. At the same time, within a larger historical context, the financial crisis takes a second place. We have seen such crisis before. What we have never seen before is the global threat to human survival that is developing in front of our own startled eyes. We are in the midst of a global environmental crisis that started with the dawn of industrialization and exacerbated with globalization, ever since the Bretton Woods institutions were created after WWII to provide a financial infrastructure for international markets and for spreading the role of markets and industrialization across the world economy. In both cases, however financial mechanisms are at work, essentially financial markets are implicated in both situations.

Both the financial crisis and the environmental crisis are essentially two aspects of the same problem. How so?

We will explain how by using simple examples available through the media that is read by the average person in the street. The urgency of the situation has become clear. For example on Tuesday June 21 2011 The Times newspaper in London writes "Marine life is facing mass extinction" and it explains: "The effects of overfishing, pollution and climate change are far worse than we thought. The assessment of the International Program on the State of the Oceans (IPSO) suggests that a "deadly trio" of factors - *climate change, pollution and overfishing* – are acting together in ways that exacerbate individual impacts, and that "the heath of the oceans is deteriorating far more rapidly than expected. Scientists predict that marine life could be on the brink of mass extinction." Observe that *all the three causes* of extinction just mentioned – overfishing, pollution and climate change -- are attributable to the industrialized world who consumes the majority of the marine life used as sea food, and generates over 60% of the global emissions of carbon dioxide and uses 70% of the world's energy, all this while housing only 20% of the world's population. Industrialization is at work in the impending destruction and mass extinction in the earth's seas, the origin of life as we know it.

The complexity of the problem is baffling scientists. Normally the Earth self-regulates, but now we are tying the Earth's hands in self -regulating itself out of the problem industrialization has created.

There is no quick fix. The standard way that the planet regulates carbon, for example sucks carbon from the atmosphere to maintain a balance, is by using its vegetation mass, which breathes CO_2 and emits oxygen. Animals – for example humans - do exactly the opposite. Animals breath oxygen and emit CO_2. In balance, the two sets of species – vegetation mass and animals - maintain a stable mix of CO_2 and oxygen, and therefore since CO_2 in the atmosphere regulates its temperature, a stable climate. But the enormous use of energy by industrial societies is tipping the scales, preventing the planet to readjust. On the same date, page 17 of The Times, writes: "Planting trees does little to reduce global warming" and explains how a recent Canadian report (The Times, 2011) has found that "even if we were to plant trees in all the planet's arable land – an impossible scenario with the global population expected to rise to 9 billion this century – it would cancel out less than 10 percent of the warming predicted for this century from continuing to burn fossil fuels." Observe that it is not the developing nations with 80% of the world's population that are causing this problem. This is because over 70% of the energy used in the world today is used by 20% of the world population that lives in industrial nations, who emit 60% of the CO_2 therefore. These are the same industrial nations that created the Bretton Woods Institutions in 1945 and have consumed since then the overwhelming amount of all the Earth's resources (Chichilnisky1995,1998)

For these reasons I say that the financial crisis and the environmental crisis are two sides of the same coin.
They are at the foundation of the current model of economic growth in industrial nations and of its voracious use of the Earth's resources. The world's financial crisis and the global environmental crisis – the two sides of the same coin - both require a new model of economic growth.

This opinion is not just mine. Indeed, the newly created international group G 20, the first world leading group of nations that includes developing countries, met in Pittsburgh, USA, on September 24 -- 25, 2009. Their Leader's Statement (G-20 Leader's Statement, September 2009) states: "*As we commit to implement a new, sustainable growth model, we should encourage work on measurement methods so as to better take into account the social and environmental dimensions of economic development.*" "*Modernizing the international financial institutions and global development architecture is essential to our efforts to promote global financial stability, foster sustainable development, and lift the lives of the poorest.*" "*Increasing clean and renewable energy supplies, improving energy efficiency, and promoting conservation are critical steps to protect our environment, promote sustainable growth and address the threat of climate change. Accelerated adoption of economically sound clean and renewable energy technology and energy efficiency measures diversifies our energy supplies and strengthens our energy security. We commit to: - Stimulate investment in clean energy, renewables, and energy efficiency and provide financial and technical support for such projects in developing countries.- Take steps to facilitate the diffusion or transfer of clean energy technology including by conducting joint research and building capacity. The reduction or elimination of barriers to trade and investment in this area are being discussed and should be pursued on a voluntary basis and in appropriate fora.*" "Each of our countries will need, through its own national policies, to strengthen the ability of our workers to adapt to changing market demands and to benefit from innovation and investments in new technologies, clean energy, environment, health, and infrastructure. It is no longer sufficient to train workers to meet their specific current needs; we should ensure access to training programs that support lifelong skills development and focus on future market needs. Developed countries should support developing countries to build and strengthen their capacities in this area. These steps will help to assure that the gains from new inventions and lifting existing impediments to growth are broadly shared." "*We share the overarching goal to promote a broader prosperity for our people through balanced growth within and across nations; through coherent economic, social, and environmental strategies; and through robust financial systems and effective international collaboration*", and "*We have a responsibility to secure our future through sustainable consumption, production and use of resources that conserve our environment and address the challenge of climate change.*" I could not have written this better myself. **The G 20 knows the problems all right. What they don't know is the solutions. For this, read on.**

Green Capitalism

The task in front of us is nothing less than building the human future. In the midst of the 6th largest extinction of planet earth, facing potentially catastrophic climate change and extinction of marine life in the world's seas - the Basis of Life on Earth – we can fairly say that this qualifies as a global emergency. And with the adult humans in charge we came so close to the brink that it would appear right now that only the young can help.

A green future is about sharing the wealth and saving the planet. Is this an impossible mandate? We need to stave off biodiversity extinction and reduce carbon emissions, while rebuilding the world economy and supporting the needs of developing nations. Is this possible?

It is, and to understand the solutions we need to look closer at the root of the problem so we can change it.

The World since WWII

Rapid expansion of international markets since WWII – which were led by the Bretton Woods institutions – led to enormous consumption of resources. Industrialization is resource intensive. It was fueled by cheap resources from developing nations – forests, minerals, biodiversity.

These resources were and continue to be exported at very low prices – and as a result poverty grew in resource exporting regions and provided 'competitive advantage' in the form of cheap labor and cheap resources that exacerbated and amplified resource overconsumption in the North. Resources were over-extracted in poor nations desperate for export revenues, and over consumed in industrial nations – thus leading to an ever expanding Global Wealth Divide. Globalization since WWII increased together with an increasing Global Divide between the rich and the poor nations – the North and the South (Chichilnisky, 1994).

This is how the global financial system that was created by the Bretton Woods Institutions in 1945, which is tied up with the financial crisis of the day, is also tied up with the global environmental problems we face, and with the global divide between the North and the South (Chichilnisky, 1994). Since energy use goes hand in hand with economic progress, and most of the energy used in the world today is fossil (87%), GDP growth is closely tied with carbon emissions today. Industrial nations consume about 70% of the world's energy, and the North - South divide is therefore inexorably connected to the carbon emissions that are destroying the stability of our global climate. Of course the same North - South Divide is the stumbling block in the Climate Negotiation as it was clear in the last global United nations negotiations on climate issues, in Copenhagen Denmark Convention of the Parties of the UNFCCC (COP) 15 and then Cancun Mexico COP 16. The problem is: Who should use the world resources? Or, otherwise put, who should abate carbon emissions? , Chichilnisky and Heal (1994).

It can be said that we are re-living last century's Cold War conflict, but this time it is a conflict between China and the USA (Chichilnisky, Time Magazine 2009). Each party could destroy the world as they are the largest emitters and can by themselves change the world's climate. Each wants the other to "disarm" – namely to reduce carbon emissions – first. This time the conflict is between the rich nations represented by the USA and the poor nations represented by China. This time it has become clear that the solution requires that we overcome the North - South Divide, the use of the world's resources between the rich and the poor nations.

Otherwise put, global justice and the environment are two sides of the same coin. Poverty is caused by cheap resources in a world where developing nations are the main seller of natural resources into the international market, resources which are consumed by the rich nations. This perverse economic dynamics is destroying the stability of the atmosphere of the planet, undermining climate patterns and causing the 6th largest extinction in the history of the planet.

Humans are part of the complex web of species that makes life on Earth. How long will it take until this situation reaches its logical limits and victimizes our own species?

How to avoid extinction?

The Gordian knot that we must sever is the link between *natural resources, fossil energy and economic progress*. Only clean energy can achieve this. But this requires changing a $US55 trillion power plant infrastructure, the power plants that produce electrical power around the world (see *IEA*), because 87% of world's energy is driven by fossil fuels and power plants produce 45% of the global carbon emissions.

In short - how to make a swift transition to renewable energy?

Who Needs a Carbon Market?

Energy is the mother of all markets. Everything is made with energy. Your food, your home and your car, the toothpaste and the roads you use, the clothes you wear, the heating of your office, your medicines: everything. Changing the cost of energy, making dirty energy more expensive and undesirable and clean energy more profitable and desirable – changes everything.
It makes the transition to clean energy possible. We have the technologies – we just have to get the prices right. Is it possible to thus change the price of energy? Yes, it is. And it has been already done, although it requires more input at present to continue this process after 2012, as discussed below. This is what my life is all about now. This is what this presentation is all about.

Here is the background and a summary of the current situation. In 1997, the Carbon Market of the United Nations Kyoto Protocol was signed by 160 nations. In it, and after a long period of lobbying and designing the carbon market, I was able to write the structure of the carbon market (cf. Chichilnisky and Sheeran: Saving Kyoto, 2009) The Kyoto Protocol became international law in 2005 when the protocol was ratified by nations representing 55% of the world's emissions - and the Kyoto Protocol and its carbon market have now been adopted as law by 195 nations. The US is excluded. In creating the carbon market I helped change the value of all goods and services in the world economy because the carbon market changes the cost of energy the world over: it makes clean energy more profitable and desirable and dirty energy unprofitable. This changes all the prices of products and services in the world – since everything is made with energy - and drives the economy to use cleaner rather than dirty energy sources. It is more profitable and less costly to use clean energy that reduces emissions of carbon now, this is precisely the role of the carbon market that I designed and I wrote into the United Nations Kyoto Protocol in Kyoto, December 1997.

The carbon market of the Kyoto Protocol is now trading carbon credits at the EU Emissions Trading System EU ETS, and as already stated, it is international law since 2005. The World Bank reports on its progress in its report "Status and Trends of the Carbon Market" which is published annually since the carbon market became international law in 2005. The report documents that by

2010 the EU ETS is trading \$200 Bn/year, and has decreased the equivalent of 20% of EU's emissions of carbon. Through the carbon market, those nations who over-emit compensate those who under emit – and throughout the entire KP process the world emissions' remains always under a fixed emissions limit that are documented in Annex 1, nation by nation emissions limits for OECD nations. A 'carbon price' emerges from trading the 'carbon credits' or rights to emit, which represents the monetary value of the damage caused by each ton of CO_2. The carbon market therefore introduces a 'carbon price' that corrects what has been called the biggest externality in the history of humankind (cf. Stern, 2006)

The carbon market cuts the Gordian knot and makes change possible. It does so because it makes clean energy more profitable and dirty energy less profitable, and therefore encourages economic growth without environmental destruction: it fosters green development. The carbon market itself costs nothing to run, and requires no subsidies except for minimal logistics costs. In net terms the world economy is exactly in the same position before and after the carbon market – there are no additional costs from running the carbon market, nor from its extremely important global services.

The over-emitter nations are worse off, since they have to pay. But every payment they make goes to an under- emitter, so some nations pay and some receive, but in net terms the world economy is exactly in the same position before and after the carbon market is introduced. There are no costs to the world economy from introducing a carbon market, nor from the limits on carbon emissions and environmental improvement that it produces. It is all gain.

What is the status of the carbon market ?

As of 2010, it has been ratified in 195 nations, and this includes all the industrial nations except the US. It is international law since 2005. Its nation by nation carbon limits expire in 2012 but the Kyoto Protocol itself – its overall structure and the structure of the carbon market do not expire – they are and continue to be international law. All we have to do to keep the carbon market's benefits is to define new emissions limits nation by nation for the OECD nations – something that we should be doing in any case as they are the major emitters and without limiting their emissions there is no solution to the global climate issue.

What is the current status of the carbon market in the US, which is the single industrial nation that has not yet ratified the Kyoto Protocol? There are cross-currents in US, since it is a politically divided nation. But the US has already a carbon market for 10 North eastern US States, called RGGI, which is operating but timidly – the limits on emissions are small and so are the prices for carbon credits therefore. The economic incentives of Kyoto Protocol's carbon market are enormous. China, for example, created a reported 1 million new jobs and became the world's main exporter of clean tech equipment since 2005 after signing on and ratifying the Kyoto Protocol in 2005 and benefitting from US\$40 billion from its carbon market and Clean Development Mechanism. China is right now introducing its own carbon market. Many in the US want part of the carbon market advantages. President Obama said he wishes to ratify Kyoto the Protocol, and by now 22 States are planning to create a Carbon Market of their own including California. Hundreds of cities and towns support the carbon market in the US. In the Fall 2007 the US Supreme Court greed that Federal government and the EPA can enforce carbon emissions limits without requiring Congressional approval. Every effort to deem this regulation illegal by Republican representatives has failed so far. It is generally accepted that global businesses (for example the automobile industry) will benefit from KP's guidelines, and could suffer economic losses without the benefit of KP economic incentives at home. This is because the automobile industry is global, and cars that do not sell in other OECD nations create huge losses and lead to bankruptcies. Since all OECD nations are buying carbon efficient cars, because they ratified the KP, the US car industry is commercially isolated. For these reasons, in 2010 the EPA imposed automobile emission limits of 36.7 miles per gallon, an efficiency requirement that has been increased further by the Obama administration in 2011. The automobile industry voluntarily supported a rise to 54 MPH in 2011. Furthermore in December 2011 EPA announced that it would impose limits on stationery sources like power plants, which is the beginning of a US carbon market, but the issue is still hotly contested by the Republican Party which freezes decision making since we are close to another presidential election. Nevertheless a leading Republican candidate for president, Mitt Romney who was formerly a Governor of Massachusetts, endorses the creation a "cap and trade" system or a carbon market. A similar sequence of events took place when the SO2 market was created at the Chicago Board of Trade 20 years ago – first it was quite controversial, but the SO2 emission limits were eventually passed for US power plants and then traded in an SO2 market at the CBOT, which is now widely considered to have been very successful in eradicating acid rain in USA.

Are the new EPA carbon limits the beginning of the US carbon market as were the SO2 limits 20 years ago? History is being written right now.

Green Markets are the answer –they will transform Capitalism in the 21st century

What is a green market and why does it matter? A shining example of a green market is he Kyoto Protocol Carbon Market just discussed, which I introduced in 1997 and became international law in 2005. The EU ETS is trading $200 billion annually today and has transferred already $50 Bn to developing nations for clean technology private projects that promote sustainable development, and has decreased about 20% of the EU emissions since becoming law in 2005. Another successful example of a green market is the SO2 Market in Chicago Board of Trade that was created about 20 years ago, which is quite different from the carbon market because SO2 concentration is not a "global commons" since it varies city by city while CO2 is the same uniformly all over the planet. There are more green markets in the works. Today the UN is exploring markets mechanisms for biodiversity and for watersheds. As in the case of the Kyoto Protocol carbon market, these are markets that would trade rights to use the global commons – the world's atmosphere, its bodies of water, its biodiversity – and therefore have a deep built-in link between efficiency and equity. In the carbon market of the Kyoto Protocol, by design, the poor nations are preferentially treated, having in practical terms more access and more user rights to the global commons (in that case the planet's atmosphere). This is not the case with SO2 which is a simple "cap and trade" approach as SO2 is not a public good, as was discussed above.

Efficiency with equity is what it's all about. They are really two sides of the coin. One is equity and the other is efficiency. Both matter. The carbon market provides efficiency with equity. How? Through its Clean Development Mechanism the Kyoto Protocol provides a link between rich and poor nations – the only such link within the Kyoto Protocol -- since poor nations do not have emissions limits under the KP and therefore cannot trade in the carbon market. But developing nations still benefit from the CDM of the carbon market – how so?

Developing nations have benefitted from the KP. Since 2005, when it became international law, the KP carbon market funded US$50 Bn in clean technology (CDM) projects in poor nations – see World Bank "Status and Trends of the Carbon Market" (2005-2010) – and the CDM projects have decreased so far the equivalent of 20% of EU emissions. The CDM works as follows. Private clean technology projects in the soil of a developing nation – China, Brazil, India - that are proven to decrease the emissions of carbon from this nation below its given 'UN agreed baseline' are awarded "carbon credits" for the amount of carbon that is reduced that are themselves tradable for cash in the carbon market – so as to recognize in monetary terms the amount of carbon avoided in those projects and fill the role of shifting prices in favor of clean technologies. These CDM carbon credits – by law – can be transformed in cash in the KP's carbon market. This is the role of the carbon market in the CDM, and this is how the KP has provided $50 Bn in funding to developing nations since 2005 (The World Bank, "Status and Trends of the Carbon Market" 2005 – 2010)

The North-South conflict – namely, who should abate first - puts all this at risk. To move forward in the global negotiations we must overcome the China – US Impasse, which is in an intense form of the same conflict that prevails between rich nations and poor nations as a whole – the North and the South (see Chichilnisky, Time Magazine: Special Issue on Heroes of the Environment, last page, December 2009). But is it possible to overcome the North South divide? Yes, it is.

But the interests of the industrial and developing nations are so opposed that once again, we need a two - sided coin. This is the same dual role that the carbon market played in the Kyoto 1997 global negotiations, where it provided market efficiency that the US and the OECD wanted, while limiting only OECD nations emissions which is what poor nations wanted. This os what I saw then, and how by introducing the carbon market into the wording of the KY I saved the negotiations and the Kyoto Protocol was voted by 1960 nations. Equity and efficiency are the two sides of the coin. We need both.

Organizing Principles for Green Capitalism

At this point the reader may think that this is about doom and boom, but offers few details about how to fix the problem. Worry no more, that part is coming now.

I will show how Green Capitalism is the solution, and it remains to be explained how this works.

Green capitalism a way forward that is consistent with US technology and leadership, and with future emissions reductions by developing nations, China and India. The basis was explained in Time Magazine Chichilnisky 2009 (op.cit). The Kyoto Protocol CDM can play a critical role as a foundation of a major technology - driven financial investment that benefits from and propels the renovation of the Kyoto targets post 2012.

Here are three building blocks for the global UNFCC negotiations:

(i) Efficient US Carbon Negative Technologies (ii) The Kyoto Protocol carbon market and its CDM, and (iii) Global Capital Markets

Carbon Negative Power Plants for developing nations (cf. Chichilnisky and Eisenberger, Cryogas International, 2011)

There are today cost efficient technologies that capture CO_2 from air. Global Thermostat LLC is an example. The firm is commercializing a technology that takes CO_2 out of air and uses low cost residual heat to drive the capture process, making the entire process of capturing CO_2 from the atmosphere very inexpensive. There is enough residual heat in a coal power plant that it can be used to capture twice as much CO_2 as the plant emits, thus transforming the power plant into a 'carbon sink'. For example, a coal plant that emits 1 million tons of CO_2 per year can become a sink absorbing a net amount of 1 million tons of CO_2 instead. Carbon capture from air can be done anywhere and at any time, and so inexpensively that the CO2 can be sold for industrial uses or enhanced oil recovery, a very profitable opportunity. Any source of low (100 C) heat will do. In particular renewable (solar) technology can power the process of carbon capture. This can helps advance solar technology and make it more cost efficient. This means more energy, more jobs, and it also means economic growth in developing nations, all with less CO2 in the atmosphere.

(ii) **The Kyoto Protocol carbon market**.

The role of the Kyoto Protocol Carbon Market and its CDM is critical, as it can provide needed funding and financial incentives for investment to build carbon negative power plants that were described above in developing nations. The CDM can be used to provide "offsets", which are contracts that promise to buy the electricity that is provided by carbon negative power plants for a number of ears and therefore unlock banking resources for the investment.
The scheme covers fixed costs and greatly amplifies private profits

(iii) A US$200 Bn a year Private/Public Fund – Green Power Fund - to build carbon negative power plants in developing nations, particularly in Latin America and Africa

This Green Power Fund was named and proposed by the author in writing to the US Department of State in Copenhagen COP 15 December 2009, and it was also published by the author in the *Financial Times* in 2009. It was accepted and two days later was publicly offered by US Secretary of State Hillary Clinton in the global negotiations COP 15 and subsequently in COP 16. It is making the rounds in the negotiations, where it has received substantial support although the entire scheme has not been incorporated, and its very positive connection with the Kyoto Protocol was not made explicit. The scheme proposed is a private – public Green Power Fund raised from global capital markets to invest in investment grade firms that build carbon negative power plants in developing nations, with CDM funding to provide off-takes to by the ensuing electricity, as mentioned above. The background and feasibility of the Green Power Fund are as follows.

As already mentioned, existing technologies (www.globalthermostat.com) can efficiently and profitably transform coal power plants and solar thermal sources of energy in a way that reduce atmospheric carbon concentration. Investment is needed to build carbon negative power plants in developing nations and elsewhere, to renovate the US$55 trillion power plant industry infrastructure worldwide (IEA), which is 87% fossil today. What is required is about $200 Bn/year for 15 years. This amount of money will go to investment- grade power plant builders (General Electric, SSE, Siemens, Linde, etc) to build carbon negative power plants in developing nations, which is exactly what the carbon market is trading today per year (US$200 Bn, see World Bank's "Status and Trends of the Carbon Market" 2010) and therefore the financial target proposed here is eminently achievable.

Blueprint for Sustainable Development
The premises for Sustainable Development are
1. Clean and Abundant Energy available worldwide
2. Sustainable growth in developing nations

3. Accelerating the transition to solar energy
4. Transforming fossil fuels into a clean alternative

Green Capitalism and Traffic lights for Human Survival

New types of markets are needed to transform capitalism by providing incentives that make green economic projects more profitable than their alternatives, fostering conservation of biodiversity, clean water, a safe atmosphere -- and some of them already exist and are described above. Green markets change GDP by valuing the Global Commons (the atmosphere, biodiversity, clean water) and they also link equity with efficiency

Examples of green markets are:
Carbon Market – international law since 2005
SO2 Market in US – trading at the CBOT since 1991
Markets for Biodiversity - to emerge, they are proposed by the author and under UN consideration
Markets for Water are in the same condition

These markets provide the missing signal of scarcity that is normally provided by market prices when a good or service becomes very scarce. Such signals are tantamount to Traffic Lights for Human Survival. Here are sign posts to implement the above strategies going forward. Within the UNFCCC Global Climate Negotiations, the annual COP meetings, the next of which is COP 17 in South Africa. In Copenhagen COP 15 December 2009 we were able to insert wording into the CDM allowing carbon negative technologies to be compensated as part of the CDM. Namely, that the CDM funds negative carbon technologies

Economic Incentives for the Short and the Long Run

There is a major difference between long run and short run strategies. And long run strategies do not work for the short run. We need economic incentives for the short and for the long run. They are different because in the short run we must actually reduce carbon in the atmosphere and do so fast – a carbon negative approach – and renewable energy as the long run solution. Renewable energy is too slow for the short run, since replacing a U$55 trillion power plant infrastructure with renewable plants could take mane decades. Action is needed sooner than that. For the short run we need <u>carbon negative technologies</u> that capture more carbon than what is emitted.
Trees do that – and they must be conserved to help preserve biodiversity. Biochar does that. But trees and other natural sinks are too slow for what we need today – see the beginning of this article.

Why Negative Carbon?

Negative Carbon is needed NOW as part of a blueprint for transformation, a blueprint for Sustainable Development:

While in the long run only renewable sources of energy will do, including Wind, Biofuels, Nuclear, Geothermal, and Hydroelectric energy – all of these are in limited supply cannot replace fossil fuels. Global energy today is divided as follows: 87% fossil, namely gas coal, oil; 10% is nuclear, geothermal and hydroelectric, and less than 1% solar power – photovolteic and solar thermal. Nuclear fuel is very scarce and nuclear technology dangerous (Japan 2011) therefore it seems unrealistic to seek a solution in the nuclear direction. Only solar energy can: Less than 1% of the solar energy we receive can be transformed into 10 times the fossil fuel energy used in the world today.

The short run is the next 10 years. There is no time in this period of time to transform the entire fossil infrastructure – it costs $50 trillion (IEA) to replace. We need to directly reduce carbon in the atmosphere now. CSS works but does not suffice because it captures what power plants emit. Any level of emissions adds to the stable and high concentration we have today.

Yet we need short term strategy that accelerate long run renewable energy, or we will defeat long term goals.

The solution? Combine air capture of CO_2 with storage into biochar, cement or other materials, and use it to produce renewable gasoline (gasoline produced from CO_2 separated from air and Hydrogen separated from water). Is this therefore too expensive? No – it is already feasible at commercial and competitive rates.

We can combine air capture with solar thermal electricity using the residual heat to drive the carbon capture process, making a solar plant more productive and efficient so it can out- compete coal as a source of energy.

In sum: the blueprint offered here is a private/public approach, based on industrial technology and financial markets' leadership, self - funded and using profitable derivative markets – carbon credits as the 'underlying,' based on the Kyoto Protocol CDM, as well as markets for biodiversity and water providing abundant clean energy to stave off impending and actual energy crisis in developing nations, fostering mutually beneficial cooperation for industrial and developing nations

The blueprint proposed provides the two sides of the coin, equity and efficiency, and it assigns a critical role for women as stewards for human survival and sustainable development.

Our Vision is a Carbon Negative Economy and Green Capitalism resolving the Global Climate Negotiations – the North South Divide. The more you produce and create jobs ✳ The Cleaner the Atmosphere. Economic growth that is harmonious with the Earth resources

Summary: A Vision for Sustainable Development

Avoiding extinction is about the survival of the human species. Survival is not about violent competition & struggle. Survival is about life not death. Carbon Negative Solutions are the future of energy, and green markets lead the way to Green Capitalism, resolving the global climate negotiations and the Global Divide, providing clean energy and economic growth for the North and the South that is harmonious with the Earth's resources, and focused on creating and nurturing life. Building the future.

References

Hyun Youk & Alexander van Oudenaarden: "Microbiology: Altruistic Defense needed for Survival (*Nature* 2 September 2010)" p. 34 Vol. 467 Issue 7311.

Swift, Thomas: "A Modest Proposal for preventing the Children of Poor People in Ireland from Being a Burden on their Parents or Country, and for Making them Beneficial to the Public" Sarah Harding, London UK, 1729.

G-20 Leaders' Statement from Meeting in Pittsburgh, USA, September 24-25 2009, HYPERLINK "http://www.pittsburghsummit.gov/mediacenter/129639.htm" http://www.pittsburghsummit.gov/mediacenter/129639.htm

G. Chichilnisky "North South Trade and the Global Environment" American Economic Review (1994.)

Stern, N. The Economics of Climate Change, Oxford, (2006)

Chichilnisky, G. (1998) "The Economic Value of the Earth Resources" in American Museum of Natural History: Scientists on Biodiversity (ed. Ellen Futter) New York, 1998.

Chichilnisky, G.(1995) "Biodiversity as Knowledge" Proceedings of the National Academy of Sciences,

Chichilnisky, G.(2009) "Forward Trading: a proposal to End the Stalemate between the US and China on Climate Change", Time Magazine, Special Issue of Heroes of the Environment , last page, December 2009

The Times,(2011) page 15, Tuesday June 21 2011.

6.2 The Economics of the Anthropocene

By Sir Crispin Tickell

What is the Anthropocene? It was well explained in a recent article in *The Economist*. Briefly it is the idea that humans have so transformed the land surface, seas and atmosphere of the Earth since the beginning of the industrial revolution some 250 years ago that we need a new geological epoch to describe it. Our not so little animal species has changed the character of soils, the chemistry of the oceans and atmosphere, the selective breeding of species of all kinds and their movement round the Earth to produce a world substantially different from what preceded it. Hence the Anthropocene.

It falls to this generation to try and measure the impact on society, and work out what might be done to mitigate or adapt to change in the general human interest. Little is more difficult than learning to think differently. Yet it is hard even to define the principal problems without upsetting longstanding traditions, beliefs, attitudes and the often unspoken assumptions on which we build our lives. It took a long time for previous generations to accept the antiquity of the Earth, the mechanisms of evolution, the movement of tectonic plates, the shared genetic inheritance of all living organisms, and the symbiotic and to some extent self-regulating relationship between the physical, chemical, biological and human components of the Earth system. Some still reject the whole idea.

The impacts which together constitute the Anthropocene can be defined in many ways. In broad terms we are exploiting and in some respects running down the Earth's natural capital, including the biosphere, and damaging the ecosystem services on which we depend. This is hard to reconcile with our experience of the bonanza of inventiveness, exploitation and consumption since the industrial revolution. All successful species, whether bivalves, beetles or humans, multiply until they come up against the environmental stops, reach some accommodation with the rest of the environment, and willy-nilly restore some balance. Are we near to those stops?

In September 2009 the magazine Nature published an article by Johan Rockstrom and others identifying nine scientific stops or boundaries which humans would cross at their peril. Three had already been crossed: climate change; loss of biodiversity; and interference with nitrogen and phosphorus levels. The other six were stratospheric ozone depletion; ocean acidification; use of fresh water; changes in land use; chemical pollution; and atmospheric aerosol loading.

But these stops, however important, are only half the story. There are six more general ones where the societal responses are critical. First we need to confront the effects of our own proliferation in all its aspects; next to work out new ways of generating energy; to manage and adapt to what is in effect climate destabilization; to give higher priority to conservation of the natural world; to create the necessary institutional means of coping with global problems; and not least to look at economics in the broadest sense and the way in which we measure things. As has been well said by Lord Rees former President of the Royal Society: in the future global village we cannot afford to have too many village idiots.

There is a lot to be said about all these issues, but today I want to focus on economics and what has been labelled socio-ecology. Much current economics is built on the assumptions of more than a hundred years ago. Resources then seemed limitless; shortages were more of labour and skills than of goods; technology could solve almost any problem: wastes could always be disposed of; the other organisms on which we depended could adapt to the demands we made on them; the good functioning of society was a product of what was called 'growth' (hence the increasing use of Gross National Product and Gross Domestic Product as measuring devices); and a kind of belief (I can think of no better word) in market forces as the main if not the only drivers of health, wealth and prosperity. With this comes the belief that economics are governed by reason (often mathematically expressed) rather than by animal - herd - instincts which otherwise rule.

It may be painful but indeed we have to think again. Our society, even our animal species, is in a unique situation: as the title of a recent book put it: we have *Something New Under the Sun*. Here are some broad propositions:

We should recognise that there is no such thing as a free market, and there never has been. All markets operate within rules, whether explicit or implicit. Together they constitute a framework which if it is any good should be in the public interest and to the public good.

The question, answered differently, in different societies is to determine the character of regulation, the nature of incentives and disincentives, how best to profit from enterprise, the avoidance of market failure, and in the long as well as the short term the stability and general health of society.

Somehow we have to bring in externalities (or true costs in social as well as economic terms). Indeed externalities could be more important than internalities. Markets are marvellous at fixing prices but incapable of recognising costs.

We should be ready to admit that human population increase is a major global problem, even if it is levelling off in some areas. Associated with it is increasing unemployment as technology enables us to produce more goods and services with fewer people.

We should challenge the current models of 'development' which underline the artificiality of the distinction between developed, developing, under-developed and even over-developed countries. The true distinction is between those who have set industrialization as an ideal within and between their countries, and those who look more widely and see the future in term of their people's resources and welfare. We have majority and minority worlds across the world as a whole.

In measuring health, wealth and happiness, we have to take into account the things we most value: safety, security, food, water, cleanliness and energy. Here we must recognise that despite continuing population increase we are producing more and more goods and services with fewer and fewer people. The social costs of unemployment are enormous, and we have to reckon properly with them.

Concepts of value are controversial. For example how do we value uncut rainforest, and reward those who do not cut it? Who should take the responsibility for human-driven climate change, and pay those who suffer most for it ?

None of these points is new. Change is already under way, even if sometimes obscured by the current economic crisis. In particular efforts have been made to establish new systems of measurement: for example through the Human Development Index, the Stern Review, and the recent report of the Stiglitz Commission. There is even a effort to measure GDH, or Gross Domestic Happiness, I suppose as part of the Big Society. But we are still far from the changes of attitude that are required.

Supposing, as I hope, that the message does eventually become more widely received and understood, what would be the implications ? Frankly they go so wide that I hesitate to be very specific. Individuals, local authorities, corporations, government at all levels would need to set very different priorities and human behaviour generally would change as a result.

A pivotal factor would be our use of energy. The flow of energy affects economics, indeed life itself, every minute. It was the uses to which we put the stored energy or sunlight known as coal, oil and gas, which directly caused the industrial revolution and the consequent transformation we now label the Anthropocene. I take energy as an example of how we need to think differently.

First we must recognize that supplies of energy from fossil fuels are limited. Estimates vary all the time as technologies develop, but deposits of oil, gas and coal are by their nature finite, and the environmental penalties paid in their exploitation will become higher than society can expect. There is also a changing balance of consumption between them. For example in the European Union, electricity supplies from gas have risen to 25% and from coal have fallen to 20%. There is increasing fear of dependence on certain suppliers, whether they be in the Middle East or Russia. Energy security is now high politics. In the meantime demand continues to increase worldwide. In China energy use doubled between 1990 and 2006, and is likely to double again by 2025.

The second new factor is better understanding of the cumulative effects of fossil fuel use and combustion on the chemistry of the atmosphere and the environment generally. The general relationship between greenhouse gases and the surface temperature of the Earth is well established, and although strenuous debate continues on the degree of public responsibility for the current increase in carbon dioxide in the atmosphere, many think that the consequences of our continuing dependence on fossil fuels are more serious than the prospect of their depletion.

Hence the new interest in making more effective use of what fossil fuels remain, and such measures as sequestration of carbon or global auctions of permits to emit greenhouse gases. But the main interest has been in developing alternative sources of energy. They include nuclear power, whether fission or fusion; solar energy on the ground or through geo-engineering; power from biofuels; tidal and ocean power; a return to wind and hydro power; geothermal power using the heat beneath our feet; and a range of new electrification technologies.

Of course there are many uncertainties and complexities. We can rarely identify tipping points until we have passed them. So far the societal responses have been mixed and uncertain with wide variations between countries.

The economics of the Anthropocene demand not just a new approach but a whole new methodology. Out of date economics should be recognised as a dangerous mental condition which is driving the world in an alarmingly wrong direction. In natural terms we are tiny parts of a gigantic system of life to which we are doing increasing injury. The human superorganism has to learn its place among other superorganisms. So far it has failed to do so. The impact of our species has been so great that the term Anthropocene is more than justified. Let economists reckon with it.

6.3 Happiness, Economics and the Environment: Evidence from Australia

By Christopher L. Ambrey, Christopher M. Fleming and Matthew Manning*

Abstract

Against most objective measures Australia's economic performance in the first decade of the twenty-first century was exemplary. Against subjective measures, such as those provided by self-reports of life satisfaction or happiness, the record is less impressive; there is evidence to suggest that life satisfaction in Australia is declining. In seeking an explanation for this apparent paradox, we observe that of the social, economic and environmental domains included within the Australian Bureau of Statistics' *Measures of Australia's Progress*, it is only the environmental domain that has regressed across all indicators. Employing Geographic Information Systems data, along with data from the Household, Income and Labour Dynamics in Australia (HILDA) survey, this chapter reports the findings of three years of research investigating the link between environmental quality and life satisfaction in Australia.

Introduction

Against most objective measures Australia's economic performance in the first decade of the twenty-first century was exemplary. For the period 2001 to 2010 the following can be observed: per capita Gross National Income grew by 38.0%, compared to growth of 34.1% in the Euro area, 30.2% in North America and 35.2% for all OECD member states; household final consumption expenditure grew by 35.7%, compared to growth in the Euro area, North America and the OECD of 9.8%, 19.1% and 16.4% respectively; unemployment fell from 6.8% to 5.2%, whereas the Euro area, North America and the OECD experienced increasing unemployment; central government debt fell from 27.3% to 24.1% of Gross Domestic Product (GDP), whereas in the Euro area, North America and the OECD central government debt as a proportion of GDP increased (The World Bank, 2012). Furthermore, Australia's Human Development Index (HDI) score (measured on a scale of 0 to 1) rose from 0.915 in 2001 to 0.937 in 2010, ranking Australia second only to Norway (United Nations Development Programme, 2010).

In contrast, longitudinal data reveals that Australia has performed rather poorly, with self-reported life satisfaction declining over the period (see Figure A1 in the Appendix). In seeking to explain this apparent paradox we turn to the Australian Bureau of Statistics' Measures of Australia's Progress; a suite of indicators that measures Australia's progress across three dimensions (society, economy and environment). In the most recent (2011) release, three of the six societal indicators (health; education and training; and work) are judged to have improved over the previous 10 years, whereas three have gone unmeasured (crime; family, community and social cohesion;

and democracy, governance and citizenship). In the economic dimension, three of the five indicators (national income; national wealth; and household economic well-being) are judged to have improved, one indicator (housing) is judged to have undergone no significant movement, and one indicator (productivity) has declined. In the environment dimension, two of the six indicators have declined (biodiversity; and atmosphere), whereas four have gone unmeasured (land; inland waters; oceans and estuaries; and waste) (Australian Bureau of Statistics, 2011).

Noting that it is only the environmental dimension that has regressed across all measured indicators, the purpose of this chapter is to explore the extent to which the natural environment contributes to an individual's life satisfaction and thus offer declining environmental quality as a potential explanation for the observed decline in life satisfaction in Australia over the decade. The chapter proceeds as follows. Data and method are described in Section 2. Section 3 presents results from three cases studies. Section 4 offers final thoughts.

Data and method

Employing data from the Household, Income and Labour Dynamics in Australia (HILDA) survey, a micro-econometric life satisfaction function of the core determinants of life satisfaction is developed. The dependent variable is obtained from individual's responses to the question: *All things considered, how satisfied are you with your life?* This is an ordinal variable, with the individual choosing a number between 0 (totally dissatisfied with life) and 10 (totally satisfied with life). The life satisfaction function is then augmented by linking Geographic Information Systems data on the relevant environmental factor to the individual respondent through the collection district (CD) in which they reside (the CD is the smallest spatial unit in the Australian Standard Geographical Classification). The coefficient of the environmental factor yields first, a direct valuation in terms of life satisfaction, and second, when compared to the estimated coefficient for income, the implicit willingness-to-pay for the environmental factor in monetary terms (Frey, Luechinger, & Stutzer, 2010).

Case studies

In this section we present research exploring the association between self-reported life satisfaction and the level of three different environmental factors (air pollution, ecosystem diversity and public greenspace). Further details and additional case studies can be found in the following publications: Ambrey, Chan, and Fleming (2013) (air pollution); Ambrey and Fleming (2011) (scenic amenity); Ambrey and Fleming (2012) (protected areas); Ambrey and Fleming (in press-a) (public greenspace); and Ambrey and Fleming (in press-b) (ecosystem diversity).

Case study 1: Air pollution in South East Queensland

The negative effects of air pollution are substantial and wide-ranging. While health effects are of most concern, air pollution can also lead to loss of visibility for residents and recreationists, reduced agricultural and forest productivity, damage to buildings and structural materials, and stress on ecosystems. Together these effects impose significant economic costs on governments, businesses and households. Accurately estimating these costs is an important component of the development of efficient pollution reduction policies (United States Environmental Protection Agency, 2011).

South East Queensland (SEQ) is one of Australia's fastest growing and most densely populated regions. In 2007 Brisbane City, the principle urban centre of the SEQ region, was the second fastest growing urban centre in the developed world (Newman, 2007) and the resident population of the region is projected to increase by 44%, to 4.4 million, by 2031 (Office of Economic and Statistical Research, 2010). This growth has been accompanied by persistent exceedences of air quality standards for particulate matter with an aerodynamic diameter of less than 10 microns (PM_{10}).

While a number of existing studies clearly demonstrate a link between the region's air quality and residents' health and well-being (cf. Chen, Mengersen, & Tong, 2007; McCrea, Stimson, & Western, 2005; Petroeschevsky, Simpson, Lukman, & Rutherford, 2001; Rutherford, Simpson, Williams, Mitchell, & McCall, 2000; R. Simpson, Williams, Petroeschevsky, Morgan, & Rutherford, 1997), to the best of our knowledge, there are no publicly available monetary estimates of the cost of air pollution in the region. The purpose of this study is to fill this knowledge gap and estimate the cost of PM_{10} exceedences from anthropogenic activities.

Similar to strategies employed elsewhere in the literature (cf. Brereton, Clinch, & Ferreira, 2008; Smyth, Mishra, & Qian, 2008), an ordered probit model is used to estimate Equation 1. Similar to MacKerron and Mourato (2009) the data we employ is modelled air pollution data rather than interpolated or even extrapolated data from a finite coverage of monitoring stations (cf. Ferreira et al., 2013; Levinson, 2012; Luechinger, 2009). The model used is The Air Pollution Model (TAPM) 4.0 developed by the Commonwealth Scientific and Industrial Organisation (CSIRO) Marine and Atmospheric Research Group (Hurley, 2008). This is an airshed model commonly used for modelling the dispersion of emissions from anthropogenic sources. Figure A2 in the Appendix indicates the extent of spatial heterogeneity in the average number of days that PM_{10} concentrations have exceeded their 24-hour health guidelines by CD for 2001.

Our results indicate that the average number of days over the 12 months prior to the interview that PM_{10} concentrations within a respondent's CD exceed national health guidelines is negatively associated with life satisfaction, statistically significant at the 10% level with a coefficient of -0.0159. That is, we find that PM_{10} exceedences in an individual's local area significantly detract from that individual's self-reported life satisfaction; this result and the associated implicit willingness-to-pay are quite robust to a number of model specifications.

Following the procedure described in Equation 2, the average implicit willingness-to-pay in terms of annual household income for a one day decrease in the average number of days that the PM_{10} concentration level exceeds national health guidelines over a twelve month period is AUD 5,164. In per-capita terms, given there are on average 2.95 people living in each household in the sample, this implies a willingness-to-pay of AUD 1,751.

Our results point to substantial welfare improvements from an abatement of PM_{10}

exceedences from anthropogenic sources. They, therefore, reaffirm the goals and standards of the National Environment Protection Measure for Ambient Air Quality (Australian Government Department of Sustainability Environment Water Population and Communities, 2012) and suggest that, while the Brisbane City Council Clean Air Strategy (Brisbane City Council, 2009) is a useful initiative, there is a strong case for bringing the time frame for 'clean air' forward from the current target date of 2026.

Case study 2: Ecosystem diversity in South East Queensland

It is well recognised that biodiversity provides many direct and indirect benefits to humans. It is equally well recognised that human activity has contributed to unprecedented rates of biodiversity loss (cf. Secretariat of the Convention on Biological Diversity, 2010). Moreover, projections show continuing and, in many cases, accelerating species extinctions, loss of natural habitat and changes in the distribution and abundance of species over the remainder of the twenty-first Century (Leadley et al., 2010).

Ensuring biodiversity is more accurately valued may go some way to halt this decline. At a microeconomic level, valuation enables the benefit of biodiversity preservation (or alternatively, the cost of biodiversity depletion) to be included within benefit-cost analyses. At a macroeconomic level, valuation allows national accounts to be augmented to better reflect the impact of economic activity on a society's natural capital. Values may also be used to assess damages for litigation purposes.

While the motivation for valuing biodiversity is clear, there remains no established framework for doing so (Czajkowski, Buszko-Briggs, & Hanley, 2009; Nijkamp, Vindigni, & Nunes, 2008). On top of the usual difficulties associated with trying to place monetary values on non-market environmental goods and services (cf. Freeman, 2003), two additional challenges are apparent. First, it is not immediately obvious which quantifiable indicator of biodiversity is best to use. Second, indicators preferred by ecologists are often not understood by the general public, from whom values must be elicited. That is, there is often a disconnect between the 'goods' demanded by the public and ecologists' understanding of what is important for ecosystem functioning (Spash, 2008).

This study uses data on self-reported life satisfaction along with a spatially disaggregated Simpson's diversity index (E. Simpson, 1949) to place a monetary value on ecosystem diversity in SEQ. In terms of addressing the first challenge, while the two terms are not synonymous, a considerable number of ecologists advocate the measure of biodiversity at the level of ecosystem diversity (Nunes & van den Bergh, 2001). In regards to the second challenge, a key advantage of the life satisfaction approach is that it does not require respondents to have specific knowledge of the good in question, nor does it ask them to perform the unfamiliar task of placing a monetary value on a non-market good. The approach may therefore be ideally suited to the valuation of complex environmental goods. To our knowledge, this is the first attempt to use this approach to value ecosystem diversity.

The strategy in this study is to estimate Equation 1 via both ordered probit and ordinary least squares; while the former is more theoretically correct, the latter permits easier interpretation of marginal effects and facilitates comparison with existing studies. Ecosystem diversity data is constructed via a Biodiversity Assessment and Mapping Methodology and provided, for each remnant unit in the SEQ bioregion, by the Department of Environment and Resource Management (Queensland Environmental Protection Agency, 2007). Within the Biodiversity Assessment and Mapping Methodology, ecosystem diversity is measured via the Simpson's diversity index (E. Simpson, 1949). This index incorporates the ecosystem diversity concepts of 'richness' (number of different ecosystems) and 'evenness' (relative abundance), and ranges between zero and one, with high scores representing areas of high densities of regional ecosystems and ecotones (transitional areas between ecosystems). The Simpson's diversity index is spatially weighted for each CD. The spatial variation of the index over the CDs in the study region is illustrated in the Appendix (Figure A3). The level of ecosystem diversity in the sample ranges from 0 to 0.73.

Our results indicate that ecosystem diversity, as measured by the Simpson's diversity index, is found to have a positive and significant (at the 5% level) effect on life satisfaction, with an estimated coefficient (in the ordered probit model) of 0.0469. That is, increases in ecosystem diversity have a positive and economically significant effect on life satisfaction. Again following the procedure described in Equation 2, the average implicit willingness-to-pay in terms of annual household income for a one-unit improvement in ecosystem diversity is AUD 14,288. Given, on average, there are 2.5 people living in each household in the sample this implies a per-capita willingness-to-pay of approximately AUD 5,700. Our results also indicate that the welfare effects for marginal reductions in ecosystem diversity are most severe for individuals located in areas with existing low levels of ecosystem diversity.

These results suggest that there are significant life satisfaction impacts of increased ecosystem diversity and that the preservation, or improvement, of existing levels of ecosystem diversity is welfare enhancing. The challenge for policy makers is to adequately manage the pressures of projected population and economic growth in rapidly growing regions such as SEQ.

Case study 3: Public greenspace in urban Australia

It is estimated that over 50 per cent of the world's population now reside in urban areas. Moreover, the United Nations (2010) projects that the world's urban areas will absorb all of the global population growth over the next four decades, as well as continue to draw some of the rural population. Policy-makers and urban planners therefore face a significant challenge to design urban areas in such a way as to accommodate this growth, while maintaining residents' well-being.

Despite a large land mass and comparatively small population, Australia is heavily urbanised, with 89 per cent of the population living in towns and cities. Moreover, most future population growth is expected to be concentrated in existing urban centres (Commonwealth of Australia, 2010b). Within this context, a standards approach to the provision of public greenspace has been employed since the 1940s, with the standard set at a level of 7 acres (3 ha) per 1000 residents (Bryne, Sipe, & Searle, 2010). There are many instances, however, where this standard has not been met. For example, in Sydney (Australia's largest city) the inner and middle suburbs have local open space per 1000 residents ranging from 0.56 to 2.41 ha (Searle, 2011).

Somewhat surprisingly, given the wealth of evidence supporting the well-being benefits of greenspace (an excellent review of the literature is given by Bell et al. (2008)) the l, the provision of greenspace in urban environments does not appear to be high on the policy agenda. For example, the State of Australian cities 2010 report (Commonwealth of Australia, 2010b) barely mentions greenspace and the 2010 intergenerational report (Commonwealth of Australia, 2010a) all but ignores the issue (Bryne, et al., 2010). Furthermore, policies of urban consolidation have concentrated medium- to high-density residential development in inner-ring suburbs where greenspace is comparatively scarce (Bryne, 2012). This provides reason to doubt the adequacy of local open space planning to cope with intensified urban consolidation across Australian cities (Searle, 2011).

The purpose of this study is to measure the effect of greenspace on the life satisfaction of residents of Australian capital cities, paying particular attention to heterogeneity in preferences for greenspace across people depending on their characteristics or circumstances. As with Case Study 2, the strategy is to estimate Equation 1 via both ordered probit and ordinary least squares. The measure of public greenspace employed is the percentage of public greenspace in the resident's local area, defined at the level of the CD. An illustration of CD administrative boundaries and overlapping public greenspace is provided for Sydney in the Appendix (Figure A4).

Our results indicate that public greenspace, as measured by the percentage of public greenspace in the resident's local area, is found to be welfare enhancing (at the 10% level), with an estimated coefficient (in the ordinary least squares model) of 0.0032. That is, higher levels of public greenspace are associated with higher levels of welfare for residents. From Equation 2, the average implicit willingness-to-pay in terms of annual household income, for a one per cent increase in public greenspace, is AUD 1,172. Given, on average, there are 2.5 people living in each household in the sample, this implies a per capita implicit willingness to pay of AUD 469. To put these results in context, on average, a one per cent increase in greenspace from the mean is equivalent to a 143 square metres increase in public greenspace in the CD.

In regards to heterogeneity of preferences for greenspace, the dominant finding is that preferences are largely homogenous; the benefits of public greenspace do not appear to depend on gender, ethnicity, level of health, employment status, dwelling type or hours worked. We do, however, find some heterogeneity. Specifically, we observe greater welfare effects of public greenspace in areas with higher population density. This may reflect a combination of factors, including scarcity rent and high initial marginal utility attributable to what little public greenspace is available in particularly densely populated areas. In regard to the characteristics of the residents and their circumstances, we find that residents aged between 15 and 19 and between 40 and 49 are found to report lower levels of life satisfaction in areas of higher greenspace, as do those with young children. The reverse is true for lone parents and residents with an education level of year 12 or below.

In summary, our findings reaffirm the role of public greenspace in supporting well-being and the importance of protecting or enhancing the provision of greenspace in urban environments in Australia. Projected population growth in urban areas, coupled with the finding that the welfare effects of public greenspace are greater in high-density environments, suggest that the role of public greenspace in maintaining the well-being of urban residents is likely to become more important over time. This needs to be recognised by policy-makers and given appropriate consideration in future urban planning decisions.

Final thoughts

These studies provide additional evidence on the positive association between environmental quality and life satisfaction, and go some way to explaining declining life satisfaction in the face of improvements in objective measures of progress, as experienced in Australia over the first decade of the twenty-first century.

Worryingly, recent policy decisions such as the Queensland government's legislative change to allow grazing of cattle in National Parks (Tlozek & Arthur, 2013), suggests that policy-makers remain unaware of the welfare reducing effects of trading environmental quality for income growth. Further evidence of this lack of awareness can be found in the rapid development of the coal seam gas industry despite concerns about impacts on the environment and public health, and development of ports near the Great Barrier Reef despite concern voiced by international agencies (Anonymous, 2013). It is hoped that this research can go some way to increasing awareness of the environmental quality – life satisfaction trade off and, is so doing, promote more informed public debate on these issues.

References

Ambrey, C., Chan, A., & Fleming, C. (2013). Estimating the cost of air pollution in South East Queensland: An application of the life satisfaction non-market valuation approach. *Griffith University Discussion Paper in Economics and Business Statistics No. 2013-02.*

Ambrey, C., & Fleming, C. (2011). Valuing scenic amenity using life satisfaction data. *Ecological Economics, 72*(1), 106-115.

Ambrey, C., & Fleming, C. (2012). Valuing Australia's protected areas: A life satisfaction approach. *New Zealand Economic Papers, 46*(3), 191-209.

Ambrey, C., & Fleming, C. (in press-a). Public greenspace and life satisfaction in urban Australia. *Urban Studies.*

Ambrey, C., & Fleming, C. (in press-b). Valuing ecosystem diversity in South East Queensland: A life satisfaction approach. *Social Indicators Research.*

Anonymous. (2013). 'We're in the coal business': Campbell Newman slams UNESCO Great Barrier Reef warning Retrieved June 18, 2013, from http://www.news.com.au/national-news/unesco-slams-great-barrier-reef-management-youve-got-eight-months-to-fix-it/story-e6frfkw0-1226381188474

Australian Bureau of Statistics. (2011). Measures of Australia's Progress: Summary Indicators 2011, Catalogue No. 1370.0.55.001 Retrieved 17 July 2012,   from http://www.abs.gov.au/AUSSTATS/abs@.nsf/mf/1370.0.55.001

Australian Government Department of Sustainability Environment Water Population and Communities. (2012). Air quality standards Retrieved 20 January 2013, 2013, from http://www.environment.gov.au/atmosphere/airquality/standards.html

Bell, S., Hamilton, V., Montarzino, A., Rothnie, H., Travlou, P., & Alves, S. (2008). *Greenspace and quality of life: A critical literature review*. Greenspace Scotland Research Report. Stirling.

Brereton, F., Clinch, J., & Ferreira, S. (2008). Employment and life-satisfaction: Insights from Ireland. *The Economic and Social Review, 39*(3), 207-234.

Brisbane City Council. (2009). Clean Air Strategy for Brisbane Retrieved 12 January 2013, from http://www.brisbane.qld.gov.au/environment-waste/natural-environment/air-quality/clean-air-strategy/index.htm

Bryne, J. (2012). What is green space worth? *http://theconversation.edu.au/what-is-green-space-worth-4703* Retrieved 19 January 2012, from http://theconversation.edu.au/what-is-green-space-worth-4703

Bryne, J., Sipe, N., & Searle, G. (2010). Green around the gills? The challenge of density for urban greenspace planning in SEQ. *Australian Planner, 47*(3), 162-177.

Chen, L., Mengersen, K., & Tong, S. (2007). Spatiotemporal relationship between particle air pollution and respiratory emergency hospital emissions in Brisbane, Australia. *Science of the Total Environment, 373*(1), 57-67.

Commonwealth of Australia. (2010a). Australia to 2050: Future Challenges - the 2010 Intergenerational Report. Canberra.

Commonwealth of Australia. (2010b). *State of Australian Cities 2010*. Infrastructure Australia. Canberra.

Czajkowski, M., Buszko-Briggs, M., & Hanley, N. (2009). Valuing changes in forest biodiversity. *Ecological Economics, 68*(12), 2910-2917.

Ferreira, S., Akay, A., Brereton, F., Cunado, J., Martinsson, P., Moro, M., & Ningal, T. (2013). Life satisfaction and air quality in Europe. *Ecological Economics, 88*(1), 1-10.

Ferreira, S., & Moro, M. (2010). On the use of subjective well-being data for environmental valuation. *Environmental and Resource Economics, 46*(3), 249-273.

Freeman, A. (2003). *The Measurement of Environmental and Resource Values: Theory and Methods* (2nd ed.). Washington DC: Resources for the Future.

Frey, B., Luechinger, S., & Stutzer, A. (2010). The life satisfaction approach to environmental valuation. *Annual Review of Resource Economics, 2*(1), 139-160.

Hurley, P. (2008). TAPM V4 User Manual. Canberra: CSIRO Marine and Atmospheric Research Group.

Leadley, P., Pereira, H., Alkemade, R., Fernandez-Manjarres, J., Proenca, V., & Scharlemann, J. (2010). Biodiversity scenarios: Projections of 21st Century change in biodiversity and associated ecosystem services. (Vol. Technical Series No. 50). Montreal: A Technical Report for the Global Biodiversity

Outlook 3.

Levinson, A. (2012). Valuing public goods using happiness data: The case of air quality. *Journal of Public Economics, 96*(9-10), 869-880.

Luechinger, S. (2009). Valuing air quality using the life satisfaction approach. *Economic Journal, 119*(536), 482-515.

MacKerron, G., & Mourato, S. (2009). Life satisfaction and air quality in London. *Ecological Economics, 68*(5), 1441-1453.

McCrea, R., Stimson, R., & Western, J. (2005). Testing a moderated model of satisfaction with urban living data for Brisbane, South East Queensland, Australia. *Social Indicators Research, 72*(2), 121-152.

Newman, C. (2007, 19 January 2010). Lord Mayor opens landmark Brisbane event. *Council Newsroom* Retrieved 19 January, 2010, from http://newsroom.brisbane.qld.gov.au/home/news_detail.asp?ID=765

Nijkamp, P., Vindigni, G., & Nunes, P. (2008). Economic valuation of biodiversity: a comparative study. *Ecological Economics, 67*(2), 217-231.

Nunes, P., & van den Bergh, J. (2001). Economic valuation of biodiversity: Sense or nonsense? *Ecological Economics, 39*(2), 203-222.

Office of Economic and Statistical Research. (2010). *Queensland regional profiles: SEQ region.* Queensland Treasury. Brisbane.

Petroeschevsky, A., Simpson, R., Lukman, T., & Rutherford, S. (2001). Associations between outdoor air pollution and hospital admissions in Brisbane, Australia. *Archives of Environmental Health: An International Journal of Epidemiology, 56*(1), 37-52.

Queensland Environmental Protection Agency. (2007). Biodiversity Planning Assessment: South East Queensland 3.5. Brisbane: Biodiversity Planning Unit.

Rutherford, S., Simpson, R., Williams, G., Mitchell, C., & McCall, B. (2000). Relationships between environmental factors and lung function of asthmatic subjects in South East Queensland, Australia. *Journal of Occupational and Environmental Medicine, 42*(9), 882-891.

Searle, G. (2011). Urban consolidation and the inadequacy of local open space provision in Sydney. *Urban Policy and Research, 29*(2), 201-208.

Secretariat of the Convention on Biological Diversity. (2010). Global Biodiversity Outlook 3. Montreal.

Simpson, E. (1949). Measurement of diversity. *Nature, 163*(1), 688.

Simpson, R., Williams, G., Petroeschevsky, A., Morgan, G., & Rutherford, S. (1997). Associations between outdoor air pollution and daily mortality in Brisbane, Australia. *Archives of Environmental Health: An International Journal of Epidemiology, 52*(6), 442-454.

Smyth, R., Mishra, V., & Qian, X. (2008). The environment and well-being in urban China. *Ecological Economics, 68*(1-2), 547-555.

Spash, C. (2008). How much is that ecosystem in the window? The one with the bio-diverse trail. *Environmental Values, 17*(2), 259-284.

The World Bank. (2012). Data. Available: http://data.worldbank.org/?display=default Retrieved 2 August, 2012, from http://data.worldbank.org/?display=default

Tlozek, E., & Arthur, C. (2013). Qld's national parks cattle grazing laws 'disastrous' Retrieved 2 June, 2013, from http://www.abc.net.au/news/2013-05-22/qld-national-parks-cattle-grazing-laws-disastrous/4705082

United Nations. (2010). *World Urbanization Prospects: The 2009 Revision*. Department of Economic and Social Affairs. New York.

United Nations Development Programme. (2010). Human Development Report 2010: The Real Wealth of Nations (Pathways to Human Development). New York.

United States Environmental Protection Agency. (2011). The Benefits and Costs of the Clean Air Act from 1990 to 2020: Final Report. Washington DC.

Welsch, H. (2006). Environment and happiness: Valuation of air pollution using life satisfaction data. *Ecological Economics, 58*(4), 801-813.

Acknowledgement

This chapter uses unit record data from the Household, Income and Labour Dynamics in Australia (HILDA) survey. The HILDA project was initiated and is funded by the Australian Government Department of Families, Housing, Community Services and Indigenous Affairs (FaHCSIA) and is managed by the Melbourne Institute of Applied Economic and Social Research (Melbourne Institute). The findings and views reported in this chapter, however, are those of the authors and should not be attributed to either FaHCSIA or the Melbourne Institute.

We thank Griffith University for the Griffith University Postgraduate Research Scholarship and the Griffith Business School for the Griffith Business School Top-up Scholarship; funding that was instrumental in facilitating this research. This research would not have been possible without data provided by the Australian Government Department of Families, Housing, Community Services and Indigenous Affairs (FaHCSIA), the Australian Bureau of Statistics (ABS), and the Department of Science, Information Technology, Innovation and the Arts (DSITIA).

Part 7 Sustainable Healthy Cities
7.1 Strategies for a Sustainable City: Thimphu

By Jigme Tashi Tsering

Thimphu is the Capital of the Kingdom of Bhutan, a small kingdom situated north of India and South of China

Introduction

The rapid growth of cities has become the most striking feature of human civilization. Cities have depleted earth's resources by draining the fertility without replenishing it. They have exhausting the forests, watershed and in the process discarding vast quantities of waste and pollution.

Sustainability needs to be addressed if people is to continue to live in cities and continue to flourish on this planet. We need to find a viable relationship between cities and the living world – a relationship not parasitic but symbiotic, or mutually supportive (Girardet, 1992).

Photo: Jigme Tashi Tsering. Bhutan.

In this chapter an attempt will be made to describe the situation of Thimphu city and

(c) Jigme Tashi Tsering

the type of strategies that will make the city sustainable. While the city will never be entirely sustainable this attempt at reducing use of natural resources, reusing resources, use of additional renewable energy source aims to reduce the impact of the city on the environment and in the process also combat climate change.

Background and Geography

Bhutan is a land-locked country in the Himalayas having a population of 672,425 people (PHCB, 2005). Bhutan has an area of 38,394 Km^2 and borders China in the North and India in the South, East & West.

The Capital City Thimphu is located in the western region with a population of 98,676 (PHCB, 2005).

Environment

The Government has a policy of maintaining 60% of areas under forest cover. In 2005, 68% of total area was under forest cover (NECS, 2002).

Economy

The back bone of the economy is hydropower. Export of hydropower to India accounts for 60% of total revenue.

Kyoto Protocol

Bhutan is a signatory to the Kyoto protocol under the United Nations Convention on Climate Change. Bhutan's annual emission of CO_2 per-capita was 0.2 ton as compared to the world average of 4.5 ton in 2004 (UNDP, 2007).

While no targets have been set for reduction of Carbon Dioxide, Bhutan is committed to reducing GHG (NEC, 2000). Mitigation programs currently being implemented:

- Renewable energy technology options
- Improved technology to reduce fuel wood consumptions
- Introduction of fuel-efficient vehicles
- Improvement of imported fossil fuel quality

Bhutan has to date successfully constructed and commissioned a 70 kW Clean Development Mechanism micro hydropower project in Chendebji village with the objective to reduce GHG. The project commission in 2005 has reduced CO_2 emission by 593 tons, by replacing the need of kerosene, firewood and diesel by the villagers.

Energy

Bhutan generates about 1488 MW of electricity from hydropower of which it consumes 152 MW (BEA, 2005). However with global warming and glaciers receding fast, there is a need to depend on other renewable energy sources in the future.

According to the Population and Housing Census 2005, the main sources of fuels are firewood (37.2%), electricity (30.6%), LPG (25.5%) and the remaining from other sources.

While Bhutan has an abundant clean source of energy there is still abundant use of fuel wood. Even though Carbon dioxide is a GHG, fuel wood burning is not considered a

GHG as it is absorbed when trees are planted. However, the burning of wood results in deforestation which damages the environment, effects the water shed (water source) and at the same time reduces the carbon sink potential.

It was found that most of the 6,982 households and over 1000 institutions in Thimphu still use fuel wood for cooking and heating purposes. For example on an average each school consumes about 15 truckloads of firewood every year (GEF, 2006).

Strategies to reduce fuel wood demand:

Replace traditional stoves with efficient improved cooking stoves will reduce the consumption of firewood. Such stoves can save up to 40% of fuel compared to traditional stoves. This puts less pressure on forest & energy recourses in addition to reducing GHG (Shrestha, S.K & Thapa, R. 1999).

- Use of sawdust briquette as an alternative fuel source
- Switch to electrical appliances instead of wood stoves (as electricity from hydropower)
- Use of alternative renewable energy source such as solar energy
- Most institutions use fuel wood as a source of energy for heating water for having bath
- Switch to solar hot water system (SHWS) would result in decrease of demand for fuel wood
- For example a nunnery in Thimphu used to use five truck load of fire wood per year. With use of SHWS, three truckloads of fuel wood use is reduced a year (GEF, 2006)
- Solar power generation is considered a prominent form of clean energy that avoids GHG Emissions
- One KW of Solar power capacity avoids one MT of annual CO_2 emissions (Kaur, R. 2008)

Building Designs

Houses in Thimphu are poorly designed. Improving the designs of house can result in saving of energy and money in the long run.

One of the main sources of CO_2 is energy required for space heating. Improvements in building design can reduce energy consumption. In a new house, windows typically account for 15% to 30% of the total heat loss. With good design, large areas of glass window can save energy through passive solar heating gains. While initial cost of glazed window is high they will eventually pay for itself – for example, window with low energy coating cost about 10-15% more than conventional double glazed units, but they reduce energy loss up to 18% (Woolley, T & Kimmins, S. 2000).

In the same way using advance insulation materials can actually reduce the energy consumption of buildings by as much as 90% (Girardet, H. 1992).

Bhutan has a strict procedure to approve building designs prior to construction. In addition to checking structural integrity, the government agency should encourage eco-friendly practices. While initial cost might be more, building with good energy saving features can be viewed as an *eco-friendly* house and will eventually have greater market value as energy saving would compensate for the higher investment. This is in contrast the current practice of poorly insulated houses being constructed at the lowest possible cost. The result is that building owners also charging minimal rent but energy consumption of individual households are high. While the financial outcome may be same, there is more energy use in the latter.

The documentation of design and materials used in building now, is a good practice. This provides the ideal opportunity for incorporating building efficiencies. In addition during demolition of buildings it helps in efficiently sorting materials which can be later be used for recycling (Lawson, B. 1996).

Use of energy saving devices

Most buildings in Thimphu use incandescent bulbs. Switching to use of low-energy fluorescent light can save 70% power. Although they cost more initially they last longer and soon pay back the extra cost in the energy saving they make (Elliott, D. 2003).

Strategy for energy conservation

Environment preserved by:
- better fuel efficient stoves
- better building design
- reduced use of fuel wood due to use of alternate energy
- Social
- decrease in health hazard from indoor air pollution
- improved quality of life
- Economic
- While initial economic costs of these investments are high, in the long run they will pay back / benefit the community
- government can play a major part in influence the demand by affecting the supply cost by either taxation or subsidy such as by:
- No tax on electrical heaters and rice cooker appliances
- Subsidy on energy saving appliances
- Subsidy on briquette stoves to encourage use of sawdust briquette
- Subsidy on house insulation materials
- Increase in royalty on fuel wood
- Cost sharing basis by government for renewable energy

Transport

Bhutan imported about 70,047 metric tons of oil equivalent in 2005 which were used for *transportation*, lighting, cooking and heating purposes (DOE, 2005).

With inadequate public transport, cars have been an essential means of mobility by which individuals commute. As per the Road Safety and Transport Authority (RSTA), there are 19,000 vehicles in Thimphu in 2008 with the number increasing at 17% annually (RSTA, 2003).

A major source of air pollution in Thimphu is the combustion of fossil fuels from vehicle emission. Study conducted by the National Environment Commission (NEC) found that emission levels was found to be high in vehicles with 60% of petrol and 96% of diesel engine vehicles not meeting Indian emission standards (BSoE, 2001).

In fact, it was found that pollutants of vehicle as one of the main causes for acute respiratory tract diseases in Thimphu. A health study showed that acute respiratory tract disease had increased from 10.08% in 1990 to 14.02% in 1998 (BSoE, 2001).

More cars mean more pollution. In addition use of cars has a disadvantage to community. Cars not only pollute the atmosphere but also take away valuable space. It is estimated that "one hundred people in a bus need only 40 square meters of road space" whereas "one hundred people in cars travelling by themselves need some 2000 square meters" (Girardet, 1992).

Car based planning are destroying public spaces, and detaching bonds within community. High volume and speeding traffic causes people to retreat from street-based community. This results in social disintegration and isolation. Reliable public transport is therefore the only option to give back more public space to the community.

Vehicles not only need resources for production but also needs energy during operation. Pendakur (cited in Girardet, 1992) reports that "cars use 1860 calories per passenger mile, bus 920, rail 885, walking 100 and bicycles 35 calories per passenger mile". Hence we can see that the bus uses much less energy than car and should be the mode of travel.

From Pendakurs report we can see that bicycles use the least energy. To encourage bicycle usage, and to ensure that it is save and convenient as possible, it is vital that roads and facilities are of suitable standards. Hence Roads Authorities should constructed or rebuilt road with minimum recommended lane width so the bicycles can be safely included in the general flow of traffic (Healey, K. 1996).

The strategy for a sustainable city aims to reduce energy demand, reduce pollution & free more space for the community.

Strategy for the transport sector
- Impose high tax on import of cars
- Policy to import fuel efficient vehicles
- Import good quality fuel
- Legal framework to control vehicle emissions
- Introduce reliable public transport system
- Subsidy for buying bicycles
- Improved footpath for pedestrians

A good public transport for Thimphu can be a bus or tram system that runs on electricity as the source of energy from renewable hydropower is within Bhutan.
Economic
- With less car pollution there will be decrease in health related illness, which will decrease health expenses of the government *as health care in Bhutan is free*
- Government health sector resources could be invested into the transport sector

- Higher tax on cars can help fund public transport
- Socially
- *class barriers* are not created, which will allow for an environment for interaction between people
- No financial pressure to invest limited resources in expensive vehicle. Hence it frees resources of people to be used in other meaningful ways

Environment
- Use of public transport and bicycle will put less pressure on the atmosphere
- Decrease in demand for non renewable *petroleum* based fossil fuel

Water Demand
With a population of 98,676 people (PHCB, 2005) and with water demand at 125 liters per person per day (DUDES, 2006), Thimphu required 12,335.5 cum of water per day. Thimphu's two water treatment plants supply of 15,000 cum per day is more than adequate currently.

However with the population growing rate of Thimphu of 10% per annum (NEC 1998), the current water supply of 15,000 cum per day will only be able to provide water for a population above 120,000. Hence water conservation measures have to be taken to ensure that water is available in the future.

Strategy for water sector

Rain water harvesting systems
- Thimphu is an ideal city for rain water harvesting as most building have Corrugated Metal Sheet roofing
- rainwater harvesting is sustainable as there is rainfall throughout the year
- Government needs to promote rainwater harvesting by inculcating social acceptance and pride in technology that preserves the environment
- Financial investment is minimal with building owners required to purchase *gutter* for channeling of water to tank, a tank, and an electric motor to pump the water from lower tank to existing tank
- Saving on water is an economic incentive for people
- Less energy is required to treat water thereby benefiting the environment
- The government can influence the demand by affecting the supply cost by either taxation or subsidy.
- Increasing the tariff on water to discourage use
- Subsidize water saving devices such as efficient shower heads, shower timers etc.
- Policies could be implemented such as all new construction being required to use dual flush toilets, water less urinals, all gardening to be done by grey water.

Planning

Thimphu was establishment in 1955 as the capital of Bhutan. Since then Thimphu has undergone many changes. The town plan of 1998 was to make Thimphu a dream city with a vibrant culture which is people and environment friendly.

With rapid increase in automobile numbers and pressure on public health infrastructure in the town centre, a new plan called the Thimphu Structural Plan was implemented in 2003. This plan after implementation would ensure Thimphu to be a sustainable and livable city.

This new structural plan put restriction on plot coverage as well as building height. While the objective was the reduce pressure at the center this also allowed for other considerations:

- With residential buildings restricted to three floors, *lifts* are not needed thereby elimination the use of electricity
- Concept of elders residing on ground floor, middle class on second floor and young couples at the top floors encourages older generation to live in cities
- With no lifts *there is more free space*

The structure plan being implemented is aimed at improving the access of people to services. This structural plan requires the creation of 15 urban villages which is created through participatory land pooling. All villages will have its own village square with shopping centers, playground, gardens and an express bus link connecting it to the urban centre. This ensures a local communal environment where all activities are close together and walking and cycling can be the mode of transport (DUDES, 2003).

The urban villages provide communal public areas which are essential for people to interact. Young people especially require public meeting space where they can strengthen their links with people around them. Otherwise they may turn to crime and increasingly to suicide (Healey, K. 1996).

Strategy to improve the life of the community:

- Coordinate social gathering that ensures communal spirit and bonding
- Initiate communal service centers such as washing machine services. Instead of each individual buying a machine, communal washing machine can still serve the needs of people and ensure optimal use. These actions reduce GHG.

The establishing urban villages are being implemented. As the urban villages get completed the villages remove the pressure on the urban center, which will allow the city centre to also become more livable.

Solid Waste

Thimphu has grown rapidly in the last few decades. With rapid urbanization, rural-urban migration, change in consumption habits and the high population growth rate have resulted in increase of waste generated.

Thimphu which generated 10 tons of waste daily in 2000 (USPS, 2000) is currently generating 64.5 tones of waste daily (Penjor, 2008). The waste generation of 0.3 kg per capita per day in 2001 (BSoE, 2001) has risen to 0.56 kg per capita per day in 2007 (Penjor, 2007). These wastes are being disposed of at Thimphu's only landfill site.

The tariff charged by the Municipal Corporation for the disposal of Solid waste is low. There is no limit restriction to the amount of waste disposed. Being a cheap method for waste disposal, there is no incentive for other viable economic methods of waste management.

As per a survey by Penjore (2008), the composition of waste by weight was 25% organic, 14% cardboard, 12% paper, glass 10%, plastic 5%, metal 4% and other the remaining. This revealed that recycling of waste at household level was minimal. In addition organic and green wastes are not composted. The decay of organic matter in absence of air also releases methane a harmful GHG.

The success of management of solid waste is crucial in the attitude and behavior of humans to the environment. The strategy for solid waste management should be to *reduce waste to the landfill:*

Strategy for solid waste sector

- Tariff for the waste for landfill should be charged based on quantity
- Increasing tariff would result in people reducing waste to land fill. Only waste with no value will be disposed as it cost people money to dispose of it. Waste such as paper, glass, metal, organic waste which have value could either be sold off for recycling
  With increased tariff for waste disposal, recycling option can become economically viable. Recycling will:
- preserve the environment as the recycled resource does not require new raw materials
- uses less energy in processing recyclable materials than processing from raw materials

   With increased tariff for waste disposal composting options can become economically viable

- Composting of organic matter and greens can produce manure
- Composting done properly would not generate methane, a GHG
- Manure can be sold
- Effective composting requires a right Carbon to Nitrogen (C/N) ratio of about 25-30:1. For example the mixing high C/N ratio such as sawdust, with low C/N ratio such as glass clippings or vegetable peels resulting with C/N ratio of 30 would allow compost activity to take place at optimum rate (Mason, J. 2003, p.43, 44).

- Waste such as sawdust from sawmill could be used in composting or converting to alternate source of fuel such as briquette.
- This would also encourage reduction of waste disposed into landfill and in the process promote value from waste material

  Government should finance and provide technical expertise to encourage private business to take up recycling and composting

  Cost of purchasing different bins for different waste should be subsidized. This will encourage segregation of waste at source

  Increase in cost of disposal of construction waste will have positive impact on initiative to reuse old material
- most current industrial practices and systems are currently ecologically unsustainable
- Tucker and Treloar (1994) recommends that from an energy conservation and CO_2 emission viewpoint, recycling of building materials should be encouraged based on research
- It is essential to make use of resources a more natural systems, which are typically characterized by cyclical process (Lawson, 1994) and symbiotic, mutually dependent relationships (Allen,1994) for sustainability

These methods will:

- conserve materials and energy;
- generating less waste for landfill

Economic

- With the increase in tariff of disposing waste to the landfill, it becomes economically viable to compost which is valuable nutrient that has economic value

Social

- people can eat food from natural nutrients and not artificial fertilizers

Environmental

- With composting, valuable nutrients which could other wise have been lost is replaced back into the soil, closing the nutrient cycle

Sewerage

As per L. M Austin and S. J. Van Vuucen, human being excretes 500 liters of Urine and 50 liters of faeces per year.

While 50 liters of faeces is not difficult to manage, the mixing of faeces and urine when flushed with water as sewerage becomes a problem. That means 50 liters of faeces becomes 550 liters of polluted and unpleasant sewage.

The sewerage of Thimphu is piped into a sewerage treatment plant which currently has a treatment capacity of 3,060 m3/day (TCC, 2005). With increase in population, there is increase in demand of water for flushing and increase in energy needed for treating sewage.

Strategy for sewage sector

One strategy to reduce water demand for flushing in toilets and reduce energy demand for treatment of waste is to introduce the Urine Separating toilets (UST). What UST does is that, it separate urine (nutrients N,P,K from mixing with faeces matter.
Advantage of the UST is:

- Lower water use with 0.1 to 0.3 liters of water is required to flush urine (Johansson et al., 2002) which is 90% reduction compared to half flush from standard 3/6 dual toilet
- Nutrients from Urine (N,P,K) can be used as concentrated fertilizer with only limited treatment prior to land application
- Energy consumption for nutrient removal at Sewage treatment plants can be reduced by source separation technology resulting in lower nutrient wastewater for treatment.

Based on calculations presented in *Annex A*, there is potentially a saving of 2250 m³ of water per day. In addition there is a reduction of 2250 m³ of sewage that does not require treatment per day and hence less energy use.

In addition to water saving and energy reduction, a life cycle analysis of different removal and recovery technology (Table 1) found that nutrients can be recovered energetically at *source* more efficient that either their *removal* at the Sewage Treatment Plant or from *new* production from natural source (Maurer et al. 2003).

Nutrients	Specific Energy required (de-nitrification and precipitation) at Sewage Treatment Plant	Specific Energy for production of traditional fertilizer
N	13 kWh/kg	13 kWh/kg
P	14 kWh/kg	8 kWh/kg

Table 1: Comparison of energy required for treatment at Sewage treatment plant & production of fertilizer
Source: Maurer et al. 2003

Hence, nutrient segregation at source is the most environmental friendly approach as it requires the minimal energy demand, which reduces GHG emission which otherwise would be emitted during the sewage treatment or during production of new fertilizers.
In effect UTS closes the nutrient circles as nutrients can again be put back into the fields as fertilizer.
Economic

- Practical problem is difficulty in collection of urine separately. With the existing sewage network, what can be done is that the urine is stored separately during the day. At night, the urine could be released and collected separately at the sewage treatment plant. This *method does not require infrastructure investment*
- Concentrated Urine with minimal treatment can be sold as fertilizer
- Urine separating toilet with flush provision can be easily retrofitted in standard toilet

- Additional land not required for expansion of sewage treatment plant

Social

- Urine separation with flush provision will make it more appealing
- *Reduces demand for water*, making it cheaper for people
- While use of urine as fertilizer may seem revolting, people are very adaptable in Bhutan and cheap cost will be a major incentive for use

Environmental

- *Reduces discharge of nutrients* to sewage treatment systems
- *Reduce volume of water demand*
- *Reduces demand for energy to treat waste*
- It potentially closes the nutrient cycle by returning nutrients to the field, which contributes to sustainability

Conclusion

According to the International Union for the conservation of Nature, "sustainable development improves people's quality of life within the context of the earth's carrying capacity'.

While Thimphu is a relatively small city by modern standards, the demands and impacts of the city's existence is clearly visible. This chapter has identified issues that are crucial in making the city more sustainable:

- Energy efficiency
- Energy and water conservation
- Use of more renewable energy
- Efficient public transport
- Urban planning and livability of citizens
- Recycling of solid waste
- Solid waste composting

By reducing the demand on the natural resources and improving the living condition of people, the city will not only have a circular metabolism existence for sustainability but also have a liveable city where people can live in harmony with the environment.

Photo: Jigme Tashi Tsering. Bhutan.

Annex A – Water saving and sewage reduction. (Note: Volume of water required and volume of sewage generated is calculated in Annexure B)

<u>Water saved</u> and <u>sewage reduced</u> when <u>comparing full flush toilet and urine separation toilet</u>

(for Thimphu city population per day)

Toilet type	Volume of water required per person per day (liters)	Population of Thimphu	Total water saved (liters)	Total water saved (cubic meter)	Remark
Full flush toilet	30				Total toilet use is 5 times per day x 6 liters of water = 30 liters

					toilet use is 1 time for faeces and 4 times for urine = 1 x 6 liters + 4 times x 0. 3 liters = 7.2 liters
Urine Separation toilet	7.2				
	22.8	98676	2249813	2250	

Toilet type	Volume of sewage per day	Population of Thimphu	Total sewage reduction (liters)	Total sewage reduction (cubic meter)
Full flush toilet	31.54			
Urine Separation toilet	8.74			
	22.8	98676	2249813	2250

Annex B – Calculation for water use and sewage generated
(Note: Calculation of water use in toilet and sewage generated is per person per day)
Assumption (taken from L. M Austin and S. J. Van Vuucen):

a) 1 human uses toilet 5 times daily (1 time for faeces and 4 times for urination)
b) each human being urinates quantity is 0.35 liters each time (500 liters / 365 days / 4 times daily)
c) each human being faeces quantity is 0.14 liters (50 liters / 365 days / once daily)
d) each full flush requires 6 liters, half flush 3 liters and use of urine separation 0.3 liters

Toilet use: Full Flush

Toilet use type	volume of human waste (liters)	Volume of water for flushing	Total volume of sewage per toilet use	Number of times toilet was used	Total sewage = Total volume of sewage per toilet use x no. of times toilet was used

faeces	0.14	6	6.14	1	6.14
urine	0.35	6	6.35	4	25.4
					31.54

Toilet type: Half flush

Toilet use type	volume of human waste (liters)	Volume of water for flushing	Total volume of sewage per toilet use	Number of times toilet was used	Total sewage = Total volume of sewage per toilet use x no. of times toilet was used
faeces	0.14	6	6.14	1	6.14
urine	0.35	3	3.35	4	13.4
					19.54

Toilet type: Urine Separation Toilet

Toilet use type	volume of human waste (liters)	Volume of water for flushing	Total volume of sewage per toilet use	Number of times toilet was used	Total sewage = Total volume of sewage per toilet use x no. of times toilet was used
faeces	0.14	6	6.14	1	6.14
urine	0.35	0.3	0.65	4	2.6
					8.74

Photos: Jigme Tashi Tsering. Bhutan.

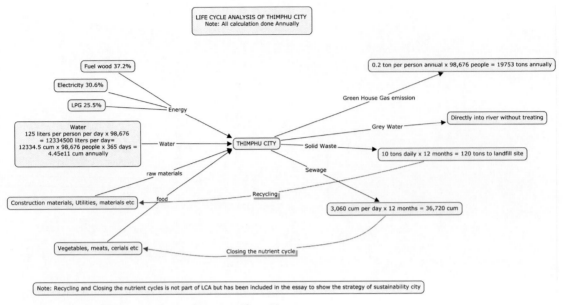

Diagram: Life Cycle Analysis for Timphu City

7.2 Urban Sprawl in Eastern Europe

By Michelle Wishardt (UK)

Urban sprawl is a form of 'land take' associated with expanding urban areas, generally associated with suburbanization or residential and non-residential de-concentration. Previously eastern European cities typically exhibited a more compact urban form with high densities, reflecting the 'strong centralised planning regimes and substantial reliance on public transport that prevailed during the communist era' (Ott, 2001; Nuissl and Rink, 2005). However it is in this region that sprawl is now most dramatic and the development of so-called 'bagel cities' are in evidence. Here employment and settlement in the core cities is shrinking but expanding in suburban, out-of-town areas. The pattern is well documented in metropolitan areas such as Brno and Gdansk. It is of concern as this outward growth is causing significant impact on physical morphology and land use patterns, many irreversible with serious environmental implications.

Causes - why it's particularly prevalent in CEE

The driving forces behind the sprawling metropolis phenomena in Eastern Europe are multi-faceted, however dominant among them are clearly the liberation of the land market, changing housing preferences, the massive growth in private car ownership and use, improving economic prospects creating new pressures for low density urban expansion together with less restrictive planning controls. As the European Environment Agency has noted, 'privatisation in Central and Eastern European Member States has led to private housing estate companies building massively in peri-urban areas with few constraints on architectural quality, land use or possible master plans' (2006). At a personal level a push factor drawing people to re-locate outside cities include the desire for better quality housing with more living surface per capita in what is perceived to more attractive, family-friendly and greener surroundings. In non-residential sprawl, one strong factor has been the new inflows of foreign investments, particularly in the retail, warehousing and industrial sectors.

Why it's a problem – impacts

The sprawling trend is critically important because of the significant impacts that are evident in increased or overconsumption of energy, land and soil resources. This in turn contributes to the emissions that cause climate change, as well as elevated air and noise pollution levels which directly affect quality of life.

Urban sprawl development is often 'patchy, scattered and strung out, with a tendency for discontinuity, leap-frog(ing) over areas, leaving agricultural enclaves'. Inevitably it therefore results in the loss of agricultural land and a growing proportion of soil sealing, with associated flood risks in urban areas. Finally, urban sprawl with the expansion of artificial surfaces at the cost of grasslands, wetlands and eco-systems adds to the loss of biodiversity and more broadly sustainability.

How to deal with what has become a vicious circle of urban expansion is extremely difficult. Competition to maximise revenue from land sale is a particularly intractable issue and involves complex layers of governance, as well as the interests of property developers and business. Spatial plans in Poland which recognise the problem have focused on quality and cost in core cities, with regeneration initiatives and co-ordination between municipalities. However counter-acting or inhibiting urban sprawl effectively in Eastern Europe is an enormous challenge.

7.3 A sense of community and Permaculture Practice in Kibbutz Lotan

By Ryota Koike and Eli Gregory

Introduction

The term *Permaculture* comes from 'permanent agriculture' developed by David Holmgren and Bill Mollison in the 1970s. According to Holmgren (2002), Permaculture is about respecting both nature and human beings by re-designing a society in a way that it satisfies human needs within the ecological capacity. Based on such an underlying philosophical framework, Permaculture consists of three pillars: earth-care, people-care, and fair-share with twelve design principles:

- observe and interact

- catch and store energy

- obtain a yield

- apply self-regulation and accept feedback

- use and value renewable resources and services

- produce no waste

- design from pattern to details

- integrate rather than segregate

- use small and slow solutions

- use and value diversity

- use edges and value the marginal

- creatively use and respond to change

Earth-care is about understanding how human activities affect the surrounding environment. People-care is building environmentally sustainable living spaces to maximise the benefit of nature for people without destroying the environment. Fair-share is recognition of the limits in the ecological capacity. As its philosophy implies, the ethics of Permaculture is contrary to the mainstream modernisation theory that Permaculture practice does not attempt to destroy and conquer the environment. Rather it protects the nature and brings an environmental awareness such as recognition of limited resources to individuals, encouraging their participation in every day life.

Why Permaculture?

The idea of prosperity in Permaculture ethics is not driven by quantitative growth of materials, but achieved by focusing on human well-being in the people-centred approach. What is remarkable about Permaculture is that it does not require any academic qualifications such as PhD in a specific field or a large source of finance, but ordinary people can practice it (Holmgren 2002: Morrow 2006). People, for example, can start from rethinking of the product life-cycle. In a current economic model, the production method is one-way and dead-end since the beginning of manufacturing, and they end up with being a worthless scrap. In addition, those scraps often become the source of pollution in the third world.

As Diamond (2005) points out, developed nations such as the United States transfer tonnes of waste to developing countries like China by paying a handful of money, and such toxic wastes go directly to the poor who sell usable electronic materials from the mountain of garbage. As such, this sort of pollution transfer causes health problems in the third world. This is just one of the examples, but if consumers are more aware of such facts, they might choose locally produced products with a greater sense of responsibility.

Also, since Permaculture values harmonious interaction between people and the nature, it encourages a practice of sharing in a community and maximises the value of indigenous knowledge which is alive amongst local people inherited from their ancestors. This accumulation of human capital is an important element in sustainability that they tell the best use of natural resources. As such, Permaculture is now leading the lifestyle change and seen as one of the solutions to the climate change and the resource scarcity.

This chapter thus presents a narrative of Permaculture practice in Kibbutz Lotan in Israel, explaining how Permaculture ethics works and how people can live in ecological sustainability.

Ecological Life in Lotan in Israel

Every Friday evening with the setting sun, 200 parents, children, volunteers, workers, family, and friends make their way slowly toward the dining hall, pausing often to say hello with one another and to welcome the Sabbath. After a full and long 6-day workweek, the Sabbath becomes a time to break bread and share wine. It's a time where one can own an achievement or a story of the past week and share it with the rest.

Embodying the three ethics of Permaculture, earth care, people care, fair share, we find ourselves in the humble desert community named Kibbutz Lotan, a late addition to Israel's Kibbutz Movement. A completely socialist living community, Kibbutz Lotan remains true to the founding principles of the collective living Kibbutz lifestyle - give according to your abilities and take according to your needs. Like many of Israel's Kibbutzim (the word 'Kibbutz' pluralized) in Israel, much of their income is generated through various team-effort industries. Unlike many Kibbutzim, Lotan operates not only for profit, but also with mission.

Unique to the region and much of the world, on Kibbutz Lotan you can find the Center for Creative Ecology. The CfCE is an educational initiative founded by a group of very bright, motivated and conscious people offering international students a chance to not only learn Permacultural and alternative sustainable living techniques but a chance to live them as well. Students from around the globe flock to this small Israeli desert community to participate in the 'Green Apprenticeship' program. Students find themselves living in the 'Bustan' – a prototype neighborhood for sustainable living, working in the organic garden (yes, in the desert!), learning sustainable earth building, cooking using alternative technologies, practicing composting, and living a completely communal lifestyle.

In the 'Bustan' alone, students are housed in geodesic domes made of earth materials and straw bale insulation. They cook dinner in an open-air communal kitchen with such amenities as solar ovens, a parabolic solar cooker, an efficient burn rocket stove, and a traditional adobe mud brick oven or 'taboon' oven. They share three showers with hot water generated by solar energy. They even go to the restroom using waterless compost toilets that produce 'hummanure' (it's truly not gross at all).

You won't find Lotan applying basic Permacultural principles in their educational programs alone, they strive to apply them to as many other facets of life and work on the Kibbutz.

As one might imagine, there are inherent problems associated with the agriculture industry, a major source of revenue for Lotan, when you live in the desert. These problems become especially evident when you operate a dairy farm. A dairy farm requires exponentially more water to maintain than the water required by the rest of the Kibbutz combined. Cows need to be kept hydrated, cool, and clean. After all, a desert is not the typical habitat for a cow. So what did Lotan do with the excess wastewater? Easy, they built a constructed wetland that filters out toxins naturally while simultaneously providing a habitat for migratory birds to eat, drink and rest during their bi-annual migration and thus creating flourishing bird watching tourism. To keep the cows cool, the dairy farm offers giant roofs under which the cows take refuge; a cow can't sit out in the blistering sun all day. This is required. So Lotan extended the purpose of these roofs by building a row of solar panels on top that feed back in to the main grid offsetting energy costs and reducing dirty coal burning electricity production.

I'm sure one can imagine that working outdoors all day can work up quite an appetite. The people of Lotan cook a lot and eat a lot they also manage to leave a lot of food behind. So what does Lotan do with the food scraps of 200 hard working desert dwellers? Create a compost pile (three really) and encourage everyone to separate the organic material from the non-organic material as they clear their plate and use the newly composted soil in the community garden, the same garden that is maintained by the international 'Green Apprenticeship' students. Even conscious about the used cooking oil from falafel Fridays, Lotan finds use for what would normally be discarded as the outer most coating used to repel rain for the geodesic domes made of earth plaster and straw bales in the Bustan neighborhood.

Rooted in *'Tikun Olam'* – Hebrew for 'Repairing the World', Lotan considers itself an ecological crusader of sorts but like many other human endeavors, Lotan is not perfect and they know it, but they strive daily to be the best they can.

References

Burnett, G. (2008) Permaculture A Beginner's Guide. (2nd ed.) Essex: Spiralseed.

Diamond, J. (2005) *Collapse: How Societies Choose to Fail or Succeed.* London: Penguin Books.

Holmgren, D. (2002) Permaculture Principles and Pathways Beyond Sustainability. Australia: Holmgren Design Service.

Holmgren, D. (2009) Future Scenarios: How Communities Can Adapt to Peak Oil and Climate Change. Devon: Green Books.

Morrow, R. (2006) Earth User's Guide to Permaculture. (2nd ed.) United Kingdom: Permanent Publications.

7.4 10 Key Points for the Renewable Energy Society in the 21st Century

By Ryota Koike

1 Breaking the monopolistic or oligopolistic energy industry.

Since the energy industry is capital intensive, it is under either monopoly or oligopoly around the world. Although this natural monopoly is effective in terms of cost performance, it is actually harmful to the people and the environment when considering its inherent issues of the emergence of power elites and corruption in governance. The oil industry is one of the clearest examples that since oil revenue shares a huge proportion of national cash inflow in oil producing countries, oil extracting multinational corporations possess economics and political power over the host governments. Also, the same problems can be found in other energy industries that for example, Japan had a regulatory capture between the government regulatory body and the electric company, which partly caused Fukushima catastrophe. Therefore, there is a need for a reformation of monopolistic energy industry.

2 Localisation and decentralisation of electric power companies.

Given the problems raised above, localisation and decentralisation of electric power companies must be considered. Some may argue that it is unrealistic, but in reality the current mainstream approach (market-based Kyoto mechanisms and technological fixes) to the global climate change is insufficient in terms of a real GHG emissions reduction. Such mitigation processes mark the sound results in the name of environmental protection with the technological advance, but they are actually just repeating a misbehaviour in a slightly better way. Therefore, however these strong mitigation policies are indeed very crucial, now it must consider redesigning the energy life-cycle and choosing renewable energy over the current fossil fuel based energy production. In fact, since the potential gains from the renewable energy depend largely on local geographical and ecological features, it is more efficient to adjust electricity production methods to the local needs rather than producing and distributing the energy from the centre and losing some before reaching the periphery.

3 Government subsidies to the local energy production.

In order to recover from the global economic crisis, some countries have established new growth strategies such as Obama administration's 'Green New Deal'. However, since the governments focus only on stimulating the market for the economic growth, they are more likely to give subsidies for existing lower risk projects, and thus the investors tend to spend their money in such projects, maximising a short-term benefit with the minimum risks. As such, small venture projects often do not have enough capital to develop their technologies. Also, although natural monopoly has advantages that it can provide stable supply of energy with lower production costs, it gets limitlessly bigger by draining capital, disallowing other competitors to grow, and capital never reaching the local.

Despite the need for localisation and decentralisation of mega-energy corporations, they will inevitably lead to an increase in the energy prices in the market, possibly marginalising the marginalised further such as those who already suffer from energy poverty. Therefore, there is a need for subsidies for energy commodities and the local renewable energy development such as the Feed-in-tariffs system from the government. This use of subsidy is similar to microfinance in the poverty eradication in a sense that it aims to provide a ladder to those in need and encourage their self-help afterwards.

4 Stabilisation of the economy and solving debt services.

Since the collapse of Lehman Brothers in 2008, the global economic crisis massively destabilised the economy. Furthermore, the Euro crisis triggered by the excessive debt accumulation caused a further blow to the already struggling world economy. Despite the economic struggle, increasing jobless rates, and persistent poverty, there is a mystery in the world that the world spent $1.74 trillion in total on military expenditure, recording a growth over the past 13 years since 1998, and also the oil money only circulates within the oil industry. It indicates that although it seems the world does not have sufficient fund to solve the said problems, it is because of the allocation of resources. Therefore, if the world fairly distributes its abundant capital to wherever is appropriate such as green industry, it will help create new technologies, job opportunities and better livings for the people. Thus, the governments must reallocate their resources and stabilise the economy. Without this step, the governments cannot ensure the step 3.

5 Reduction of the use of fossil fuel for energy production

As seen in the oil shocks in the 1970s and the current political conflicts in the Middle East, the oil producing countries are occasionally unstable and this significantly affects petroleum prices as well as other commodity prices such as food. Therefore, the energy production should not be dependent on petroleum or other finite source of energy.When the above steps (local energy production and government financial support) are ensured and the renewable energy development progresses, it will change current structure of energy supply that the role of fossil fuels will become less important, being replaced by the renewable energy. This means that the amount of fossil fuel consumption will decline and the energy will be produced and consumed locally, and thus cause less environmental damages.

6 Building public transport systems

At the Rio+20 Earth summit, the several regional and world development banks made an announcement that they will shift their investment pattern from the roads construction to building transport systems with a $175 billion fund over the next 10 years. Such a policy change is very important because motor vehicles emit a large amount of GHG and causes environmental pollutions as well as health problems. In fact, it is estimated that the car use in the world consumes one third of total oil consumption. Also, IEA highlights in its report in 2011 that 23% of world carbon emissions were produced from a transport sector in 2009. Thus, building transport systems and reducing the car use will help cut GHG emissions, decontamination costs, and healthcare costs. Moreover, motor vehicle companies are developing new technologies such as electric cars, hydrogen vehicles, and compressed air cars. Although they are technically not yet brought into the market at affordable prices, these technologies will definitely lead the car industry in the age of environmental concern. Building public transport system and introducing new technologies to the public motor vehicles must lead the green innovation.

7 Halting nuclear reactors construction and replacing them with renewable energy

Because the current capacity and technological development of renewable energy are insufficient to cover ever increasing energy demands, some countries, notably in Asia, construct new nuclear power plants with a huge amount of investment. However, when analysing the externalities of nuclear energy such as risks of a natural hazard, high level radioactive waste, and human errors, nuclear energy is not the best option for securing energy supply and environmental protection. It is true that the nuclear technology is still one of the options for solving the energy issues, but it should not be expanded unless the safety is 100% ensured; however, it is impossible in reality. Therefore, we must develop the renewable energy and halt the construction of nuclear power plants.

8 Improving transparency in the energy industry

As is an inherent issue in monopolistic industries, governance is one of the biggest problems in the energy industry. Massive corporations often exploit their power to cover up unpleasant facts and keep them away from the public scrutiny. Even though regulatory agencies are established to monitor such corporations, there is a risk of regulatory capture as seen in the oil industry in Nigeria and the nuclear industry in Japan. Hence, improving transparency in governance by opening the information to the public must be ensured.

9 Strengthening a safety guideline for a nuclear hazard

Although nuclear energy involves huge risks, it is in fact unrealistic to abandon all the nuclear power plants, especially where nuclear energy covers more than 50% of the energy production such as in France, Lithuania, Slovakia, and Belgium. Therefore, what is urgently needed is strengthening regulatory systems and establishing a safety guideline for an emergency. In both Chernobyl and Fukushima cases, it is pointed out that because of a lack of a clear emergency guideline, the governments failed to take appropriate actions such as distributing potassium iodide to the citizens in the affected areas and worsened the situation. Thus, re-examining the emergency guideline must be the first consideration to minimise the possible risks.

10 Conducting the careful re-assessment of nuclear risks

Even though assessment of risks of natural hazards is already done, it must be carried out at regular bases with a third party monitoring system. Fukushima accident is one example that the earthquake and tsunami were unpredictable even with the modern technology and were expectedly massive, which caused the worst catastrophe in the history. Therefore, risk assessments must take into account of 'unpredictable factors' to ensure safety.

Since the current approach to the climate change is based on mitigation, it does not change the fundamental structure, and people are repeating the same thing in a different way with a help of the technological innovation. Although some have made such an argument since the 1970s, the majority of people are ignorant and reluctant to make a lifestyle change. It must be noted that mitigation polices alone are insufficient in accomplishing sustainable development. In the world of resource scarcity and the global climate change, we must recognise the limits in our ability to conquer the nature. People in the past perhaps believed the resources are bottomless, abundant, and free to exploit, and developed means to squeeze finite resources with a science innovation since the emergence of industrial revolution. However, in this modern era, people have far more sophisticated technologies and knowledge. Therefore, we should no longer make an excuse for what human activities have caused to the environment and must make a decisive step towards a practical sustainable development.

7.5 Renewable Energy Development in Japan: Kuzumaki Town Local Innovation

By Ryota Koike

Green House Gasses Emissions Reduction Policy in Japan

At the Kyoto Earth Summit, Japan set its GHG emissions reduction target as 6% against its 1990 standard, and actually managed to cut GHG emissions by approximately 7% from 2007 to 2008. Despite such a promising start Japan is in fact struggling to achieve the goal that the GHG emissions in 2010 increased by 3.9% from 2009 due to a recovery from the global economic crisis in 2008 (Ministry of Environment, 2010). It is also evident that Japan was the 5th highest emitting country in 2009 after China, US, India, and Russia (IEA 2011), producing 8.58 tonnes of CO_2 per capita in 2009, which was about twice as large as the world average of 4.29 tonnes (Ministry of the Environment 2009). This indicates that relatively lower GHG emissions between 2008 and 2010 were not achieved by a radical structural change but as a by-product of the economic recession.

Despite the above facts, the government has an over- optimistic vision and a passive posture towards the issue, and is showing its reluctance to make a structural change and claims that it expects to cut 3.8% of GHG emissions by plants' carbon absorption through forest management and 1.6% through carbon trading, joint implementation, and Clean Development Mechanisms under the market-based Kyoto mechanisms. The 0.6% balance of the reduction target is expected to be achieved by decreasing 53% of GHG emissions through improving energy efficiency, 29% by increasing the number of nuclear power plants, and 18% through renewable energy development (Kuzumaki-town, 2004). Such estimations especially regarding nuclear energy, however, are likely to fail because of the aftermath of Fukushima catastrophe in 2011, which led to a widespread public demand for a policy change.

Slow government-led Development

Prior to the nuclear accident, Japan did not have any clear strategies for a renewable energy development, because the government initially planned to increase a nuclear energy capacity to 40% by 2030, replacing conventional fossil fuels such as oil and coals. This policy regrettably left the renewable energy industry unattended. As such, it has become clear that, while the demands for renewable energy have increased, Japan lacks the infrastructure, and failed to provide sufficient incentives to domestic firms. This is a huge disadvantage for private firms mainly because the construction of infrastructure is both time and capital consuming, and it is estimated to take at least 5 years and cost 1 trillion yen. While there is an urgent need for establishing the infrastructure with long term funding, Japan faces an increasingly threatening financial problem in that its national debt reached 709 trillion yen in 2012 which is equivalent to the amount of 17 years tax revenue, marking a 210% proportion of GDP ratio (Ministry of Finance Japan, 2012), and thus is now unable to fund such a huge development project.

Therefore, although Japanese companies have high levels of technology, they chose to operate their businesses abroad rather than within Japan. Mitsubishi Heavy Industries (2010), for example, has launched its offshore wind energy project in the UK with a £14 million funding from the UK Department for Business Innovation and Skills. Similarly, other leading companies such as Sharp, NGK Insulators, Sumitomo Corporation, Showa Shell, and Eurus Energy operate their renewable energy projects in Europe and the Middle East (Ministry of Economy, Trade and Industry, 2010). Thus, it can be seen that while Japan has sophisticated technology, paradoxically, it has failed to utilise such resources to innovate its own energy market.

Local-led Renewable Energy Development

However, although large scale government-led development failed to stimulate the renewable energy industry, there have already been some successful local-led projects being operated in Japan. One of such examples is 'Kuzumaki-town Green Project' in Kuzumaki town in Iwate prefecture. The town has developed the projects with its wise investment in the third sector, the joint venture firms between public and private capitals, and gains renewable energy such as solar, wind and biomass by taking advantage of their local knowledge and resources.

The feature of the town is that 86% of the land is covered with forest and 46.6% of the population is a stockbreeder, and thus its economy is based largely on stockbreeding, mainly exporting dairy products such as milk and cheese to other areas. Contrary to economic growth, depopulation became one of the biggest issues since the 1960s that the scale of the population has decreased from 15,946 at its peak in 1960 to 8,020 in 2004 (Kuzumaki Town, 2003). Combined with the depopulation, the environmental concern also urged immediate reactions that the Kyoto earth summit in 1997 raised environmental awareness, especially to global climate change and the importance of GHG emissions reduction. Thus, the Kuzumaki town established a new administrative policy in 1998.

Kuzumaki-town Green Project

Since the policy change in the 1990s, Kuzumaki town has implemented following policies:

- 'New Kuzumaki energy vision' in 1999

- 'Kuzumaki-town energy efficiency vision' in 2004

- 'The 2nd Kuzumaki-town energy efficiency vision' in 2010,

In these policies is recognised the importance of the balance between human economic activity and the ecological capacity (Kuzumaki-town website). The town, therefore, set three pillars of development: improving telecommunication infrastructure, stopping the depopulation, and promoting renewable energy for environmental protection, in an attempt to revitalise the town by creating new green jobs through its participatory future-oriented city planning of environmental sustainability.

In the 'new Kuzumaki energy vision', the town firstly established the joint venture 'Green Power Kuzumaki Wind Power Factory' with the government's financial support in 2001. The establishment of wind power facility was a wise investment because the fact that 97% of the land is 400m above the sea level provides a suitable environment for wind energy generation. In fact, it produces 54 million kW per year, which is twice as much as the annual electricity consumption of the whole town, covering 16,000 households' demands (Kuzumaki-town website). The town also makes extra revenue by selling a surplus of electricity to the Tohoku Electric Power Company, and by which it covers the costs of the operation.

Furthermore, the town launched the energy efficiency project in 2004, in which it established other renewable energy facilities to take advantage of its rich natural resources. For instance, a livestock waste biomass system enables farmers to convert 13 tonnes of wastes into biomass energy per day. Also, since 97% of the town is covered by the forest, it produces a large amount of the wood waste from the forest management. Thus, the town established a woodchip biomass system, which provides 3 tonnes of woodchip biomass energy per day. In addition to these green energy projects, the town has built a solar energy facility at the Kuzumaki junior high school for green education and young generations' participation. The town is now planning to launch 'Kuzumaki-town biomass project', which aims to redesign current energy life-cycle to consume only what it produced by expanding its existing renewable energy capacity as well as develop new technologies (Kuzumaki town, 2012).

Such projects thus are run by taking advantage of local knowledge and resources, and what is significant about the project is that they encourage active participation from the citizens with subsidiary to green related commodities. As a result, the projects have contributed to an energy consumption reduction by 22.1% in 2010 compared to the 1990 standard. Despite the fact that the total electricity consumption has increased by

47% in the decade between 1994 and 2004, such an increase was covered by the renewable energy production, marking 184.5% of the energy self-sufficiency ratio as well as 46.3% of carbon emissions reduction per year.

Implications

This small local-led movement shows several advantages for rural communities such as;

1. securing local energy self-sufficiency with less GHG emissions

2. attracting potential private capital to renewable energy development

3. creating new job opportunities in the field of green jobs

4. raising environmental awareness amongst households with their participation in the project in a close proximity to the issue.

Because small rural towns have the depopulation issue and are often financially marginalised, it seems difficult to implement new large-scale projects, but the Kuzumaki Green Project provides a good example of how a small town can tackle the issue by developing small and local green projects. In fact, these rural areas are not resource poor but, in many cases, rich in natural resources, as the government approximated the potential gains of 1.9 billion kW from wind, 100 million kW from solar, 15 million kW from hydroelectricity, and 10.5 million kW from geothermal energy (Ministry of the Environment, 2011). Therefore, it is possible to spread green innovation even in a small town, if it takes small local-based development with cooperation between the public and private capital.

Rebirth of Japan: A Comprehensive Strategy

Since the implementation of the new energy policies, some big firms accelerate their businesses in the renewable energy market. In October in 2009, a Net Metering Policy was introduced which allows those who produce solar energy to sell their surplus of electricity to the electric power companies with reasonable price settings. Also, Japan has made a small distributed capacity investment of $8.1 billion in solar PV projects in 2011, marking a growth rate of 25% compared to the previous year (UNEP 2012). Given these efforts, solar power generators became more affordable and available to private entrepreneurs as well as individuals, so that the amount of production doubled to27 million kW in 2011 from 11 million kW in 2008. (Japan Photovoltaic Energy Association, 2012).

In addition to the NMP, Japan has introduced the new *Feed-in-Tariffs Policy*, replacing NMP since July 2012. This policy also mandates electric power companies to purchase surplus of electricity, but what is different from the previous system was that it covers other renewable energies, including wind, geothermal, hydroelectricity, and biomass energy. The purchasing prices were set to 42yen/ kWh for solar power and 23yen/ kWh for wind power with 20 years guarantee. It is thus expected that such policy implementations will provide an incentive for the market and boost further renewable energy production in Japan. Also, in 2012, the government introduced a new economic growth strategy, in which it claims to create 1.4 million of job opportunities by expanding the green energy industry by 2020. Furthermore, it aims to increase the renewable energy capacity from the current level of less than 1% to 25-30% in the next 20 years, reflecting lessons from the nuclear disaster in 2011 (National Policy Unit, 2012). Thus, the government has facilitated the renewable energy development in the past few years by establishing a guideline for private entrepreneurs. Given that, there are some renewable energy facilities being established since the implementation of the new policy. For example, Fushimi city in Kyoto prefecture has invested £96 million and started running a large scale solar power plant, which covers electricity consumption of 1,000 households (The Kyoto Shimbun News 2012). Similarly, SB Energy, one of subsidiaries of Softbank group, has funded several solar energy projects in Japan, including Kyoto, Osaka, Totori, Tochigi, Gunma, and Tokushima prefecture. The 'Softbank Totori Yonago Solar Park' project in Totori prefecture, for instance, is expected to begin its operation in July 2013 with the capacity of 39.5 million kW per year, equivalent to 11,000 households' electricity consumption (SB Energy, 2012).

With these projects with sufficient funds of private capital and revitalised rural economy, there possibly will be a rapid expansion in the renewable energy market. There are some problems ahead though Japan is beginning to proceed to the renewable energy era, in the post-Fukushima energy policy change.

References

International Energy Agency. (2011) *Energy Balances of OECD Countries.* [Online] Available at: http://wds.iea.org/wds/pdf/documentation_OECDBAL_2011.pdf [Accessed: 5 July, 2012].

Japan Photovoltaic Energy Association. (2012) *Domestic Solar PV Share.* [Online] Available at: http://www.jpea.gr.jp/04doc01.html [Accessed: 4 July, 2012].

Kuzumaki Town Website. [Online] Available at: http://www.town.kuzumaki.iwate.jp/index.php?topic=kankyo

Kuzumaki Town. (2003) *Kuzumaki Town Energy Efficiency Vision.* [Online] Available at: http://www.town.kuzumaki.iwate.jp/images/library/File/kankyo/04kanene/h15-vision.pdf [Accessed: 3 September, 2012].

Kuzumaki Town. (2010) *2nd Kuzumaki Town Energy Efficiency Vision.* [Online] Available at: http://www.town.kuzumaki.iwate.jp/images/library/File/kankyo/04kanene/-vision.pdf [Accessed: 3 September, 2012].

Kuzumaki Town.(2012) *Kuzumaki Biomass Town Project.* [Online] Available at: http://www.town.kuzumaki.iwate.jp/images/library/File/kankyo/04kanene/h20-biomass.pdf [Accessed: 4 September, 2012].

Kyoto Shimbun. (2012) *Kyoto's Mega-solar Electric Generation Starts Running with Supply of 1,000 Housholds*. [Online] Available at: http://www.kyoto-np.co.jp/top/article/20120701000097 [Accessed: 4 July, 2012].

Ministry of Economy, Trade and Industry. (2010) *Energy White Paper in 2010*. [Online] Available at: http://www.meti.go.jp/ [Accessed: 2 September, 2012].

Ministry of Environment. (2011) *Study of Potential for the Introduction of Renewable Energy*. Climate Change Policy Division, Japan.
[Online] Available at: http://www.env.go.jp/earth/report/h23-03/ [Accessed: 30 May 2012].

Ministry of Finance. (2012). *The Amount of National Debt of Japan*. [Online] Available at: http://www.mof.go.jp/gallery/20110308.htm [Accessed: 5 July, 2012].

Ministry of the Environment. (2009) *The Source of CO2 Emissions in the World*. [Online] Available at: http://www.env.go.jp/earth/ondanka/shiryo.html#06 [Accessed: 4 September 2012].

Ministry of the Environment. (2010a) *Press Release: Green House Gasses Emissions in 2010*. [Online] Available at: http://www.env.go.jp/press/press.php?serial=14564 [Accessed: 4 September, 2012].

Ministry of the Environment. (2010b) *Total GHG Emissions in 2010*. [Online] Available at: http://www.env.go.jp/earth/ondanka/ghg/2010gaiyo.pdf [Accessed: 4 September 2012].

Ministry of the Environment. (2012) *The World's Commitment to CO$_2$ Reduction*. [Online] Available at: http://www.env.go.jp/earth/ondanka/stop2012/stop2012_ch4.pdf [Accessed: 4 September, 2012].

Mitsubishi Heavy Industries, Ltd. (2010) *Press Information: Signing a Contract with UK Government on Offshore Wind Power Plants*. [Online] Available at: http://www.mhi.co.jp/news/story/1002264910.html [Accessed: 30 August, 2012].

National Policy Unit. (2012) *Rebirth of Japan: A Comprehensive Strategy*. [Online] Available at: http://www.npu.go.jp/policy/ [Accessed: 1 September, 2012].

SB Energy Corp. (2012) *Press Release*. [Online] Available at: http://www.sbenergy.co.jp/ja/business/index.html [Accessed: 2 September, 2012].

United Nations Environment Programme. (2012) *Global Trends in Renewable Energy Investment*. [Online] Available at: http://fs-unep-centre.org/publications/global-trends-renewable-energy-investment-2012 [Accessed: 4 July, 2012].

Photo Miriam Kennet. Solar panels on a house-boat on the RiverThames

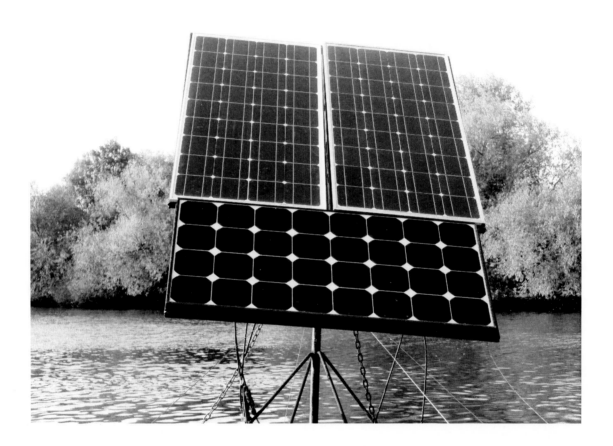

Part 8: Special Master Class theorising Care

Dressed to Care, Locating Feminist Contributions to Care in the Economy

by Professor Vinca Bigo and Professor Virginie Martin

The aim of this chapter is to locate the vast array on research on the subject of care in the economy right across the academic landscape. The chapter explores both orthodox and heterodox economic research on care, and focuses especially on a branch of heterodox economics, which has vastly contributed to this topic, called Feminist Economics. For a comprehensive view, however, we must consider feminist contributions, more widely. Our chapter is original in its endeavor to a) map and b) assess contributions on the topic of care in the economy, not only across the traditional orthodox-heterodox divides of the economics academy, but in its examination of contributions by non-economic feminist scholars. In our conclusion, we uncover important obstacles to the academic advancement of research on care in the economy. We put forward key recommendations needed to lift barriers to progress, and to address the global care crisis that assails countries around the world.

Introduction

The aim of this chapter is to locate research on care on the map of economic scholarly output. We are interested in contributions to care and its role in the economy[1]. We will find academic contributions are equal neither in quantity, nor in quality. Second, the majority of contributions come out of a branch of heterodox economics called Feminist Economics, as well as from feminist academics located in other disciplines.

Should there be any doubt of the importance of correctly understanding what care entails, and of its role in the economy, we need only to remind ourselves that we are in the midst of a global care crisis. Academic researchers, and other commentators, or informed observers, who study the situation of carers and care work, report conditions that are so inadequate that the discussion everywhere is couched in terms of national and/or global care crises, and of 'care deficits', and such like (Vinca Bigo 2010). These contributors point to substandard care centers, shortages of care workers, poor conditions of care workers, a lack of training, etc. Should there be any doubt, let us briefly note some of the explicit findings by relevant observers. Jane Lewis and Susan Giullari note that the "American feminist literature is replete with references to the 'care crisis'" (Susan Giullari and Jane Lewis 2005:96).

Mignon Duffy, for example, focusing on the US, notes not only the desperate conditions of care workers, the low pay that care workers receive, but also the concentration of women, particularly 'women of color', in these low-wage jobs:

"Recently, scholars and activists have focused attention on the contemporary crisis in care in the United States, particularly on the inadequacy of care resources and concomitant low wages and high turnover in care jobs. The combination of increased women's participation in the paid labor force and a dramatic aging of the population has left the United States with what Arlie Russell Hochschild (1998) has called a "care deficit". Amid stories of substandard day care centers, unhealthy conditions in nursing homes, and shortages of qualified nursing personnel in hospitals, there is mounting concern about the quantity and quality of care available for children and the elderly as well as for those who are ill or disabled. Feminist scholars have been among those making the connection between these social problems and the low wages and poor working conditions of day care providers, health aides, and other workers who provide care for pay in the labor market. Especially concerning to feminists is the concentration of women, particularly women of color, in these low-wage jobs" (Mignon Duffy 2005:66-7).

We draw lessons from the specific landscape of contributions to care in the economy. We shall note, in particular, the need for more methodological debate, as well as for the adoption of inter disciplinary and pluralist orientations to lift obstacles and facilitate progress in the field. Below, we first turn to the much disputed distinction between orthodox and heterodox economics, before examining both strands in turn.

Orthodox or heterodox?

Modern economics comprises a number of strands or schools of thought. We can identify two groups in particular. They are mainstream (or orthodox) economics, and heterodox economics. Orthodox or mainstream economics is that strand of economics that has come to increasingly dominate the scene of the economics academy since WWII, in terms of resources, appointments, teaching curriculum, and publications.

In this context, heterodox contributions are by and large ignored by the powers that be, where the former are not consider as usefully contributing to economic scholarship. In keeping, heterodox economics departments can be noted for their rarity (Andy Denis 2009). The recent student protest at Harvard University is a testimony to the state of affairs. In a letter dated November 2nd, 2011, the students of Economics 10 class, an introductory course taught by Greg Mankiw, former advisor of the Bush administration, complains of "the bias inherent in this introductory economics course" and of the "specific—and limited—view of economics" it advances (praxispamphlet 2011). The same letter says:

"A legitimate academic study of economics must include a critical discussion of both the benefits and flaws of different economic simplifying models. As your class does not include primary sources and rarely features articles from academic journals, we have very little access to alternative approaches to economics. There is no justification for presenting Adam Smith's economic theories as more fundamental or basic than, for example, Keynesian theory." (praxispamphlet 2011).

The Economics 10 class students have noticed that they are exposed to a curriculum that is quintessentially orthodox. Their wish is, legitimately, to be informed of non-orthodox voices that exist in economics, and to be introduced to different world-views, methodologies and economics theory.

Now, given the diversity of contributions in both mainstream and heterodox economics, is there a feature that consistently distinguishes the two groups? Such a feature does seem to exist. The element that characterizes orthodox or mainstream contributions consistently over time is that the orthodoxy insists on the use of mathematical deductive[2] models and econometrics methods (Lawson 1997).

Heterodox economists, on the other hand, are united in that they do not insist on the use of mathematical deductive methods, or any method in particular for that matter. The heterodoxy is critical of any dogmatic insistence on any one particular method. Instead, they believe that all methods should be included in the economist's toolbox. The choice of method, in heterodox economics, has typically been motivated by the relevance of any given method to examine and theorize the object under study.

Such differences do not preclude heterodox and orthodox economists from exploring similar themes. Indeed, claims to allegiance to, say, Marxist, Keynesian, New Institutional, and Feminist Economics, are made by orthodox and heterodox economists alike. The difference, once more, lies essentially in the methodologies and implicit ontologies[3] subscribed to. Moreover, there may well exist, within the schools we identify as heterodox, scholarly work, which makes use of mathematical deductive methodology. The difference is, once more, that the heterodoxy will not insist on the ubiquitous use of any one method.

The lack of pluralism that pervades the economics profession is such that the UK based Association for Heterodox Economics has finally voiced its concern with the relevant academic governing bodies, as to the lack of pluralism in the economics academy (Andy Denis 2009). Below, we begin with an examination of mainstream or orthodox research on care in the economy.

Orthodox conceptions of care

Mainstream or orthodox scholarship on care in the economy, tends to emphasize formal and paid care labor, rather than informal and/or unpaid forms of care labor. Definitions of care in this strand of economics can be noted for their absence (Colin Danby 2004; Marianne Ferber and Julie Nelson 2003).

One of the orthodox schools most concerned with care in economics is New Household Economics (NHE). Its cornerstone is the conceptualization of household activity as involving the joint welfare maximization of its members through the production of goods (the objects of utility), and by an amalgamation of household labour, technology and accrued assets (Gary Becker 1974, 1981; Jacob Mincer 1958, 1962)[4]. Unpaid care work, it is assumed, is carried out in the home by a female worker (typically the mother) in a male-headed household (not withstanding the increasing numbers of single parent, typically, female-headed households). The arrangement is considered to be willingly chosen, for being the most efficient deployment of his and her skills.

A tentative challenge to prevailing accounts of the household has comes from New Institutional Economics (NIE) (Robert Pollak 1985), recognizing that power, and not (only) benevolence, characterizes intra-family decision making processes. Using the language of transactions-costs, NIE applies the bargaining model to decision making situations. NIE is more sophisticated in its analysis, as it does away with the concept of joint-preference ordering. Processes of bargaining affect how the gains from cooperation are distributed within the family unit (Shelly Lundberg and Robert Pollack 1992; Marilyn Manser and Murray Brown 1980; Amartya Sen 1982)[5].

One of the problems is that treatment of care by the NIE, the successor of the NHE, remains rooted in neoclassical theory. Indeed, according to Alexandra Benham herself, Secretary of the Ronald Coase Institute (Coase is seen by many as the forefather of NIE),

"New Institutional Economics incorporates a theory of institutions into economics. It builds on, modifies, and extends neoclassical theory. It retains and builds on the fundamental assumption of scarcity and hence competition - the basis of the choice theoretic approach that underlies microeconomics" (Alexandra Benham 2010).

Simon Duncan makes similar observations, when he argues that

"new institutional economics' sits closest to the neo-classical account in trying to incorporate criticisms of conventional economics while keeping the discipline intact... In essence institutions only arise to 'correct' the real world so that the neo-classical model can properly operate" (Simon Duncan 2000: 7)[6].

In other words, NIE is still subject to the limits inherent in the neoclassical approach we have discussed above.

There have been attempts by feminist critics to transform existing mainstream theories in a concern to make them more relevant for policy (Gunnel Gustavsson 1997). Notburga Ott (1992), for example, argues that though the division of work based on comparative advantage is efficient in the short term (Gary Becker 1981), in the long run, she suggests, it is a sub-optimal solution, for it implies decreased bargaining power and decreased access to extra-household opportunities for the partner specializing in household work. Asa Rosen (1993) suggests, on the other hand, that there exists a stable discriminatory equilibrium in the job market that leads to inefficient outcomes in the long run. Although these interpretations draw attention to the fact that mainstream conclusions are often biased against women, and seek to produce theory that overcomes this limitation, they remain rooted in the standard assumptions of atomistic optimizing agents. The result has been, less to successfully transform existing theory in this domain, as to give it a certain legitimacy.

Before we turn to alternative approaches to care in the economy, let us below first examine why mainstream research on care has not been more successful. For, in order to progress, we must have a clear idea of the causes of failure. Else, the same mistakes will likely be reproduced time and time again.

An explanatory critique[7] for the lack of success

In the neoclassical strand of mainstream economics, economic agents are fictitious entities referred to as *homo economicus* (Steven Ziliak and Deirdre McCloskey 2008). The latter has unlimited desires, which he seeks to satisfy, with a view to maximizing his utility. He has no real agency or free will. His behavior is determined by a mathematical formula. Orthodox economic research typically assumes rational, optimizing, 'utility' seeking behavior in order to understand care relations.

Paula England and Nancy Folbre (2003) have pointed out that, although mainstream economics allows for agents to derive utility from acting altruistically, independence, autonomy and narrowly conceived self-serving behavior are nonetheless presupposed by the assumption of independent utilities (Nancy Folbre 1994b; Virginia Held 2002; Susan Himmelweit 1999; Neila Kabeer 2001; Julie Nelson 1996). *Homo economicus* is typically neither needy, nor dependent, features that do not sit well with the interdependence that characterizes relation of care in reality. As such, mainstream or orthodox scholarship on care necessarily fails to portray the relational aspect of the care situation.

Further, women, and others on the margins, are still everywhere the principal providers of care labor. Their participation is not actively taken into account in mainstream economic research on care in the economy. Structural inequalities that contribute to systematically limiting women's skills, whilst favoring those of men, are ignored. Processes of gender stereotyping are in mainstream economic theory mostly overlooked, whilst the benefits of sexual divisions of labor accruing to men are not acknowledged (Barbara Bergmann 1989; Francine Blau and Barbara Ferber 1992). Indeed, where power is discussed, a male, heading the household, is assumed to exercise it in a rational and altruistic manner, leaving no room for exploring the lack of and potential for women's empowerment in the household (Neila Kabeer 2001).

Charitable critics of the unified household model are of the opinion that mainstream models describe the status quo, and so merely reflect existing gendered roles. Feminist economists have long argued that the division of labor cannot be justified by biological differences, indicating that such divisions are social rather than natural (Esther Boserup 1970; Marianne Ferber and Bonnie Birnbaum 1977; Lloyd and Niemi 1979; Paula England 1993;). Unfortunately, mainstream models that describe care arrangements do not offer a framework for thinking through more equitable arrangements (Marianne. A. Ferber and Bonnie Birnbaum 1977; Isabel Sawhill 1977; Jane Humphries and Jill Rubery 1984).

A further problem is that even when the determining factors, such as power and dependency, are in some way represented in mainstream theory, such as in NIE, they are expressed in numerical terms, via a mathematical relationship, and hence still lack *realisticness.* In the end, the realities of the care worker and the care relation are not taken into account.

Now the lack of realisticness, we contend, is the result of their specific methodological choice. Mainstream scholarship on care in the economy is constrained by a self-imposed and ubiquitous *methodological straight jacket.* In other words, it suffers from the use of, and an insistence on, mathematical deductive modeling.

Good science, of both a natural and social kind, however, is first and foremost about achieving *explanatory* success, not *predictive* success. A similar view is expressed by certain economic geographers, who

> "would argue that is the mathematical model-builders who are deluding themselves into believing their deductivist theorising is somehow superior, and that discursive modes of theorising permit the construction of much richer 'maps' or representation of reality" (Ron Martin 1999: 82).

Indeed, where and when the NHE and the NIE adopt deductive tools, they have great difficulty incorporating norms and institutions to arrive at a dynamic and realistic representation of the care relation. To fit the models, agents, firms, institutions, etc., are portrayed atomistically, that is, they are decontextualised. We can thus quite easily explain why theories on care and its provision, that emanate from the mainstream literature, (necessarily) lack realism and relevance.

To arrive at methods that are appropriate to studying care, the logic must be inversed. That is, we should start with our best understanding of the nature or ontology of the subject under study before deciding on most appropriate methods. On closer inspection, the ontology (be it implicit or explicit) of the economy, presupposed by the heterodoxy, is one of an open system, in the sense of strict event regularity not occurring therein. Care has a strong human relational element, so that methods, such as mathematical deductive models that presuppose closed systems, are not especially suited to its study (for a full discussion of open and closed systems and methods in economics, see Vinca Bigo 2006). Below, we turn to research on care made by heterodox economists, more specifically, by a branch called Feminist Economics,

Feminist Economic contributions to care in the economy

Various branches of heterodox economics have contributed on the topic of care in the economy. Groupings to have done so quite explicitly include Health Economics, Post-Keynesian Economics, Institutional Economics, Evolutionary Economics, Nursing Economics, Welfare (State) Economics, Social Economics, Marxist Economics, Austrian Economics, Development Economics, Ecological Economics, Environmental Economics, and Green Economics. But he heterodox group to have most contributed to the subject of care is Feminist Economics. It is to their research that we turn below.

One of the most encompassing definitions for care labour coming out of Feminist Economics is supplied Paula England, Michelle J. Budig and Nancy Folbre. Summarizing their position, Paula England and Nancy Folbre define care labor as "work providing face-to-face services that develop the capabilities of the recipient (England, Budig and Folbre, 2002). Capabilities refers to health skills, or proclivities that are useful to the individual themselves or to others. These skills include physical and mental health, and physical, cognitive, and emotional skills, such as self-discipline, empathy, and care. Such care services are provided by parents, other family members, friends, and volunteers, but also by people who are paid, such as teachers, nurses, childcare workers, elder-care workers, therapists, and others" (Paula England and Nancy Folbre 2003).

Beyond *mis*-representations of care in the mainstream economic literature, its *under*-representation in the orthodoxy stems from the fact that care is not easily identified and measured. The above definition is giving us a sense of this difficulty. Much, if not most, of the provision of care takes place outside the formal sector (whether paid or unpaid). In fact, the majority of care provided is in the form of unpaid work done by women outside institutional settings. Whilst non-market activities are not necessarily more complex than market ones, they tend not to be captured by conventional quantitative measures that have become the norm in mainstream economics. The result is often a failure of orthodox economic theory to adequately incorporate care that is unpaid and/or informally provided, in deference to market based transactions.

Indeed, when taking full account of women's contribution to the economy, the share of care labour in GDP turns out to be considerable. Feminists to actively defend and develop this position include Diane Sainsbury (1999) in political sciences, Siv Gustafsson (2005) in economics, Jill Rubery (2006) in economics, Diane Elson (2010) in sociology, and Martin Seeleib-Kaiser (2008) in social policy and social work. When taking full account of women's contribution to the economy, the share of care labor is considerable (Lina Gálvez-Muñoz, Paula Rodríguez-Modroño and Mónica Domínguez-Serrano 2011). Feminist economist, Vinca Bigo, and human geographer, Mia Gray, have coined the term 'background care' to indicate that the economy, as a whole, and collectively organized formal care, in particular, rely heavily on, and would not survive without, the vast amount of informal and/or unpaid care provided mostly by women ('background care') (Vinca Bigo and Mia Gray 2009). Not surprisingly, certain scholars argue explicitly for the need to gender mainstream economic theory and research on the welfare state (see, for example, the Women Budget Group in the UK).

Feminist Economics scholars have further pointed to the tendency for policies to aim at increasing the labor participation of women. But the focus on participation *per se* ignores the ways in which reproductive work burdens its providers. Amongst the publications by the United Nations Research Institute for Social Development, the following passage makes the point eloquently:

"the pressing policy concern that of simply increasing the volume of explicit female employment, since simply adding on recognised "jobs" may in fact lead to a double burden upon women whose household obligations still have to be fulfilled. Instead, concern has to be focused upon the quality, the recognition and the remuneration of women's work [...], as well as the conditions facilitating it, such as alternative arrangements for household work and child care." (Jayati Ghosh 2004).

Happily, an increasing number of contributions examine care with a specific focus on the experience of carer providers, and of the care relation. These take the vulnerability of carers and dependents seriously, and explore the complexities of dependency. In this context, Diana Strassmann (1993), Paula England (1993), Marianne Ferber and Julie Nelson (1993), Edith Kuiper, Jolande Sap, Susan Feiner, Otto Notburga and Zafiris Tzannatos (1995), Drucilla Barker and Susan Feiner (2004), and Marion Turkel (in Nursing Economics) (2001) are amongst a number of heterodox scholars to have written extensively on the subject of economic agents as related and (inter) dependent, whose emotions do not stand in opposition to rationality and reason.

Further contributions to discussions bearing on the burden placed on care workers come out of development economics. Scholars in this area points out that women are the first to suffer from the adverse consequences of development, in great part caused by Structural Adjustment Programmes (see for further discussion of these questions Bina Agarwal 1997; Lourdes Beneria 1979; Edward Bergman 1986; Simon Duncan and Rosalind Edwards 1997; Susan Feiner and Bruce Roberts 1990; Judith Galtry 1997; Gillian Hewitson 1999; Amartya Sen 1984; Diana Strassmann and Livia Polanyi 1995). This is so, given the burden of multiple caring responsibilities, not only for off springs, but also for the elderly and the sick (including HIV infected persons), that falls upon girls and women. Their situation as carers is often rendered worse by environmental degradation, which typically complicates the task of providing decent food and sanitation.

Reflecting this reality, in a recent conference on "The Political and Social Economy of Care", the UNRISD identifies care as a priority topic (2009). It examines issues such as epidemiology, welfare, socio-cultural and demographic changes, new forms of family structures, regional developments, and poverty, more generally. The conference proceedings emphasize the importance of care as a lens of analysis: "The 'care diamond' analogy put forth by the [UNRISD] project illustrates the multiplicity of sites and institutions involved in care provisioning." (UNRISD 2009: 4).

Thus, heterodox economic research on the topic of care in, provided especially by Feminist Economics scholarship, is prolific indeed. Here, care is studied under its multiple and complex relational, personal and inter personal, aspects. This is possible precisely because, the heterodoxy is not constrained by any method in particular. Indeed, no heterodox economist insists on mathematical deductive methods. Economic theories that aim to improve the material conditions of well being in developing countries and elsewhere will gain in pertinence, when they reflect the agential and contextual complexities of the care relation, including the reality of the burden placed on carers.

Although, some of the scholars cited above, as others to research the topic of care in the economy, are seated outside economic departments, many consider themselves economists, and/or may attend events organized by associations such as the

International Association for Feminist Economics, or publish in the association's journal, *Feminist Economics*. For this reason, we have included them in this section. Nonetheless, if many insightful contributions to care come out of feminist economics (wherever they are located), many others, still, emerge out of other subject areas. In the section below, we develop an overview of the research on care in the economy, developed outside economics. This concerns scholarship produced by feminist scholars that work in other disciplines, yet concern themselves with the topic of care in the economy.

Beyond Feminist Economics

To start, research on the welfare state, social policy analysis and policy formulation, concerned with the (equitable) distribution and provision of adequate care, exists a number of disciplines. Debates centre on the respective roles of the state, the firm, the family, the community, and charitable organizations in providing and financing care (Gosta Esping-Andersen, Duncan Gallie, Anton Hemerijck and John Myles 2002; Gosta Esping-Andersen 2008 from sociology). A portion of this literature discusses the effects of the gender pay gap on the provision of care (see for example the focus of GeNet 2009).

Another part concentrates on the difficulties of juggling a career and looking after dependents, as reflected in work-life balance dilemmas (see for example, Jude Browne 2006 in sociology; Shirley Dex and Heather Joshi 1999 in education; Jane Lewis 2008 in social policy).

Relatedly, Sophie Bowlby in geography, Susan Gregory in health, and Linda McKie in law and social sciences have uncovered 'caringscapes'. In their own words, "the concept of 'caringscapes' can help look at the relationship between work and caring responsibilities in a different, multi-dimensional way, leading to a better understanding of the demands and needs of those combining work and care", a concept they developed with a view to aiding policy decisions and implementation (Linda McKie, Susan Gregory and Sophia Bowlby 2004). In a similar vein, Laura Balbo (1987) in the humanities developed the idea of "crazy quilts" as a metaphor for the complex web of responsibilities that carers juggle with on a daily basis.

Further, Liz Bondi in social geography offers a framework of analysis to better understand the often ambivalent nature of the care relationship (Bigo 2010). She suggests " [psychotherapeutic approaches] provide frameworks within which to understand the sometimes contradictory and paradoxical qualities of the emotions associated with giving and receiving care. Emphasising the mutual constitution of feelings and relationships, psychotherapeutic formulations enrich understandings of the gendering of care work as well as offering spatial metaphors within which to articulate subjective experiences of caring and being cared for." (Liz Bondi 2008: 262).

Research in psychology also offers useful insights into the kinds of resistances faced when promoting shared parenting. It is still a challenge for men to find their place as more involved fathers. They and society at large are still constrained by norms and expectations (Corinne Grenier et Virginie Martin 2010). The topic of fathers as possible carers is discussed by social psychologists, such as Andrew Bainham, Shelley Day Sclater and Martin Richards (1999) in psychosocial studies, Andrea Doucet (2011) in sociology and anthropology, Tabitha Freeman (2008) in family research. Indeed, when encouraging men and/or women to become active carers, welfare state policies have to contend with collective, but also with personal difficulties, that touch on the carer's identity.

Further research argues convincingly that, at the collective level, conceptions of citizenship must incorporate duties and responsibilities incumbent on citizens to provide care (Virginia Held 1995 in philosophy; Selma Sevenhuijsen 1998 in medical ethics and medicine; Kari Wearness 2004 in sociology). There is growing awareness of the value of care giving to society as a whole. Crucially, different conceptions of citizenship will imply different welfare policies.

Relatedly, other scholars put forward an analysis of care that is not just about provision, or as care labor *per se*, but also about care as an ethical orientation. Carol Gilligan's (1982) challenge to Lawrence Kohlberg's morality for neglecting differences in moral development and dispositions of girls and boys sparked a vast body of literature on the ethics of care. Whilst care in economics is almost exclusively focused on care as work, it is care in the sense of motivation, or responsibility, that is, 'caring about' that is being referred to here. An ethics of care puts the need to value contributions made by carers firmly on the agenda, joining those who favor definitions of citizenship in relation to care. It is also a framework that challenges the foundations of liberal economic thinking, since an ethics of care emphasizes the importance of empathy (Bigo and Gray 2009; Braunstein in Community and Behavioral Health; van Staveren in Development Economics; Daniele Tavani in Economics 2011). As such, it does not sit well with methodological individualism that portrays economic agents acting in an atomistic fashion.

Debates on the commodification of care offer a further perspective on the care worker, by focusing on the effects of financially compensating care work. The context of the northern welfare states is one in which private sector care has grown significantly. Consumers can now purchase services ranging from direct care (health care, child care, elderly care) to "intimate care" (such as buying gifts and cards for significant anniversaries, planning your child's party, and so on). Arlie Hochschild (2003) in politics explores the caring sector's demands on employees, and argues that managed emotions become part of the "product". In this context the care worker runs the risk of becoming alienated to the detriment of providing quality care.

The limits to the commodification of care are extensively discussed in heterodox scholarship. Contributors focus on the limits in productivity gains that can be achieved in the provision of care, and ask whether care can and/or should be commodified (feminist economist Susan Himmelweit 1999). Perceptions of the private-public divide play an important part in these discussions, and tend to vary according to the positions individuals occupy (of mother, father, employee, etc.). Gender theorists have actively questioned the sharpness of the divide between the two spheres (Christine Delphy 1995; Viviane Zelizer 2006 in sociology and their research on intimacy). Stressing the divide rather than envisaging a continuum between the private and the public sphere affects the theorization of care, and how resources are allocated to caring occupations.

More generally, to understand why women consistently find themselves in positions of subordination, as carers and otherwise, social scientists, including political philosophers and psychoanalysts, have examined the ways in which patriarchal structures underpin and cooperate with capitalist ones, whilst explaining how the two can and do also run into contradictions (Azizah Al-Hibri 1981; Ann Ferguson 1996; Sulamith Firestone 1972; Arlie Hochschild 1989; Lucie Irigaray 1985; Juliet Mitchell 1974; Mary Molyneux 1985)[8].

Heidi Hartmann (1979, 1981) argues, in what Iris Marion Young (1981) later calls the 'dual system theory', that capitalism and patriarchy support, each after their own fashion, the 'family wage' (an individual's wage sufficient to support a family). The family wage model centers on the male breadwinner, without giving adequate consideration to women doing care work in the home (Susan Giullari and Jane Lewis 2005). The latter are a vulnerable category, for financially dependent on the male and/or the state. Concurrently, these women supply the capitalist system with an (reserve) army of labor 'for free' (Zillah Eisenstein 1979; Sheila Rowbotham 1972). The availability of cheap and/or free care labor is indeed a fundamental feature of capitalist economies. Understandingly, Marxist and other scholars call for such work to be both to better valued and rewarded.

The notion of care is also employed in corporate social responsibility discourse, and in the ecofeminist literature (Sarah Cook 2008; Sherilyn MacGregor 2004; Steve May, George Cheney and Juliet Roper May 2007). Indeed, the term is now widely used by corporations, who portray themselves as caring for their employees, their customers, the environment, and other stakeholders. The caring discourse is typically used because of the positive value care denotes, even if, it must me added, much amounts to mere lip service (Robertson and Nicholson 1996).

We now have a more comprehensive picture of research on care in the economy in the academic landscape. Not surprisingly, orthodox and heterodox contributions vary in quantity and quality. What is more surprising is the number of scholars located outside the economics academy making contributions, relevant to furthering our understanding of care and its dynamics in the economy. What lessons can we draw from our analysis? We can draw a number of key conclusions. To these we now turn.

Conclusions

Our objective has been to locate research on care in the economy in the academic landscape, to identify obstacles impeding progress, and to point to possible ways forward. Amongst the vast array of academic contributions spanning several decades up to this day that we have reviewed in both mainstream and heterodox economic scholarship, as well as research located in other disciplines, on care in the economy, we made the following observations.

First, *orthodox* economic contributions to the study of care continuously lack realism. The care relation is portrayed by the orthodoxy as a mathematical function, in which the complexities of human interactions are largely ignored. Additionally, discussion of practices, norms, and institutions in relation to gender inequality are missing, and consequently a relatively impoverished analysis ensues. Thus, the orthodoxy offers limited discussion of 1) the agency of actors involved in the delivery and reception of care, and 2) the structural context that disadvantages both. This is true though we know such structural constraints play an important part in reproducing much of the conditions that characterize the care sector, such as the inequalities that disadvantage women, racial and ethnic minorities, the poor, and the less educated.

Second, we saw, heterodox economists are united in their concern with offering a realist account of economics, and in the adoption of a pluralist methodological toolkit. Their objective is to use the method that can best explain the complexities brought by spatial and temporal changes. Whilst relinquishing some of the elegance that comes with mathematical formalism, the group incorporates historical and geographical data, drawing on a range of qualitative methods, as well as on descriptive (and possibly other forms of) statistics, where appropriate. Thus, not surprisingly, *heterodox economics*, in particular, that branch called *Feminist Economics*, research has been prolific in producing more realistic accounts of care in the economy, not least because the heterodoxy is not constrained by method.

Third, we have been able to observe a virtual total absence of heterodox economists in mainstream economics departments. Yet heterodox economics scholars have all but disappeared. The fact is that they have now successfully established themselves in *other disciplines*. Indeed, many heterodox economists conducting research on care have moved to other areas, where they have found the intellectual freedom to pursue their research. We noted further that scholars may be making contributions to economic theory, without necessarily seeing themselves as economists[9]. Thus, another key assessment of this paper is been that much research on care in relation to economic issues appears to be very often fruitfully conducted outside, rather than in the confines of, research academies and positions that are formally labeled as economics. Invaluable contributions can be found across disciplines, such as business studies, geography, politics, gender studies, sociology, and so on.

The limitations identified in the paper, we are confident, can be overcome by the adoption of three principal strategies.

First, where methods limit the development of realistic and so relevant research to care in the economy, ontologically informed *methodological debates* should be reopened throughout the economics academy. We suggest that to uncover most appropriate methods, we should start with our best conception of the nature, or the ontology, of the subject studied, and not the other way round. This, of course, includes the mainstream academy. Ultimately, appropriate methods for the study of care, must be freely established and adopted.

Second, being open to alternative methods means adopting a *pluralist orientation*. Of course, pluralism, though anti-dogmatic, is by itself not enough to guarantee progress. Amassing a large array of views and contributions can have the counter productive effect of merely fragmenting or diluting research efforts. Thus, conjointly, it is necessary to find ways to piece together research output, as well as dialectically resolve different conflicting contributions, to consolidate and advance knowledge (for further discussion of fragmentation, integration and pluralism, see Vinca Bigo and Ioana Negru 2008).

Third, given the tendency for economics to be increasingly studied outside formal economics departments, scholarship on care in the economy stands to gain by developing a stronger *inter disciplinary* engagement (a prerequisite being of course a pluralist orientation here too). In other words, research on care in the economy should actively engage with scholarship on care in other disciplines, a move that is further justified by the multi faceted nature of care.

This third conclusion warrants a final word on inter disciplinarity, and specifically on the scope of economics in relation to other disciplines. Different schools of thought in heterodox economics can be seen to divide the labor of investigating the economic realm by focusing on particular questions or topics, Feminist Economics on relations, Keynesianism on uncertainty, Institutional Economics on continuity and change, and so on. So too, the various disciplines of the social realm can be seen to ask questions belonging to aspects of the same interconnected social whole studied under its different aspects (Vinca Bigo and Ioana Negru, 2011). Thus, economics focuses on provisioning, sociology on collective phenomena, history on the past, geography on space, psychology on affects and mind processes, and so on. Max Weber recognizes the need for a division of labor (a term he himself employs), and argues that to do economics requires inter disciplinary work. In his own words:

> "The explanation of everything by economic causes alone is never exhaustive in any sense whatsoever in any sphere of cultural phenomena, not even in the "economic" sphere itself" (Max Weber 1897).

Indeed, the topic of care in economics cannot be studied in isolation. We saw in the paper how other disciplines produce numerous insights that concern care in the economy, where part of this dispersion is due to the academic relocation process described above. So long as we are clear as to the mission of the economics discipline, and the scope of care therein, we can venture out with some confidence.

And to ensure that research on care in the economy continues to progress, we recommend the adoption of two key strategies, both of which presuppose a pluralist orientation. First, the reopening of ontologically informed methodological discussions to help produce scholarship that is both realistic and relevant. Second, the production of interdisciplinary work that builds on all relevant contributions to the topic of care in the economy, however the scholarship is 'dressed' and 'disciplined'.

We would like to conclude with a quote by Julia T. Wood. In her book, *Who Cares,*

Women, Care and Culture, we are reminded just how all encompassing the topic of care is. In her preface she states:

"*Who Cares?* is about what is and what can be. It is a warning about the mounting care crisis confronting us as we stand on the brink of the twenty-first century. It is an effort to understand highly personal issues of caring that come up in our individual lives. It is an inquiry into the discursive means that create and sustain attitudes toward caring and women within our culture. It is an argument for positioning care more centrally in our cultural life and enacting the structural and symbolic changes required to realize that reconfiguration. Finally, it is an invitation to participate in reforming our society and ourselves so that we are more humanly responsive and responsible." (Julia Wood 1994: ix).

The quote above comes to corroborate our firm belief that both a strong theoretical grounding and an inclusive research orientation constitute two primal pillars to select, consolidate and develop the best possible research on the topic of care in the economy.

References

Agarwal, Bina. 1997. Bargaining and gender relations: Within and beyond the household. *Feminist Economics* Vol 3 (1): 1-51.

Al-Hibri, Azizah. 1981. Capitalism is an advanced state of patriarchy; but marxism is not feminism. In *Women and revolution: A discussion of the unhappy marriage of marxism and feminism*, pp.165-94. Boston: South End Press.

Arrow, Kenneth. 1963. Uncertainty and the welfare economics of medical care. *The American Economic Review* 53: 941-73.

Bainham, Andrew, Sheila Day Sclater and Martin Richards eds. 1999. *What is a parent?*. Oxford: Hart Publishing.

Balbo, Laura. 1987. "Crazy quilts: Rethinking the welfare state debate from a woman's point of view". In *Women and the state*. pp. 45-71. London: Hutchinson.

Barker, Drucilla and Susan Feiner, eds. 2004. *Liberating economics: Feminist perspectives on families, work, and globalisation*. Michigan: The University of Michigan Press.

Becker, Gary. 1974. "A theory of marriage: Part ii". *Journal of Political Economy* 82: 511-26.

Becker. Gary. 1981. *A treatise on the family*. Cambridge: Harvard University Press.

Becker, Gary. 2008. *Human capital*. The concise encyclopedia of economics: Library of Economics and Liberty
http://www.econlib.org/library/Enc/HumanCapital.html (accessed October 2010).

Ben-Porath, Yossef. 1980. "The f-connection: Families, friends an firms and the organization of exchange". *Population and Development Review* 6: 1-30.

Beneria, Lourdes. 1979. "Reproduction, production and the sexual division of labour". *Cambridge Journal of Economics* 3: 203-25.

Benham, Alexandra. 2010. *About new institutional economics.*

http://www.coase.org/newinstitutionaleconomics.htm. (Octobre 2010).

Bergman, Edward M. 1986. *Local economies in transition : Policy realities and development potentials Duke press policy studies*. Durham: Duke University Press.

Bergmann, Barbara R. 1989. "What the common economic arguments against comparable worth are worth". *Journal of Social Issues* 45: 67-80.

Bhaskar, Roy. 1997. "On the ontological status of ideas". *Journal for the Theory of Social Behaviour* 27: 139–47.

Bigo, Vinca. 2006. "Open and closed systems and the cambridge school". *Review of Social Economy* 64: 493-514.

Bigo. Vinca. 2008. "Explaining modern economics (as a microcosm of society)". *Cambridge Journal of Economics* 32: 527-54.

Bigo. Vinca. 2010. "The care paradox: Devaluing and idealising care, the mother, and mother nature". *International Journal of Green Economics* 4: 117-33.

Bigo, Vinca and Mia Gray. 2009. "Constructing care: For love or money". *The Review of Eonomic Philosophy: Special Issue on Ethics and Healthcare* 10 (1): 103-124.

Bigo, Vinca and Ioana Negru. 2008. "From fragmentation to ontologically reflexive pluralism". *Journal of Philosophical Economics. Special issue on Pluralism* 1: 127-50.

Bigo, Vinca and Ioana Negru. 2011. "Theorising care: a possible defence of interdisciplinarity in economics". *International Journal of Green Economics* 5(2):109-125.

Blau, Francine and Marianne Ferber. 1992. *The economics of women, men and work*. Englewood Cliffs, New Jersey: Prentice Hall.

Bondi, Liz. 2008. "On the relational dynamics of caring: A psychotherapeutic approach to emotional and power dimensions of women's care work. Gender, Place and Culture" *A Journal of Feminist Geography* 15: 249-65.

Boserup, Esther. 1970. *Women's role in economic development*. New York: St. Martins Press.

Braunstein, Elissa, Irene van Staveren, Daniele Tavani. 2011. "Embedding Care and Unpaid Work in Macroeconomic Modeling: A Structuralist Approach". *Feminist Economics* 17 (4): 5-31.

Browne, Jude. 2006. *Sex segregation and inequality in the modern labour market*. Bristol: The Policy Press.

Cigno, Alessandro. 1991. *Economics of the family*. Oxford and New York: Clarendon Press and Oxford University Press.

Cook, Sarah. 2008. *Customer Care Excellence: How to Create an Effective Customer Focus*. London: Kogan.

Cuyler, Anothony. and Joseph Newhouse, eds. 2000. *Handbook of health economics*. Amsterdam: Elsevier.

Danby, Colin. 2004. "Lupita's Dress: Care in Time". *Hypatia* 19(4): 23-48.

Davis, John B. 2001. *The social economics of health care*. London, New York: Routledge.

Delphy, Christine. 1995. "The invention of french feminism: An essential move".

Yale French Studies 87: 190-221.

Denis, Andy. 2009. "Pluralism in economics education". *International Review of Economic Education* 8: 6-22.

Dex, Shirley and Heather Joshi. 1999. "Careers and motherhood: Policies for compatibility". *Cambridge Journal of Economics* 23: 641-59.

Doucet, Andrea. 2011. "What Impedes Fathers' Participation in Care Work: Theorizing the Community as an Institutional Arena" in Catherine Krull and Justyna Sempruch (eds.) *A Life in Balance? Reopening the Family-Work Debate,* pp. 115-129Vancouver: UBC Press.

Doyal, Leonard and Ian Gough. 1991. *A theory of human need*. London: Macmillan.

Duffy, Mignon. 2005. "Reproducing Labor Inequalities: Challenges for Feminists Conceptualizing Care at the Intersections of Gender, Race, and Class". *Gender and Society* 19 (66): 66-82.

Duncan, Simon. 2000. *Challenging rational action theory*. prepared for workshop one: Frameworks for understanding policy change and culture. http://www.leeds.ac.uk/cava/papers/paper5simon.htm (last accessed October 2011).

Duncan, Simon and Rosalind Edwards. 1997. "Lone mothers and paid work: Rational economic man or gendered moral rationalities?" *Feminist Economics* 3 (2): 29-61.

Eisenstein, Zillah, ed. 1979. *Capitalist patriarchy and the case for socialist feminism*. New York: Monthly Review Press.

Elson, Diane, ed. 1995. *Male bias in the development process*. Manchester: Manchester University Press.

Elson, Diane. 2010. "Strengthening local economies through gender responsive budgeting: interview with Diane Elson". *Development* 53: 308-12.

England, Paula. 1993. "The separative self: Androcentric bias in neoclassical assumptions". In Marianne A. Ferber and Julie A. Nelson, eds. *Beyond economic man: Feminist theory and economics*, pp. 37-53. Chicago: University of Chicago Press.

England, Paula, Michelle Budig and Nancy Folbre. 2002. "Wages of virtue: The relative pay of care work". *Social Problems* 49 (Nov) 455-73.

England, Paula and Nancy Folbre. 2003. Contracting for care. In Marianne A. Ferber and Julie A. Nelson, eds. *Beyond economic man: Feminist theory and economics*, pp. 61-79. Chicago: University of Chicago Press.

Esping-Andersen, Gosta. 2008. "Childhood investments and skill formation". *International Tax and Public Finance* 15: 14-49.

Esping-Andersen, Gosta, Duncan Gallie, Anton Hemerijck and John Myles, eds. 2002. *Why I need a new welfare state*. Oxford: Oxford University Press.

ESRC. 2009. *Gender equality network (genet), part of the economic and social research council's (esrc) priority network programme*. http://www.Genet.ac.uk/ (ast accessed October 2010)

Feiner, Susan and Bruce Roberts. 1990. "Hidden by the invisible hand: Neoclassical economic theory and the textbook treatment of women and minorities". *Gender and Society* 4: 159-81.

Ferber, Marianne A. and Bonnie G. Birnbaum. 1977. "The 'New home economics': Retrospects and prospects". *Journal of Consumer Research* 4: 19-28.

Ferber, Marianne. A. and Julie .A. Nelson, eds. 1993. *Beyond economic man: Feminist theory and economics.* Chicago: University of Chicago Press.

Ferguson, Ann. 1996. "Sex and work". In Kai Nielson and Robert Ware, eds. *Exploitation*, pp. 272-80. New York: Humanities Press.

Fine, Ben. 2000. "Economics imperialism and intellectual progress: The present as history of economic thought?". *History of Economics Review* 32: 10-36.

Firestone, Sulamith. 1972. *The dialectic of sex: The case for feminist revolution.* London: Paladin.

Folbre, Nancy. 1994a. "Children as public goods". *American Economic Review* 84: 86-90.

Folbre, Nancy. 1994b. *Who pays for the kids? Gender and the structures of constraint.* London: Routledge.

Folbre, Nancy. 2001. *The invisible heart : Economics and family values.* New York: New Press.

Folbre, Nancy and Michael Bittman, eds. 2004 *Family time: The social organization of care.* London: Routledge.

Freeman, Tabitha. 2008. "Psychoanalytic concepts of fatherhood: Patriarchal paradoxes and the presence of an absent authority". *Studies in Gender and Sexuality* 9: 113-39.

Galbraith, John K. 1973. *Economics and the public purpose.* Boston: Houghton Mifflin.

Galtry, Judith. 1997. "Suckling and silence in the USA: Costs and benefits of breastfeeding". *Feminist Economics* 3(3): 1-24.

Gálvez-Muñoz, Lina , Paula Rodríguez-Modroño and Mónica Domínguez-Serrano. 2011. "Work and Time Use By Gender: A New Clustering of European Welfare Systems". *Feminist Economics* 17(4), 125-157.

Ghosh, Jayati. 2004. *Informalisation and women's workforce participation: A consideration of recent trends in India.* http://www.Unrisd.Org/unrisd/website/document.Nsf/0/24ef649b47eedbfec12 56fdc003bb860?Opendocument (accessed October 2010).

Gilligan, Carol. 1982. *In a different voice: Psychological theory and women's development.* Cambridge, Massachusetts: Harvard University Press.

Giullari, Susan and Jane Lewis. 2005. "The adult worker model family, gender equality and care: the search for new policy principles and the possibilities and problems of a capabilities approach". *Economy and Society* 34 (1): 76-104.

Grenier, Corinne and Virginie Martin. 2010. "Quand le relationnel est aussi affaire d'expertise-Proposition d'une grille de lecture non genrée du care". Conference Proceedings. Lausanne, 2-3 September.

Gustafsson, Siv. 1997. "Feminist neo-classical economics: Some examples". In Geske Dijkstra and Janneke Plantenga, eds. *Gender and economics: A european perspective*, 36-53. London: Routledge.

Gustafsson, Siv. 2005. "Assortative mating by education and postponement of couple formation and first birth in britain and sweden". *Review of Economics of the Household* 3: 91-113.

Gustavsson, Gunnel. 1997. "Strategies and practical considerations". In Gunnel Gustavsson, M. Eduards , and M. Rönnblom, eds. *Towards a new democratic order: Women's organizing in sweden in the 1990s*, pp. 46-67. Stockholm: Publica.

Hagenaars, Aldi and Sophia R. Wunderink Van Veen. 1990. *Soo gewonne, soo verteert : Economie van de huishoudelijke sector*. Leiden: Stenfert Kroese.

Hansmann, Henry. 1996. *The ownership of enterprise*. Boston and London: Harvard University Press.

Hartmann, Heidi. 1979. "Capitalism, patriarchy and job segregation by sex". In Zillah Eisenstein, ed. *Capitalist patriarchy and the case for socialist feminism*, pp. 206-47. New York: Monthly Review Press.

Helburn, Suzanne W. 1999. "The silent crisis in U.S. Child care". *The Annals of the American Academy of Political and Social Sciences* (May) 8-219.

Held, Virginia. 1995. "The meshing of care and justice". *Hypatia* 10: 128-32.

Held. Virginia. 2002. "Care and the extension of markets". *Hypatia* 17: 19-33.

Hewitson, Gillian. 1999. *Feminist economics: Interrogating the masculinity of rational economic man*. Northampton, MA and Cheltenham, UK: Edward Elgar.

Himmelweit, Susan. 1999. "Caring labour in emotional labour in the service of the economy". *Annals of the academy of political and social sciences* 561: 27-38.

Hochschild, Arlie R. 1989. *The second shift: Working parents and the revolution at home*. New York: Penguin.

Hochschild, Arlie R. 2003. *The managed heart: Commercialization of human feeling*. Berkeley Los Angeles London: UNIVERSITY OF CALIFORNIA PRESS

Humphries, Jane and Jill Rubery. 1984. "The reconstitution of the supply side of the labour market: The relative autonomy of social reproduction". *Cambridge Journal of Economics* 8: 331-46.

Irigaray, Luce. 1985. *This sex which is not one*. Ithaca NY: Cornell University.

Kabeer, Naila. 2001. Family bargaining. In *International encyclopedia of the social and behavioural sciences*, pp. 5314-19. London: Elsevier.

Kosfeld, Michael., Markus Heinrichs, Paul J. Zak, Urs Fischbacher and Ernst Fehr. 2005. "Oxytocin increases trust in humans". *Nature* 435: 473–76.

Kuiper, Edith, Jolande Sap, Susan Feiner, Otto Notburga and Zafiris Tzannatos, eds. 1995. *Out of the margin: Feminist perspectives on economics*. London and New York: Routledge.

Lawson, Tony. 1997. *Economics and reality*. London: Routledge.

Lewis, Jane. 2008. "Work-family balance policies: Issues and development in the UK 1997-2005 in comparative perspective". In Jacqueline Scott, Shirley Dex and Heather Joshi, eds. *Women and employment : Changing lives and new challenges*, pp. 387-92. Cheltenham: Edward Elgar.

Lloyd, Cynthia and Beth Niemi. 1979. *The economics of sex differentials*. New York: Columbia University Press.

Low, Nicholas and Brendan Gleeson. 1998. *Justice, society and nature: An exploration of Political ecology*. London: Routledge.

Lundberg, Shelly and Robert A. Pollak. 1992. "Separate spheres bargaining and the marriage market". *IFPRI-World Bank Conference on Intra-household Resource Allocation: Policies and Research Methods*. IFPRI, Washington, DC.

MacGregor, Sherilyn. 2004. "From Care to Citizenship: Calling Ecofeminism Back to Politics". *Ethics & the Environment* 9(1): 56-84.

Manser, Marilyn and Murray Brown. 1980. "Marriage and household decision making: A bargaining analysis". *International Economics Review* 21: 31-34.

Martin, Ron. 1999. "Critical survey. The new 'geographical turn' in economics: Some critical reflections". *Cambridge Journal of Econmics* 23: 65-91.

Matthaei, Julie. 1999. "Patriarchy". *The elgar companion to feminist economics*, pp. 592-99. Cheltenham, UK and Northamptan, MA, USA: Edward Elgar.

May, Steve, George Cheney, and Juliet Roper, eds. 2007. *The debate over corporate social responsibility*. Oxford ; New York : Oxford Universinty Press.

Mcelroy, Marjorie and Mary Horney. 1981. "Nash bargained household decision-making". *International Economic Review* 22: 333-49.

Mckie, Linda, Susan Gregory and Sophia Bowlby. 2004. *Caringscapes: Experiences of caring and working*. Research briefing no. 13. Edinburgh: Centre for Research on Families and Relationships, CRFR, University of Edinburgh.

Mellor, Mary. 1997. *Feminism and ecology*. Cambridge: Polity Press.

Mincer, Jacob. 1958. "Investment in human capital and personal income distribution". *Journal of Political Economy* 66: 281-302.

Mincer, Jacob. 1962. "Labour force participation of married women: A study of labour supply". In H. Greg Lewis, ed. *Aspects of labour economics*, pp. 63-97. Princeton, New Jersey: Princeton University Press.

Mitchell, Juliet. 1974. *Psychoanalysis and feminism*. London: Penguin.

Molyneux, Mary. 1985. "Mobilization without emancipation? Women's interests, state and revolution". *Feminist Studies* 11: 227-54.

Nelson, Julie A. and Nancy Folbre. 2006. "Why a well-paid nurse is a better nurse". *Nursing Economics* 24: 127–30.

Nelson, Julie A.1996. *Feminism, Objectivity and Economics*. Londo: Routledge.

Nelson, Julie. 2008. "Economists, value judgments, and climate change: A view from feminist economics". *Ecological Economics* 65: 441-47.

Nursing-Economic$. 2010. http://www.Nursingeconomics.Net/cgi-bin/webobjects/necjournal.Woa/wa/viewsection?S_id=1073744457. (accessed October 2010).

O'hara, Sabine. 1998. "Economics, ethics and sustainability: Redefining connections". *International Journal of Social Economics* 25: 43-62.

Ott, Notburga. 1992. *Intrafamily bargaining and household decisions Microeconomic studies*. Berlin; New York: Springer-Verlag.

Pollak, Robert A. 1985. "A transaction cost approach to families and households". *Journal of Economic Literature* 23: 581-608.

Praxispamphlet. 2011. http://praxispamphlet.wordpress.com/2011/11/04/harvard-economics-students-walk-out-in-protest-over-biased-course/(accessed November 2011).

Robertson, Diane C. and Nigel Nicholson. 1996. "Expressions of corporate social responsibility in UK Firms". *Journal of Business Ethics* 15: 1095-106.

Rosen, Anna. 1993. "Temporarily asymmetric information and labour contracts". *Labour Economics* 2: 105-05.

Rowbotham, Sheila. 1972. *Women, resistance and revolution*. New York: Random/Vintage Books.

Rubery, Jill. 2006. Shifting responsibility, changing labour market. *Shifting Responsibilities*. Conference report. Amsterdam: Amsterdam University Press.

Sainsbury, Diane, ed. 1999. *Gender and welfare state regimes*. Oxford: Oxford University Press.

Sawhill, Isabel. 1977. "Economic perspectives on the family". *Daedalus* 106: 115-25.

Schultz, Theodore W. 1974. *Economics of the family: Marriage, children, and human capital*. A conference report of the national bureau of economic research.

Scott, Jane. 2009. *Gender inequality in production and reproduction: A new priority research network funded by the ESRC*. http://www.allacademic.com/meta/p_mla_apa_research_citation/1/0/8/6/9/p ages108694/p108694-13.php. (accessed October 2010)S.

Seeleib-Kaiser, Martin. 2008. *Welfare state transformations*. Basingstoke: Palgrave.

Sen, Amartya. 1982. *Poverty and famines : An essay on entitlements and deprivation*. Oxford: Clarendon Press.

Sen, Amartya. 1984. *Resources, values and development*. Boston: Harvard University Press.

Sevenhuijsen, Selma. 1998. *Citizenship and the ethics of care: Feminist considerations on justice, morality and politics*. London: Routledge.

Sofianou, Eva. 1995. "Post-modernism and the notion of rationality in economics". *Cambridge Journal of Economics* 19: 373-89.

Strassmann, Diane. 1993. "Not a free market: The rhetoric of disciplinary authority in economics". In Marianne Ferber and Julie Nelson, eds. *Beyond economic man: Feminist theory and economics*, pp. 54-68. Chicago: University of Chicago Press.

Strassmann, Diane and Livia Polanyi. 1995. "The economist as storyteller: What texts reveal". In Edith Kuiper and Jolande Sap, eds. *Out of the margin: Feminist perspectives on economics*, pp. 249-70. London and New York: Routledge.

Treitman, Donadl J. and Heidi Hartmann, eds. 1981. *Women, work, and wages: Equal pay for jobs of equal value*. Washington DC: National Academy Press.

Turkel, Marian C. 2001. "Models of Service/Education Partnerships Struggling to Find a Balance: The Paradox between Caring and Economics". *Nursing Administration Quarterly* 26(1): 67-82.

UNRSID. 2008. Political and social economy of care. *Programme Area: Gender and Development*. GENEVA: UNRISD. http://www.unrisd.org/80256B3C005BB128/(httpProjectsForResearchHome-en)/37BD128E275F1F8BC1257296003210EC? OpenDocument&panel=relatedinformation. (accessed October 2010).

UNRSID. 2009. The political and social economy of care. In *Conference News*.

Geneva: UN.
http://www.unrisd.org/80256B3C005BCCF9/search/171609FF03432B2BC1257
65E004EB76A?OpenDocument. (accessed October 2010).

Wearness, Kari, ed. 2004. *Dialogue on care*. Bergen: Center for Women's and Gender Studies University of Bergen.

Weber, Max. 1897. *Max weber, sociological writings*. Continuum 1994. Wolf Heydebrand, ed. Transcribed: by Andy Blunden in 1998. http://www.Marxists.Org/reference/subject/philosophy/works/ge/weber.Htm. (accessed October 2010).

Women's-Budget-Group. 2010. Gender budget analysis. Hhttp://www.Wbg.Org.Uk/gba.Htm. (accessed October 2010).

Wood, Julia T. 1994. *Who cares? Women, care, and culture*. Carbondale: University of Southern Illinois Press

Young, Iris. 1981. "The limits of dual systems theory". In Lydia Sargent, ed. *Women and revolution: A discussion of the unhappy marriage of marxism and feminism*, pp.43-70. Boston: South End Press.

Zak, Paul J., Robert Kurzban and William T. Matzner. 2005. "Oxytocin is associated with human trustworthiness". *Hormones and Behavior* 48: 522–27.

Zelizer, Vivian A. 2006. *The purchase of intimacy*. Princeton: Princeton University Press.

Ziliak, Steven and Deidre N. Mccloskey. 2008. *The cult of statistical significance: How the standard error costs us jobs, justice, and lives*. Ann Arbor: University of Michigan Press.

[1] By economics, we mean the organisation of material resources for human well being. The origins of the word comes from "Middle French *yconomie,* from Medieval Latin *oeconomia,* from Greek *oikonomia,* from *oikonomos* household manager, from *oikos* house + *nemein* to manage" (online Miriam Webster dictionary, accessible on line via http://www.merriam-webster.com/dictionary/economy). Going on the origins of the word economy pertains to the household. The term thus defined gives an obvious place to caring activities, which in large part take place in the household.

[2] A deduction is a valid inference from more general premises to a less general, that is, more specific conclusion. A valid deduction is one in which the conclusion is a necessary consequence of the premises, so that the conclusion cannot be false if all the premises are true.

[3] Ontology is (the study of) the basic structure of (a domain of) reality.

[4] This field is often referred to as Economics of the Family (Alessandro Cigno 1991; Theodore Schultz 1974), or simply as Household Economics (Aldi Hagenaars and Sophia Wunderink van Veen 1990).

[5] The NIE approach models intra-household allocations on the assets and earning potential of individual members, as well as on the collective income of the household as a unit. It uses the term contract as a metaphor to analyse the evolution of non market institutions and long term relationships, a metaphor also adopted in the

study of the social organisation of care (Yossef Ben-Porath 1980; Paula England, Michelle Budig and Nancy Folbre 2002; Paula England and Nancy Folbre 2003).

[6] Siv Gustafsson (1997) and Evanthia Sofianou (1995) make a similar critique of post modern attempts to 'reform' neo-classical economics.

[7] The term 'explanatory critique' is used by Roy Bhaskar (1997) to describe a process whereby scientific enquiry moves from what is, to what ought to be, in aid of a possible process of human emancipation.

[8] We take patriarchy as referring to "a society whose social relationships systematically privilege and empower men" (Julie Matthaei 1999: 592).

[9] When not positioned in economics departments, contributors may or may engage with economists, publish in (heterodox) economics journals, and belong to economic associations, such as the Association for Heterodox Economics, the International Association for Feminist Economics, the European Association for Evolutionary Political Economy, and the like.

Part 9: Green Economics for health and well being
9.1 Ten Key Values of Green Economics
By Miriam Kennet, Jeff Turk and Michelle S. Gale de Oliveira

The ten key values of the Green Economics Institute have been defined as follows:

1. Green Economics aims to provision for the needs of all people everywhere, other species, nature, the planet and its systems, all as beneficiaries of economics transactions, not as throw away inputs.

2. This is all underpinned by social and environmental justice, tolerance, no prejudice and creating quality of life for everyone including future generations and all the current generations, including older and younger people.

3. Ensuring and respecting other species and their rights. Ending the current mass extinction of species. Ensuring biodiversity.

4. Non violence and inclusion of all people everywhere, including people with special needs and special abilities. Ensuring all nations have equal access to power and resources. Local people having control over their own destiny and resources. Increasing life expectancy, human welfare and per capita GDP in the least developed countries.

5. Ensuring gender equity in all activities. Educating, respecting, empowering women and minorities.

6. Ending current high mass consumption and overshoot of the planet's resources and returning to live within the comfortable bounds of nature in the climatic conditions under which humans built their civilisation. Choosing lifestyle changes over techno fixes and eco technology. Lowering our own carbon usage and living lightly on the earth. Changing how economics is done: from being an abstract mathematical exercise to embracing realism and the real world we all live in and share and in which we are all concerned stakeholders.

7. Valuing and respecting all people equally.

8. Poverty prevention. Climate change and instability prevention, adaptation, mitigation. Protecting the most vulnerable from risk. Ensuring the future of small island states.

9. Quickly reducing carbon per capita globally to 2 tonnes in the next 5 years and zero soon after. Limiting and reversing climate change. Moving to renewable energy sources.

10. Building a future-proofed economics to solve the current economic uncertainty and downturn which is suitable for the 21st century. Creating and nurturing an economy based on sharing, rather than greed and profit. Completely reshaping and reforming current economics to do all the above.

9.2 Green Economics: its recent development and background

By Miriam Kennet and Michelle S. Gale de Oliveira

1. Introduction
(i) Increasing interest in Green Economics and the Green Economy

Ban Ki Moon General Secretary of the United Nations, said that "We are living in an age of Global Transformation, an Age of Green Economics."

There has been a dramatic increase in interest in environmental and green economics and the transformation towards Green Jobs and a Green Economy.

Partly in response to concerns about unprecedented and rapidly accelerating anthropogenic climate change there are worries that "the very survival of the human species is at risk." We are also living in the 6th ever mass extinction of other species that the earth has ever experienced, (IUCN) with many mammals, fish and birds under threat. A growing population predicted at 9 billion, means the poor are more directly dependent than ever directly on the ecosystem, and geo political instability is becoming more common.

Inequalities between people, within and between nations, and between present and future generations as well as social and environmental injustices are now significantly affecting the world economy. The bundle of natural capital resources, (forests, productive seas, agricultural land, healthy soil, air and water, food resources, rainforests) we can leave to future generations may actually be smaller than those of today. Climate change and sea level rise mean that current and future generations may inherit a world in which there will be less land available for cultivation or habitation, as well as depletion of forests, bleaching of coral reefs, protective mangrove swamps and other resources of all kinds including viable fish stocks or productive oceans. Massive dead zones are appearing in the sea and increasing desertification and soil erosion and declining forests and whole Ecosystems services are declining and the economy will be under threat.

(ii) People and institutions are looking for alternative solutions and innovation in economics

The current economic crisis has exposed deficiencies of mainstream economic concepts and the creation of new ones. These include for example by Paul Krugman in the USA and Stigilz and Sen and Green National Accounting from President Sarkozy in France and McGlade at the European Environment Agency and more fundamental changes in economic thinking.Ecological economics (Daly) introduces absolute limits on "more is better than less." The mainstream regarded ecology related decision-making as having infinite natural boundaries, and simply aggregated human behaviour and "optimal" solutions from it.

If the air or sea is so polluted that they can't sustain life, or the soil removed, or we have passed certain thresh holds or tipping points from which the natural systems can't recover, green economists propose doing different things, rather than substitution of one raw material with another. Standard neo-liberal economics models are insufficient for today's issues and are in urgent need of not only a major overhaul and has become "unfit for purpose," but also need replacing.

(iii) The broadening of scope and the arrival of "Inclusion" in economics

According to traditional market explanations "*the invisible hand*" (Adam Smith) mechanism ensures that everyone benefits from the investment and activities of homo economicus or "rational economic man" and his spending preferences and choices. In spite of arising from selfish aims, they are presumed to benefit the whole of society. Most people on the planet are not white western educated wealthy men and cannot choose how to earn a living or how or become wealthy.

So the absolute hegemony of markets is being fundamentally questioned in all its aspects: from the need to separate investment from savings banking, to its ability to solve climate change and its ability to solve the problem of poverty for which absolute as well as relative evels continue to rise. Similarly the role of "homo economicus" in the collapse of for example Icelandic banks, has led to laws to increasing the number of women at the helm or are brought into corporate board rooms and to correct long standing imbalances of power, representation and wealth between men and women.

(iv) Mainstream economics solutions have reached a crossroads

Human economic development has always relied on technological advancement to address challenges in the past. So the switch from fossil fuels to biofuels to allow for the continuation of current transport modes, as business as usual, was a logical step which was fully embraced by large companies and large trading blocks such as the European Union. However, this competition over land uses and pushed up the price of fuel, caused a scarcity of land for dwellings, and food riots all over the world, creating more poverty and land price spikes. This increasing investment and speculation culminated in the bursting of the "bubble economy" and a complete collapse of land prices in several countries leading to a serious economic downturn. It has ended the economic period called the "Great Moderation" and we are now in a period called "The Great Contraction."

(v) Vulnerability of the economy to Global environmental change: the example of Italy

In common with many other places today, the OECD has warned that the economy of Italy in common with several other countries is particularly vulnerable to the economics effects of global environmental change. There are changes in the climate, leading to health effects of encroaching tropical vegetation, "Alien Species" invasion, malaria and dengue fever reappearing. The warming world is causing sea level rise and affecting specific environments such as the city of Venice and its lagoon and many other coastal towns and in other countries whole small island states may disappear.

The increase in temperature is causing micro climate environments, leading to more warming in certain Alpine Regions, upsetting watersheds and the available Hydroelectric Power which drive the economy and industry. In particular the warming has led to melting of the glaciers, leading to the re-emergence of "Oetzee the Ice Man" for the first time in 5000 years. These changes are affecting tourism as the mountain tops are no longer snow covered. The rich agricultural traditions such as wine, apples and meat may be damaged in South Tyrol. Slope instability, caused by changes in water courses and other global environmental changes, has meant more train derailments in mountain areas too such as occurred this year in Bolzano.

A transformation in the role of the car has led to large scale shut downs of car factories in the south and bans on using cars on certain days in larger Italian cities. Agriculture has to cope with advancing climate change and in general species moving northwards in the northern hemisphere according to some studies by up to an observed 5 metres per year. Plankton in the sea are moving significantly northwards affected by increasing acidification in the sea. In Italy tourism, a significant part of the economy, is threatened by the encroachment of a warmer tropical world, replacing it as a reliable and comfortable Mediterranean attraction and as a ski and winter walking holiday destination.

The rapidly expanding Green Economy is particularly useful in offering the hope of Green Jobs and the creation of 1000s of new ones to create a more sustainable economy.

(vi) Mainstreaming Environmental and Green Economics

The climate and biodiversity crisis solutions evolve into a blueprint for leading the world in the Green Economy. Solving the complex mesh of social and environmental justice is included in all aspects of Green Economics thinking, as are the costs and effects of climate change on the world economy. For example, the Stern Review of the Economics of Climate Change (2007) showed that spending up to 1% of GDP (recently corrected to 2%) would actually be a cheaper option than allowing runaway climate change to persist.

The TEEB Report in 2010 by Sukhdev has done similar work in highlighting the even higher costs of biodiversity loss as we are now causing the 6th ever mass species extinction. For example, bee colonies are disappearing due to microwave disturbance to their navigation systems from mobile phones, and the cost of hand pollination (already happening in China) of crops would be catastrophic in the west. Einstein said that once the bees disappear humans will only have another 4 years to survive on the planet.

Green Economics is an interdisciplinary science; on the one hand it is concerned with the theory and practical management of Global Environmental Change in all its aspects and on the other with the development Economics providing provisioning, sharing and distribution of the wealth of nature and human and naturally occurring resources.

It is a developing progressive holistic approach which cannot be explained by simplistic, typically linear mathematics and fixed preferences of individuals.

It extends beyond ecological issues to wider considerations of ideology, history of thought, evolution of society, the level of objectivity and the time specificity of solutions in a social science environment to be taken into account. These provide a much stronger basis to criticize and replace current reductionist mainstream economics. It embraces a wider set of values, including but not exclusively ecological values.

2. The arrival of Green Economics
(i) Green Economics Strategies for addressing current crises
The Green Economy Initiative of the United Nations (2008) describes the crises as "Fs", Food, Fuel and Finance" and advocates a more growthist solution and the Lisbon 2020 Agenda also suggests Smart, Green, Growth is possible and desirable.
A Green Economics perspective instead regards the crisis as a mixture of the current economics downturn, a crisis of poverty, climate change and biodiversity loss and proposes a composite set of solutions. These consist of a mixture of market instruments, such as carbon trading under the Kyoto Protocol, regulation, carbon quotas or even rationing of carbon use, as well as technological innovations and green developments. It advocates, most of all, a change in public attitudes and reduction in unnecessary consumption of the earth's resources and individual carbon footprints and for *life style changes*. A progressive holistic approach extends beyond ecological issues to wider considerations of ideology, history of thought, evolution of society, the level of objectivity and the time specificity of solutions.
The European Greens propose that the economy must adapt to what the natural environment can tolerate, aiming for ecological sustainability, equity and social justice as well as self-reliance of local and regional economies, encouraging a true sense of community, based on democracy, transparency, gender equality and the right of all people to express themselves and participate fully in decision-making.

(ii) Environmental Economics
Environmental economics aims to factor in the costs of activities and impacts external, to a particular economics transaction. Market failure, its central concept, means that markets fail to allocate resources efficiently and this occurs when the market does not allocate scarce resources to generate the greatest social welfare. The best and most

famous example is that of climate change in the Stern review. Biodiversity loss is also as serious, if not even more costly. The previous discipline of Environmental Economics has quite a main stream framework and does not specifically change activities or prevent impacts and only aims to simply find out how much things cost. Although useful information, it will not change what is done. It so omits the point that other options are available, or reassessing what is actually required.

Similarly surveys are used to establish "Willingness To Pay," for its existence of a species, or its conservation or to visit a natural amenity for an environmental benefit popularised by David Pearce are often used for example in deciding on the fate of a natural amenity such as whether to conserve a species.

The Stern Review proposes introducing a price for carbon, REDDS -debt for nature swaps and Carbon Storage and Sequestration and Discounting the future.

Common Property Rights are another concern first identified in this context by Coase and Hardin. When it is too costly to exclude people from accessing a contested environmental resource, market allocation is likely to be inefficient. Hardin's (1968) The Tragedy of the Commons popularized the challenges involved in non-exclusion and common property. "commons" refers to the environmental asset itself. Hardin theorizes that in the absence of restrictions, users of an open-access resource will use it more than if they had to pay for it and had exclusive rights and thus will often cause environmental degradation. Ostrom (1990) won the Nobel Prize this year for work on how people using real common property resources do establish self-governing rules to reduce this risk.

(iii) Ecological Economics

Ecological economics moves towards the primary role of energy and the laws of thermodynamics and energy flows and democratic decision making as subsets of the natural environment in its discourse.

Ecological economics includes the study of the flows of energy, and materials and material flows and ecosystem services that enter and exit the economic system. For the first time we have a change to the core concepts and a move towards the human economy as a subset of the natural world. Ecological Economics now is being used in global institutions. Use and non use value for measuring costs of Ecosystems services degradation are being used for example by the United Nations.

(iv) The Renaissance of Economics; the Green Economy rediscovers the roots of economics

Green Economics works in what it terms the four pillars of scope or activity, namely-1. Political and policy making, 2. academia especially science and economics, 3. business and 4. civil society including NGOs and most recently adding in a fifth, the general public and consumers.

Everyone and everything on the planet is acknowledged to have economics or provisioning requirements to achieve desired optimal conditions. Green Economics describes itself as "Reclaiming Economics, for all people everywhere, nature, other species, the planet and its systems. "As a result even the volcanic activity which cost European Economies dearly this year, was able to be incorporated. For example it has been discovered that allowing the glaciers and ice caps to melt will increase seismic activity. The earth has a self regulatory mechanism, Gaia Theory by James Lovelock) which controls the temperature at 14 degrees centigrade. Too much warming and the volcanoes erupt cooling down the planet. Too much cooling and the ice sheets form pressing down the magma and preventing earth quakes!

Green Economics a participatory approach is a development which includes natural science data and works with it, as many of its teams are physicists and natural scientists who also have economics qualifications, so it is able to weld both natural and social science together.

It is at core multi- disciplinary, and inter – disciplinary and pluralist and its decisions are based on the twin imperatives of human and natural science futures. It fully accepts that we all inhabit the earth and there is no economy outside of it. It reflects the current knowledge about the complexity of reality,. It is characterised by a holistic perspective, the involvement of nature, and is very inclusive.

It has evolved from a complete and fundamental philosophical renaissance of the origins of economics from the Greek Word oikia- meaning household or estate management, now evolved to meaning the *earth*. The "oikonomia" -of Xenophon is now the economics and provisioning for the needs of all people everywhere, nature other species, the planet and its systems and also of the "Good life" of Aristotle.

3. The Cultural, Institutional, Academic Umbrella and Positioning of the Green Economy and its Chronology
(i) The Transformation of Economics Disciplines and Schools of Thought
Under the Heterodox Economics Umbrella, are found alternative, holistic interdisciplinary, pluralistic set of methodologies and contributions. Pigou (1920) working on external effects and Coase examining the role of property rights. The USA and the UK struggle to decide who is liable for BP 's huge oil spill in American waters.

The debate is evolving into a robust economics school or discipline and widening the scope of an alternative economic framework further, into Environmental economics by authors such as Hartwick and Solow, Ciracy Wantrup, Daly, Tietenberg, Markandya, Pearce, Boulding, Jacob, Hillman, Ekins, Chichilnisky and Ecological Economics (Soderbaum, Daly, Martinez- Alier).

Green Economics is influencing the economic debate and transforming existing policies and decision-making. 'Green' and Writers include Kennet, Heinemann, Hillman, Ekins, Reardon, Porrit, Gale D'Oliveira, Dobson, Anderson, Barry, Reardon, Rao,Turk and Jociute..

A rapidly growing branch of economics, Green Economics is spreading into policy development in governments for example the Korean Government and also in Global Institutions such as the United Nations and the International Labour Organisations and the OECD. Each of these has a Green Economy Initiative or a Green Jobs Programme. Green Economics is being taught in Universities around the world and is also featured by the Dow Jones and Wall Street. The Green Economics Institute was founded in 2003 and its academic journal, *The International Journal of Green Economics* founded in 2005. Its background is in the "Green movement "hence a strong policy orientation combined with Economics Heterodoxy, as well as Environmental Science and Global Environmental Change and Management.

The discipline builds on enlightenment ideas of reason and rights, post-modern ideas of different and power struggles and elites, and Malthusian limits to growth and the search for sustainability, and on eco-feminism. The Enlightenment brought a major impact on modern understandings of economics and the role of humanity in the natural world. However it tended to look for logic and reason rather than wisdom in nature, as Bacon explains: "The human mind which overcomes superstition is to hold sway over a disenchanted nature. What men want to learn from nature is how to use it in order to wholly dominate it and other men. That is the only aim." The backlash against 10 000 years of the domestication of animals, plants and women and the colonies is in full swing within Green Economics. So it is the acknowledgement that the quest for domination is over.

Green Economics argues that nature has its own intrinsic and existence value and extends this value to all life forms, (Deep Ecology Arnae Naess) and thus seeks to reform economics to "provision for all people everywhere, all other species, the biosphere, systems, and planet."

It is sometimes part of a broader ideology, sometimes part of Bhuddist economics (Welford, Guenter Wagner 2006) advocating de-centralist, non materialist, and co-operative values and the concept of 'enoughness' or sufficiency is important, as well as leaving enough resources for future generations.

One key development was the book "Silent Spring" by Rachel Carson which exposed the effects of DDT and the practices of the chemical industry and the relationship between the economy, industry, the environment and our over all well being.

(ii) Sustainable Development Economics
Another important key development was the Sustainable Development Economics, developed by Professor Graciela Chichilnisky, and our Common Future which

addressed this area of futurity In 1987. the United Nations World Commission on Environment and Development (UNCED) issued the Brundtland Report, defining sustainable development as meeting "the needs of the present without compromising the ability of the future to meet its needs."

Sustainable Development economics gives equal weight to economics, environment and social aspects.

(iii) Green Economics as Practice
The Green Economy has been called the Economics of Sharing the earth and its economy amongst ourselves but also with other species and systems of the planet in addition but not exclusively also to ensure it remains hospitable for us and our way of life.

It is also the economics of doing and is intensely practical. For example this means that there is much focus on green supply chains and the greening of procurement with the aim of creating social and environmental justice. It also advocates greener transport methods and slower local smaller scale production, even with slow travel and more train travel, slow food and degrowth to keep within the earth's Carrying Capacity. It advocates *"Reduce, Reuse, Recycle, Repair, Restore, Relax, Recover"*

Green IT
The role of IT, once hailed as the ultimate saviour, is now regarded as a significant cause of climate change and so there is a move to decouple the big monopolies such as Microsoft and move towards more community owned human style, open source IT – and to limiting the carbon usage of server farms, saving carbon by virtualisation, using recylced and also recycling materials and managing and limiting the power usage much more.

Environmental and social dumping and checking for green and transparent supply chains

Large outsourcing of environmental and social standards to where they can't be seen (called dumping) is coming to an end. Equity, social and environmental justice are acknowledged as providing attractive competitive advantage in a modern economy.

Green Jobs
Increasing numbers of jobs are being created in this vast and innovative transformation- this green economy. The Green Jobs Initiative of the United Nations and the International Labour Organisation and the International Federation of Trades Union describes a green job as *"work in agricultural, manufacturing, research and development (R&D), administrative, and service activities that contribute(s) substantially to preserving or restoring environmental quality. Specifically, but not exclusively, this includes jobs that help to protect ecosystems and biodiversity; reduce energy, materials, and water consumption through high efficiency strategies; de-*

carbonize the economy; and minimize or altogether avoid generation of all forms of waste and pollution." A Green Economics perspective of a Green Job is anything that is sustainable and contributes to social and environmental justice.

4. Instruments and Tools in Green and Environmental Economics
(i) Geo engineering and Green Technologies

The use of technological solutions (also called Eco technology or Geo engineering or Technical Fixes). These include, solar radiation management, iron fertilisation of the sea, stratospheric aerosols, sucking carbon using giant artificial tree scrubbers, albedo management, air capture, urban albedo and algal-based CO_2 capture schemes, Carbon Storage, Sequestration or Capture.

There is increasing concern with the idea that "Unintended Consequences" could occur if for example we seed the clouds as the Chinese Government has done this year to create rain or we use Sulphur Aerosol Particles to mimic the action of volcanoes in cooling the global climate.

The "Precautionary Principle" is a major feature of a green economy which advises against trying untested technology. This would for example be used to prevent the kind of the oil spill or engineering at great depth without a clear strategy for clean up by BP.

The change to green technologies involves the use of Rare Earth Materials, which are nearly all mined in China. Significantly this year, China ceased exporting them in order to supply its own home market and so made the production of green technologies more expensive and more difficult.

"Local Production for Local Needs" will mean that the private car will be slowly replaced by modern and attractive lower carbon public transport, including car clubs, car-sharing, more cycling, and train travel. Governments introduced a green Car Scrapage scheme to encourage purchases of new cars.
Greener alternatives such as slow travel are taking off, and train-travel is once again fashionable. Slow travel, slow cities, and the Italian idea of slow food are gaining in popularity.

Lower carbon economies are now actively being created, to combat the current average of 10 tonnes carbon equivalent usage in Europe, 25 tonnes in the USA, 5 in China, and 1 in Africa. Policies include "Contraction and Convergence" firstly to limit each person's carbon to 2 tonnes of carbon equivalent per year, secondly to equalise global economies.

Additionally, the acceleration of melting permafrost and the release of catastrophic amounts of methane would set in motion rapid climate change and sea level rise. Mainstream fossil fuel dependence has unacceptable costs, including pollution damage to fisheries and geopolitical struggles over supply chains from Russia to the Middle East. Fossil fuels are being replaced by microgeneration, Renewables and SMART grids, (linking areas of high wind to areas of high solar availability) more self sufficiency. Local and micro generation of energy is possible with Feed in Tariffs introduced in Germany and the UK.

(ii) Changes in attitudes to energy production and use: Lower carbon economies

British Petrol (BP)'s Deepwater Horizon oil drilling leak in the USA is an example of how the role of oil and fossil fuels in the economy is starting to be acknowledged as a limiting factor and is being questioned. Roughly 10 per cent of UK pension funds are linked up with BP and so the cancellation of the dividend from BP has deeply affected the UK economy but the oil spill has affected the economy of the US ruining for example fisheries but also coastal tourism and wildlife. The cost of oil is also a feature of the much criticised Iraq war too which reduced public acceptability of the costs of our current life style and how the idea of freedom, liberty and nonviolence fits with the idea of safe energy supplies from hostile, undemocratic or unstable regimes. Additionally there have been concerns about the effect of CO_2 use on climate and the acceptance that the 20th century economy was characterised by mass-production and economies of scale, ending the century with huge outsourced supply chains in human conditions for workers.

(iii) Carbon trading and market solutions Climate crisis : Kyoto Protocol and the Copenhagen Conference COP15

The Kyoto Protocol, (a market-based attempt to trade carbon to solve climate change), held its regular Conference of the Parties Conference in Copenhagen COP15 in December 2009. It received unprecedented interest, and over 40 000 people and most of the world's Heads of State flocked there. Small island states would disappear unless climate change is stabilised at an agreed at 1.5 degrees of warming. Other more powerful countries decided to ask for costs of stabilisation of the climate at 2 degrees of warming. The huge response led to an actual failure of the Conference as the organisers UNFCC were completely overwhelmed with the level of interest people showed in limiting climate change.

Lord Stern said that "Climate Change was the biggest market failure the world had ever seen." Although he continues to remain within the market mechanisms promoting ever more growth as a solution, green economics tries to solve the climate problems by looking beyond only market mechanisms. Main stream Economics methods have to some extent relied on Cost Benefit Analysis and Discounting The Future but in a world where future resources may be depleted, and a weaker economy we should be doing the reverse. What is needed is to do different things differently.

(iv) Environmental Taxes and Regulations

An external effect was defined by Arrow as a "a situation in which a private economy lacks sufficient incentives to create a potential market in some good, and the nonexistence of this market results in the loss of efficiency." Externalities are examples of Market Failures in which the unfettered market does not lead to an efficient outcome, such as the costs of clean up of an oil spill, or the raising of the climate by fossil fuel use, or wastes collected and treated and can include energy products, transport equipment and transport services, as well as measured or estimated emissions to air and water, ozone depleting substances, certain non-point sources of water pollution, waste management and noise, in addition to the management of water, land, soil, forests, biodiversity, wildlife and fish stocks and on unleaded petrol and the fuels efficiency and climate change impacts of vehicles, the CO_2 emissions per km driven.

(v) Regulations

The current economic crisis was caused in part by deregulation of the banking system which had separated casino banking or speculation in investment banking from that of the savings of the small investor. Regulation is a cornerstone of a green economy. Some of which include: REACH Directive on Hazardous Chemicals and the WEEE Directive on recycling of components for electronic equipment when purchasing electrical or electronic equipment, batteries and accumulators.

(iv) The Green New Deal – Keynsian Investment

Very popular with UNEP and with the Greens and with governments, implemented by the UN and by the Korean Government and many others using a Keynsian stimulus package to pump money into the economy and targeting it towards green innovations and sustainable projects. The age of stimulus projects is now over as the big clean up starts and frugality and living within our contemporary means is the order of the day.

5. The Broader Background of the Green Economy – Changes in Focus in Economics Today
(i) The Limits to Growth

There is an increasing realization that we may have reached what has been termed the "limits to growth." We are brushing up against the finite limits to the earth's adaptability and its "carrying capacity" in the face of our human and continual onslaught on sustainable the climatic conditions, and use of resource assets have "overshot" beneficial levels. A green economics perspective argues that empowered and educated female citizens decrease population size faster while increasing a country's GDP. Some even suggest that overall "equity is the price of survival."

(ii) Prosperity without Growth

Currently gaining popularity, Prosperity Without Growth dialogues are spreading around Europe, and a fashionable Degrowth Movement has originated in France, promotes the kind of Steady State Economy envisaged by John Stuart Mill. Rather than being seen as a failed attempt at growth, Growth by Design is gaining in interest, if not in acceptance.

This is partly a result of growth actually stalling in many Western Countries and the realisation that growth above 2 tonnes of carbon equivalent per person is no longer a good long term proposition. The European Environment Agency and many other institutions are working on this and other aspects of Green Accounting and Indicators. In particular important benchmarks are progress towards the Millennium Development Goals, and the Millennium Ecosystems Services Assessment Goals, The GRI for measuring Corporate Social Responsibility, (O' Carrol) the GINI Co- efficient index,The HDI Human Development Index, the Happiness Index from the State of Bhutan and many other sustainability and social indicators as well as measurements of unemployment, trade deficit and sovereign debt. Since WW2 there has been an economics policy of encouraging high mass consumption but this has begun to be questioned. Conspicuous consumption is going out of fashion and we are moving into an age of more austerity and rebalancing. Commodity prices are fluctuating and there is a global economic downturn, large sovereign debt and rising unemployment all over Europe. Many countries and national institutions are exploring a green economy as the one ray of hope in this rather bleak landscape. The European Commission believes that this green technology will drive competitive advantage, and encourages green venture capital and Smart, Inclusive, Green, Growth as part of the Lisbon Agenda.

6. Conclusion

The Transformation into the Age of Green Economics is a very exciting period of economics innovation, offering choices of strategies from right across the spectrum. Much has happened in terms both of the evolution of Green Economics, Green Jobs and a much more effective economics system. It has spread as an important driver from Korea to the EU and as an important aspect of decision making such as in the successor to the deep sea oil spill. Environmental, ecological and green economics are all playing their part in this process as we move towards the development of an economics for the 21st century- an Age of global transformation- An age of the widely predicted 4th Industrial revolution, decarbonising our economies and working to enhance the future not to discount it!

A previous version of this chapter was first published in Encyclopedia Trecanni (in Italian), in 2010.

9.3 Green Economics
and what it means

By Miriam Kennet

We need to recalibrate what our terms mean in economics. The very word economics is from the word "oikia" or household and estate management. (Kennet and Heinemann 2006). The integrity of the household today is the last thing considered in economics and the realm of women is not included in "homoeconomicus", the basic unit in which economics modelling occurs. Green Economics moves beyond this and can be considered "post homoeconomicus" and part of a new era where economics is practised by all people everywhere, and is not "done to" or advised by one group on another group. Each person on the planet forms an equally valid economics unit. It is no longer led by white middle class western educated men trained on Wall Street or at Harvard (Kennet 2009).

Green Economics is about access for everyone and provisioning for everything on the planet. The needs of the plankton regulating our climate are as important, if not more so, in the consideration of a new construction project as the men in suits. In reality this has a two fold aspect, firstly intrinsically – their own existence value, their own right to "just simply be" part of life on earth and secondly their use to us and our survival value, or need to continue as a species, as we need them there instrumentally in order for us to survive in a non-hostile climate. This instrumental approach is often called the Ecosystem Services Approach, where the value of the ecosystem in providing human services is measured as a "use value" to us.

Similarly, one objection to the whole modelling and homo economicus approach is that most of the planet is not homo economicus. At least half is gyny oikonomika. One fifth of people are poor and hungry, and have no ability to achieve their personal buying preferences as rational economic men. Indeed their decisions are based simply on meeting their needs from day to day. In fact the very word civilisation means living in towns. We have now become "civilised" we have tamed nature and we have achieved economic superiority to other species in harnessing much of the ecosystem at the moment to provide for our own purposes. However as soon as we reached this position, it became clear that this is not an hospitable position to be in and neither is it sustainable or achievable for most people. So women, for so long excluded from economics considerations, are now starting to run banks and whole economies in a more holistic way, redressing some of the worst imbalances, for example women have started an important trading floor in Ethiopia, are running the banks in Iceland and have taken over as heads of state in several countries. A green economy is characterised as a diverse and inclusive economy with special needs and all abilities recognised and valued. Learning is regarded as a lifelong activity, rather then something done just once at school. The key to getting out of poverty and recognising the Millennium Development Goals is regarded as ending maternal mortality and educating girls and women. This is one green way of reducing population and regarded by the head of the European Environment Agency Jacqueline McGlade (2009) as the single most important aspect of creating a green economy. One of the biggest questions currently is – what is the right solution to climate change, and what is the green solution? Is there a quick fix solution to stop the runaway climate change predicted in most reports? Are we really going to get to 6 degrees of warming - as warm as the dinosaur period? (Lynas 2007) Can humans really survive into such an era? As we bask in a huge heatwave again in the northern hemisphere with a major drought, what is the right approach?

Strategic choices in a green economy
There are at least 4 strategic choices we can make.

(i) Market Mechanisms
These involve continuing to use the market to sort out the climate. In particular, the main well known method is the Kyoto Protocol, where carbon is priced and then traded using the Clean Development Mechanism in less developed countries to trade and to allow money to be exchanged towards poorer countries and those countries that have traditionally had higher carbon emissions to trade and pay for their right to pollute. This method was invented by Chichilnisky (2009) and is currently in discussion within the United Nations Framework committee to extend it to a second phase. The latest idea is to provide geo-engineering and giant scrubbers into Africa to allow Africa to go carbon negative, in other words in return for money income, they will clean up the carbon richer countries use. However although in theory- theoretical economics – this should work – in practice the Stern Review (2006) showed that "climate change is the single biggest market failure the world has ever seen". In fact more people are talking about the crisis of capitalism as a result and mainstream economics is facing some of its harshest criticism. Markets are undoubtedly part of the current mix.

(ii) Geo-engineering
However another method which is being developed is geo-engineering, where new technologies are being attempted in a rush to halt the rising tide. As has been mentioned some of these include creating artificial volcanoes, or carbon capture and storage where carbon is collected at source of a fossil fuel power station and stored under ground for many years to remove it from the atmosphere. The problem is that few of these projects have been tested and no one knows if they work, by the time we find out it could be too late as the climate would have altered significantly and dangerously.

(iii) Regulation

There are many things we can do to halt the use of fossil fuels and methane production which are causing melting of permafrost and tundra, releasing very potent greenhouse causing climate agents. It is known that the average person in the United States of America is consumes 25 tonnes per year of carbon dioxide equivalent (Kennet et al 2009, Cologna 2010). The average African uses less than 1 tonne, the average European about 10 tonnes and the average Chinese person now about 5 tonnes of carbon.

The first thing that could be done which would solve many of the issues is to educate women, as they tend to educate their children (Kennet 2008, New Scientist 2008). Secondly to create a huge push towards "contraction and convergence" (Kennet et al 2009). This would mean that the world's larger economies would contract so they would not consume as much and the world's poorest economies would be allowed and managed to increase. So there would be a convergence of levels both of economy and also of climate inducing carbon footprint eventually for equality. This was considered a radical idea when first proposed by Greens. However today, the Stern team (Stern 2009) is arguing that we need the "fastest period of growth the world has ever seen in order to pay for the technical developments we need to meet the climate change imperative." In fact they argue that such growth will peak in around 2030. This greatly enhanced growth looks increasingly unlikely to occur given the current economic downturn. And as with the last 50 years of "high mass consumption of goods" (Rostow 1960) and the artificially created demand through advertising, what has happened is an exhaustion of the world's resources and still one fifth of humanity is poor and hungry. A recipe of more of the same – and greater and accelerated growth and even more resource consumption and use – has led us to the state of massive debt which could take a generation to fix. Stern's (2009) high market growth solution does not look attractive or viable and this time we don't have time to experiment.

On the other hand, the strategy of government regulation, so that people can only use initially 2 tonnes of carbon and then negative carbon, looks more promising as if people know that they have to make changes and that everyone is doing the same they are far more likely to do it. This is effectively rationing but it does provide for everyone equally and so removes the incentive for cheating. As climate change and polar ice melting become visible realities, the acceptability of such a scheme becomes much more likely and more desirable as a preferred option, a bit like a war time adoption; everyone shares in it together equally and with pride.

(iv) Lifestyle changes

The preferred green solution is lifestyle changes. By making life style changes we argue that we are creating a new future for humanity and that it can be an exciting and high tech future. We can choose to do things differently. For example we can all cut down our carbon foot print, measuring it with a carbon calculator and cut it by 10 % every 10 weeks. We can use slow travel when moving around and switch from plane to train even for business trips, I tend to try to use the train, in one year alone having been to Montenegro, Italy and Norway and Spain using the overnight trains. The slow movement for food and for slow cities, the Citislow (Hoerschele 2010) movement is also starting to gather interest. We can choose to source locally from our community to remove embedded carbon and to recreate viable local communities and take an interest in planning in order to ensure that it meets the criteria outlined above for a longer term perspective. We can choose to cycle more and walk more.

However, conversely, we will have to severely adjust our economy and with it our built environment to live within the earth's carrying capacity and within the realms and limits that nature imposes upon us. These will be technological constraints and also economic constraints. They have been termed "The Limits to Growth", (1972) where resources and population support has reached a limit and growth must now equate to flourishing and growth as in nature. No longer can rainforest destruction, where trees are cut down for firewood be counted as growth, even if it leads to an increase in GDP, but now must be measured as destruction of natural assets or natural capital (Kennet 2007). A country clearly is less well off with a renewable resource such as a forest being depleted. It is not better off, no matter what the balance sheet or graphs are telling us.

Photo Kristina Jociute (Lithuania) Green Economists celebrating

The Green Economics Institute

Photo: Bogusia Igielska. The Green Economics Institute's *Introduction to Green Economics Course* at Oxford University

The Green Economics Institute has created a discipline or School of Economics called "Green Economics" which aims to reform mainstream economics itself into a well-defined goals-based discipline which could provide some practical answers to existing and future problems by incorporating all relevant aspects, knowledge and complex interactions into a truly holistic understanding of the relevant issues. It uses complexity, holism, pluralism and interdisciplinary working in order to widen the scope of economics, adding the science from the green aspects, and the social ideas from economics discourses. This new scope for the first time avoids partial explanations or solutions and also biased and partial perspectives of power elites. According to economics professor Jack Reardon from the USA (2007), The Institute has been very successful in creating a robust academic basis for this new idea. The Institute has influenced the methodology of mainstream economics, according to Professor Tony Lawson of Cambridge University's Economics Department (2007). It uses transdisciplinary and interdisciplinary methods so that it can factor in the complexity of nature into economics. It seeks to provide all people everywhere, non-human species, the planet and its systems with a decent level of well-being based on practical and theoretical approaches targeting both methodology and knowledge and based on a comprehensive reform of the current economic mainstream. It can, for example, comfortably incorporate glacial issues, climate change and volcanic, seismic and earth sciences into its explanations and thus in this, and many other ways, it is far more complete and reflects reality much more closely than its predecessors on which it builds. The current narrow conventional economic approach using purposely designed methods is challenged to bring areas and concepts into its scope which have been until now neglected. Existing outdated or inappropriate propositions and solutions are examined and revised to provide a realistic and more comprehensive understanding of the subject.

The Green Economics Institute argues for economic development based on economic access and decision making for all, including respect for cultural diversity and normative freedom. It does this by bringing together all the interested parties, who want to help in developing this progressive discipline, by inviting them to its events, and conferences and by means of such activities as writing books and publications and using its research, its campaigns and its lobbying and its speeches and lecturing all over the world. The Green Economics Institute created the first GreenAcademic Journal *International Journal of Green Economics* with publishers Inderscience and is now a Publishing House in its own right with 90 titles of its own and a stream of books which cover social justice questions related to poverty and health and inequality.

The Green Economics Institute has its own delegation to the Kyoto Protocol, and is a recommended UK government reviewer on the Intergovernmental Panel on Climate Change (IPCC). Members of the Green Economics Institute have lectured or worked in governments and Universities around the world, for example Surrey University, the Schumacher College, The University of Bolzano, the Tyrollean Cabinet, via Skype in Thessaloniki, FYRO Macedonia, Turkey, the National Government School in the UK with top Cabinet Officials, at University in Cambridge and Oxford, Transition Towns, Oslo, Norway, Liverpool University, Lancaster University, Abuja, Nigeria and Gondar, Ethiopia and attended conferences in many places including Cancun, Mexico and Riga, Latvia and appeared on TV and radio in Italy and Tallin in Estonia and the UK and Bangladesh amongst many others and received invitations from the President of Russia and from the governments and several universities in China and from several governments and Princes in several Gulf States as well as several parts of the United Nations and the International Labour Organisation.

Directors
Miriam Kennet, UK,
Volker Heinemann UK, Germany
Michelle S. Gale de Oliveira UK, USA, Brazil

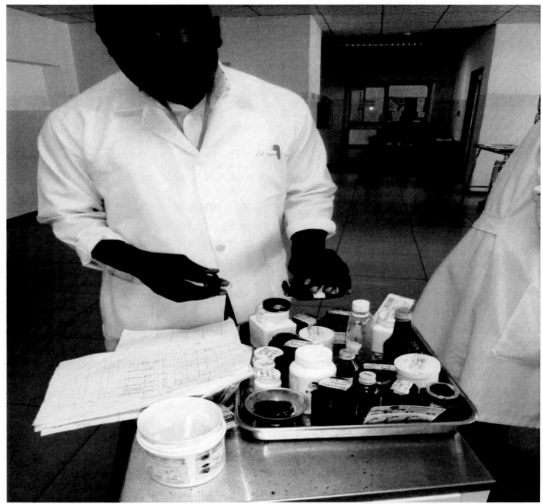

Photo Tone Berg and Aase Seeberg. Healthcare in Mozambique

Green Economics Institute Publications

Leading thinkers in the world of healthcare publish with The Green Economics Institute.

Titles available in The Green Economics Institute Book Series © include:

Green Economics Books

- The Greening of Global Finance: Reforming Global Finance © (2013) Edited By Professor Graciela Chichilnisky (USA and Argentina), Michelle S. Gale de Oliveira (USA and Brazil), Miriam Kennet, Professor Maria Madi (Brazil) and Professor Chow Fah Yee (Malaysia)
- Handbook of Green Economics: A Practitioner's Guide © (2012) Edited By Miriam Kennet, Eleni Courea, Alan Bouquet and Ieva Pepinyte
- Green Economics Methodology: An Introduction © (2012) Edited By Tone Berg (Norway), Aase Seeberg (Norway) and Miriam Kennet
- The Green Economics Reader © (2012) Edited By Miriam Kennet
- Ethics, Philosophy and Values of Green Economics, (2014) Miriam Kennet, Professor Andrew Dobson and Michelle Gale de Oliveira

Geographies of Green Economics

- Greening the Global Economy © (2013) Edited by Sofia Amaral (Portugal) and Miriam Kennet and Michelle S G Gale de Oliveira
- Green Economics: The Greening of Asia and China © (2012) Edited by Miriam Kennet (UK) and Norfayanti Kamaruddin (Malaysia)
- Green Economics: Voices of Africa © (2012) Edited By Miriam Kennet, Amana Winchester, MaheletMekonnen and Chidi Magnus Onuoha
- The Greening of Eastern Europe © (2013) Edited By Miriam Kennet and Dr Sandra Gusta (Latvia)
- Green Economics: The Greening of Indonesia © (2013) Edited By Dr Dessy Irwati and Dr Stephan Onggo (Indonesia)
- Green Economics: The Greening of Latin America © (2013) Edited By Michelle S. Gale de Oliveira (USA and Brazil), Maria Fernanda Caporale Madi (Brazil), Carlos Francisco Restituyo Vassallo (Dominican Republic) and Miriam Kennet
- Africa: Transition to a Green Economy © (2013) Edited By Dr Chidi Magnus (Nigeria), Michelle S Gale de Oliveira and Miriam Kennet
- *Forthcoming:*
- Green Economics & Bangladesh © (2013) Edited By Dr Soma Dey (Bangladesh)
- Green Economics & India © (2014) Edited by Kanupriya Bhagat & Miriam Kennet
- Greening of the Mediterranean Economy © (2014) Edited by Enrico Tezza
- Green Economics & Nigeria © (2014) By Steven Adawola

- **Social Policy Books**
  - The Greening of Health and Wellbeing © (2013) Edited By Michelle S. Gale de Oliveira, Miriam Kennet and Dr Katherine Kennet
  - Older people © (2013) Edited by Miriam Kennet
  - Citizen's Income and Green Economics © (2012) By Clive Lord, edited by Judith Felton and Miriam Kennet
  - Costing the Citizens Income Clive Lord, Judith Felton and Miriam Kennet (2014)
  - Green Economics: Women's Unequal Pay and Poverty © (2012) Edited By Miriam Kennet, Michelle S Gale de Oliveira, Judith Felton and Amana Winchester
  - Young People: Green Jobs, Employment and Education © (2012) Edited By Miriam Kennet and Juliane Goeke (Germany)
  - Education (2014) Miriam Kennet, Professor Jack Reardon (USA) and Juliane Goeke (Germany)

Energy and Climate Policy

- Green Economics and Climate Change © (2012) Edited By Miriam Kennet and Winston Ka-Ming Mak
- Green Economics: The Greening of Energy Policies © (2012) Edited By Ryota Koike (Japan) and Miriam Kennet
- Green IT (2014) Audaye Elsedy (Forthcoming)

Food, Farming and Agriculture

- Green Economics & Food, Farming and Agriculture © (2013) Edited by Michelle S. Gale de Oliveira, Rose Blackett-Ord and Miriam Kennet
- Green Economics & Food, Farming and Agriculture: Greening the food on your plate © (2013) Edited by   Michelle S. Gale de Oliveira, Rose Blackett-Ord and Miriam Kennet
- Green Food: Recipes for a Greener Planet © (2013) Edited by Rose Blackett-Ord
- Towards Sustainable Regional Food Systems: The Langenburg Forum © (2013) Edited By Miriam Kennet, by kind permission of Joschka Fischer and HRH Prince Charles Prince of Wales

Lifestyle Books

- Green Economics: The Greening of Transport © (2013) Edited By Richard Holcroft and Miriam Kennet
- Green Economics: A Book of Poetry, Art and Photography © (2013) Edited by Dr Matt Rinaldi, Rose Blackett-Ord, Friedericke Oeser Prasse and M Kennet
- The Green Built Environment: A Handbook © (2012) Edited By Miriam Kennet Judith Felton
- Economics and Culture Audaye Elsedy, M Kennet,(UK)   Anji kwi (Uganda)

Photo David Taylor: Alternative living – A Teepee.

Photo David Taylor Earthspirit. The Tree of Life Artwork

Photo Miriam Kennet. Two of our young Green Economists enjoying our conference we held at Oxford University, with our books which they have contributed to.